FOOTPRINTS OF ASSURANCE

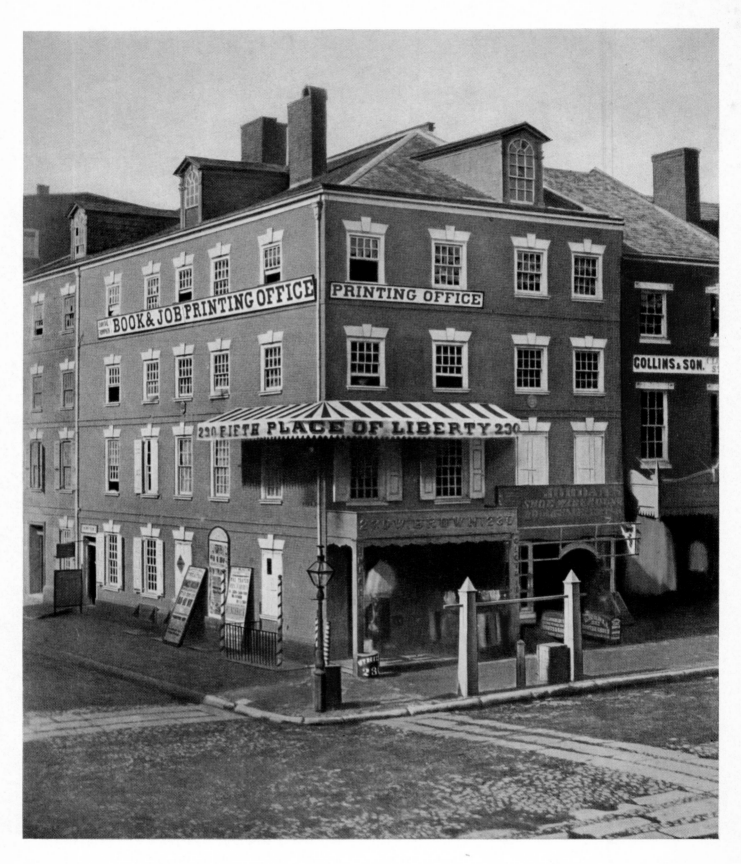

An early view of the Graff (Graaf) House in Philadelphia where Thomas Jefferson wrote the first draft of the Declaration of Independence. The fire mark of the Mutual Assurance Company which appears on the left side of this building, between the second and third floors, is now in the possession of the H. V. Smith Museum of The Home Insurance Company. See fire mark No. 25.

FOOTPRINTS OF
ASSURANCE

Alwin E. Bulau

THE MACMILLAN COMPANY: NEW YORK

1953

DESIGNED AND ENGRAVED BY THE BECK ENGRAVING COMPANY, PHILADELPHIA

DEDICATED

TO

HAROLD V. SMITH

FOREWORD

Signs and symbols have always played an important role in the lives of men. For the primitives there were the signs of the stars, the moon, and the sun—for the men of the Middle Ages there were the signs of heraldry and the guilds. Then came the signs of trade and more recently of advertising. Pioneer fire insurance companies dating back almost three centuries, as well as those of more recent origin, used a sign known as a fire mark. Since these so vividly record the struggles, triumphs, and sometimes the adversities of such concerns, they are truly "footprints of assurance."

For those who are fortunate enough to understand the signs of the ages, there is the reward of adventure and romance to be found in a review of the colorful pageantry of the past. Through the use of the fire mark, for instance, one can trace the development of a great industry from its very beginnings in Europe to its present vital role in the modern community. This same panorama covers the entire history of American fire insurance companies for a period of over two hundred years.

Here in America literally thousands of insurance carriers were established before the turn of the last century. Each was a hopeful venture launched by courageous men who perceived the need for insurance service and protection. Unaided by the protective regulations established during the past seventy-five years, however, and without the judgment that comes from seasoning and experience, all but ninety-three of the legal reserve variety of companies established prior to 1900 foundered in the storms of adversity. Although many fire insurance companies have, of course, survived to this day, hundreds of them were taken over, absorbed, or managed by concerns of accepted security standards. To these bulwarks of the fire insurance industry, whose footprints are so deeply imbedded in the sands of time, goes the credit for assuring the economy upon which this nation rests.

Fire marks first came into use in Europe and can be likened to modern trademarks, since the distinctive insignia identified the particular company which had adopted it. But in the early days, fire marks performed a much wider function than mere identifica-

tion, for European fire assurance concerns maintained their own fire brigades whose function was to fight fires only at those properties protected by their parent companies whose mark they displayed. As this subject will be enlarged upon in the pages to follow, let it suffice to say here that the use of the fire mark was directly associated with either the establishment or the maintenance of fire-fighting organizations and had a distinct influence upon their development and equipment. Conversely, it may be noted that the evolution of the fire brigades had an equal effect upon the methods by which the marks were employed and the purposes for which they were intended.

In addition to being posted upon the exterior of insured buildings, a symbol of the mark frequently appeared on insurance proposals and policy contracts. In the eighteenth century, in fact, the fire mark was an integral part of the policy contract and entered into the policy terms and the respective obligations of the insured and the company.

Fire marks were also adopted very early by the first American companies as symbols to mark the properties upon which they had written policies. Among these properties were some of our most illustrious landmarks, including the house in which the Declaration of Independence was first drafted and the State House in Philadelphia.

Commerce, which for many centuries has been the backbone of progressive civilization, relies upon competition as its motivating influence. In the insurance industry, the mark performed a valuable service in fostering a healthy opposition between the insurers by graphically presenting a challenge to widen services and coverage. It also encouraged rivalry among the early volunteer brigades and even some of the early paid fire departments, perhaps accounting in some part for the zeal and effectiveness of the intrepid fire laddies.

As the function of the fire mark slowly changed with time, so also its style, influenced by developments in the localities in which it was used, changed. Starting in Philadelphia, that "cradle" of so many things American, the fire mark was carried westward toward the frontiers. As the years passed the advance of the population was mirrored in the march of these signs. Similarly, the ever-changing appearance of the fire mark clearly reflected the transition of styles in design—the periodic changes in materials, type, and method of production — which parallel identical changes in industry and the arts. Even the imprint of prevailing ideologies has been left upon these marks, and the knowing eye can detect traces of the thinking of their period. It is hoped that a study of fire marks will be of interest to all who are inspired by the historical, economic, military, and political influences upon the arts and commerce through the decades. Possibly it will be of especial interest to that vast group of citizens engaged in the insurance business. Theirs is the industry which has been so well served and so greatly enriched by the marks which provide a tradition and a genuine historical background from which today's insurance community can take strength and inspiration for the future.

No portrayal of fire marks could be complete without a picture of those devoted and interesting men, the collectors. Over the several decades during which material was gathered for this publication, many collectors have collaborated with the author. Naturally, as happens whenever a technical exposition is involved, there may be a diversity of opinion on some of the fine points. The thoughts and ideas of all our contemporaries have been well weighed and considered in arriving at the conclusions on the following pages, however, and we are indebted to all those who have taken an informed and intelligent interest in the preparation of this book and the data it contains. The opening pages of the book will introduce the outstanding collectors of fire marks as well as the ever-increasing number of those in quest of footprints of assurance. That group continues to perpetuate by visual means the story and history of an industry in which every citizen has a direct interest—the development of indemnity for loss by fire and the preservation of property and life.

In illustrating over eighteen hundred fire marks an endeavor has been made to include all the various types of marks which have so far been located. Undoubtedly there are others which have not come to light and probably some additional ones will be located on site as the years pass on. It is our hope that further information on such new "finds" will be disseminated by a new international organization, the Fire Mark Circle, London, England, which is comprised of the most outstanding signevierists of the world.

The foregoing is only the briefest sketch of the engrossing story of the fire mark—a tale which mirrors the adventurous romance of an essential industry upon which leans the commerce of the world.

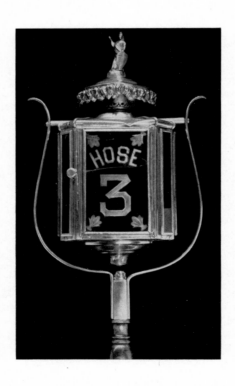

ACKNOWLEDGMENTS

In a period of well over twenty years, the research and assimilation of data accumulated for the proper arrangement of this work was made possible only through the patient assistance of many individuals. The personal encouragement of Harold V. Smith was primarily responsible for the writer's original wish to acquire a collection of fire marks, just as it was Mr. Smith's frequently mentioned desire for a comprehensive compilation of all available data on the marks of assurance which led to the present volume.

The construction of a file on the fire insurance companies of the world (and the possibility of their ever having issued a mark) necessitated the writing of over twenty-six thousand letters to one hundred thirty-eight countries. It was a mammoth task but one made less complicated by the assistance of Virginia Carson and Thelma Gorman Miller who made the chores of corresponding and indexing easier ones.

Espying a mark upon a building affords the greatest of thrills to a fire mark collector. Such compensations have gone to Mr. Smith and to the numerous collectors who gathered the marks which became a part of his great museum. That modest portion located by this author was secured from many states and cities which were visited on every holiday and vacation period for many years. To my wife and three sons, who contributed corresponding holiday periods to the assimilation of much of this historical data, goes my sincere gratitude.

Many marks and considerable written material were brought to light by other American collectors and authorities and full acknowledgment is given to all of these, especially to Norris G. Abbott, Jr., Harry F. Albershardt, Howard Bradshaw, Charles Bray, E. Milby Burton, John J. Conway, Jr., George W. Corner, Ruby Church, Earl B. Davison, C. H. Dunham, Gayle T. Forbush, Abbie G. Glover, D. N. Handy, Edward R. Hardy, Linden T. Harris, Edward P. Kiesler, Otto F. Rieg, Dwight Rutherford, Mabel Swerig, W. Emmett Swigart, C. R. Tobin, A. C. Wallace, and Verner R. Willemson.

Many years ago the great British fire mark authority, Bertram Williams, gave much counsel and assistance in acquiring and recording marks from the British Isles. During that same period advice and assistance were rendered by other overseas collectors headed by V. J. Broomfield, J. H. Buckle, C. A. Cooper, A. Bashall Dawson, Cecil E. Faulkner, D. Glendining, J. Kelly, E. Nugent Linaker, and all members of the old and new Fire Mark Circle.

In Germany, Gustav Reeker was most helpful, and many rare items were secured through the persistent efforts of Michel H. Gattegno and Alexander J. Zoides in Greece and Turkey.

Much of the recorded history of fire marks during the past decade took place in the offices of The Home Insurance Company in New York City, and there the author was assisted by Audrey Adams Baldwin and Ethyl Blass. During that period, when records were kept in the writer's Indianapolis office, the meticulous checking, filing, and arrangement was conducted by Odelia Bauman.

The final writing and preparation of this book called for a constant and intensive effort to build up an historically accurate record of fire insurance companies and their fire marks along with a pictorial exhibit of these signs. Both elements were interwoven with a narrative of corresponding import. To Martha Bulau must go the credit for having spent many months of research in libraries and museums to bring to light the historical incidents which form the background of the organization of American fire insurance companies. Audrey Adams Baldwin is responsible for the listing and checking of the descriptions of the individual marks and has been most helpful and encouraging in the successive stages of this work. For many months in London, England, the intense work of Messrs. H. A. L. Cockerell, Douglas Lawson, and A. S. Pratten has given, for the first time, a comprehensive record of the heraldry to be found upon British fire marks and they, too, have made possible the photographs of marks contained in the Chartered Insurance Institute of London, specimens of which have not yet found their way into American museums.

Important, too, was the typing of the first detailed outline of the book and the captions, by Carolyn Voss and Joan Meyers; also the successive typing of the copy by the author's own secretarial staff. The assistance of George H. Miller, in the handling of the fire marks in the museum itself, expedited the cataloging, while the technical collaboration of Benjamin Franklin Collins, King Rich, Silvio Ciancio, and Faulkner Lewis made the artistic arrangement of the book a reality.

Acknowledgment is also made to Harry Collins of Brown Brothers for the preparation of the photographic details of practically all of the illustrations. The appearance of this book has been enhanced by the engraving and printing of the Beck Engraving Company, Inc., and the author feels a deep debt of gratitude to the publishers, The Macmillan Company. The wise editorial counsel given by Thomas Ross, Charles Anderson, and Holger Cahill has been especially helpful.

To my editorial assistant, Richard Doyle, goes my unending appreciation, not only for his help in re-editing and rewriting, but also for an imaginative stimulus and sound criticism in all of the final stages of this work.

So many people, over this period of years, have been so very helpful and generous that the author feels that the credit for compiling this work should go to them. Many names could be added to the foregoing, but to those unnamed contributors also goes my sincere appreciation. Without the combined efforts of all of these individuals, this bit of history of an industry, this recording of footprints, would not have become a reality.

A. E. B.

CONTENTS

Page

The Graff House in Philadelphia *(Frontispiece)*

Foreword ... VII

Acknowledgments ... IX

Introduction ... XIII

COLOR PLATES

Facing Page

Brigade of the Sun Fire Office, 1808 ... XVI

Certificate of the Weccacoe Volunteer Fire Company ... 64

Fire Marks of American Insurance Companies ... 112

Brigades of the Phoenix and other London Offices ... 128

View of a fire in London, March 3, 1791 ... 144

A chromo of London firemen in action ... 176

British Fire Marks emblematic of heraldry ... 192

Foreign Fire Marks other than Great Britain ... 240

PART ONE

Page

Collectors and the Parallels ... 1

Development of the Coin, Stamp, and Fire Mark ... 2

Materials of Manufacture ... 5

Art and Character ... 6

Condition and Grading ... 8

Counterfeits ... 9

Collectors and Their Museums ... 10

PART TWO

AMERICAN FIRE MARKS

An Era of Colonization • 1736-1783 ... 19

In the New Republic • 1784-1800 ... 29

Page

The Decade of Reconstruction • 1801-1810 ... 38

The Decade of Despair • 1811-1820 ... 43

President Monroe's Decade or "Era of Good Feeling" 1821-1830 ... 50

A Decade of Devastation • 1831-1840 ... 55

Ten Years of Revolution in Industry • 1841-1850 ... 62

The Decade of Security • 1851-1860 ... 72

Civil Strife and Reconstruction • 1861-1870 ... 90

Survival of the Fittest • 1871-1880 ... 105

A Period of Invention and Progress • 1881-1890 ... 110

Beginning an Era of Competition • 1891-1900 ... 113

An Epoch of Speed • 1901-1940 ... 117

The Spurious and Unidentified ... 120

PART THREE

BRITISH FIRE MARKS

The Puritan Period • 1649-1714 ... 125

Era of the First and Second Hanoverians 1714-1760 ... 134

Four Decades of Royal Ascendancy • 1760-1800 ... 146

The Decline of George III • 1800-1820 ... 159

An Era of Reform • 1820-1837 ... 167

The Victorian Era • 1837-1901 ... 180

The Modern Age • 1901-1920 ... 196

The Unrecorded and Misrepresented ... 201

PART FOUR

FOREIGN FIRE MARKS

Algeria ... 205

Argentina ... 206

	Page		Page
Austria	207	Mauritius	274
Azores	210	Mexico	275
Belgium	211	New South Wales	275
Brazil	214	New Zealand	276
British Guiana	217	Norway	278
Bulgaria	218	Palestine	279
Canada	220	Panama	280
China	221	Philippine Islands	280
Colombia	226	Poland	281
Costa Rica	226	Portugal	282
Cuba	227	Portuguese West Africa	284
Czechoslovakia	228	Reunion	285
Dutch East Indies	231	Rumania	285
Egypt	233	Russia	287
Estonia	234	South Africa	288
Finland	235	South Australia	289
France	235	Spain	289
Germany	245	Straits Settlements	293
Gibraltar	255	Sweden	294
Greece	255	Switzerland	294
Holland	257	Tasmania	298
Hungary	261	Turkey	299
India	263	Uruguay	300
Indo-China	263	Venezuela	300
Italy	264	Victoria	301
Japan	270	Western Australia	303
Latvia	271	Yugoslavia	303
Lithuania	272		
Luxembourg	273	Bibliography	307
Madeira	273	Index	309

INTRODUCTION

Mr. Bulau's documentary record of fire marks is another of the valuable contributions to American everyday history made possible by the H. V. Smith Museum of The Home Insurance Company, which has previously given us two volumes on the history of fire insurance and fire fighting. Fire marks make up one of the many categories of material in this remarkable museum collection, unquestionably the most comprehensive of its kind. Mr. Bulau here sets down the story of one of the fascinating paths of private enterprise which has branched out into the broadest and most beneficent service to the community, and of the emblems that express its ideals and reveal something of its beginning and development.

The section of the book that holds the greatest interest for the American reader is the one devoted to fire marks made in America. This section is the most complete and it presents material which will bring the pleasant shock of recognition to those who are familiar with the bypaths of our urban scene of an earlier day, and that of surprise to the rest of us. Mr. Bulau sketches the history of fire insurance in this country by decades and tells us a good deal about our craftsmanship in the decorative arts, particularly as it has affected the making of trade signs which are the forerunners of present-day advertising.

Fire marks are trade signs. They are the handprints of the craftsmen who designed and made articles of use, adornment, display and communication and whose work is an important chapter in the everyday history of America. Articles of everyday use have much to tell us about human culture. One might say that they are the plain chant of the civilizations against which has been played the counterpoint of great and dramatic events, the military and political happenings which loom so large in written history. The story of the ancient world of which we have no written record is largely reconstructed from these everyday things. Even where there is some written record they help to round out the story. That they have influenced the outcome of the great events of history is a truism to any one who has studied the impact of our industrial culture upon the modern world.

The makers of early American fire marks belonged to the class of men who made the tools with which we conquered the wilderness, the men who developed the long rifle-barrelled firearm, the so-called Kentucky rifle, which was used with deadly effectiveness on the frontier, in the Revolution and in the War of 1812, the beautifully balanced American axe, the steel spades and forks and hoes and other hand tools of the early 19th century, the light and efficient plows of the sodbusting western pioneers. The men who made these articles of everyday use were the heirs of a tradition with its roots in the immemorial past, its trunk in the industrial development of their own time and its living branches in contemporary industrial know-how, which as much as any other factor, has made the United States the great and prosperous nation it is today.

This tradition developed in a hand-tool relationship, a thinking with the hands, as the French say, a kind of thinking much more important than might appear at first glance. The tool is the material analogue of the concept. Without the concept there could be no scientific or philosophical thought as we know it. Without hands skilled in thinking with tools contemporary industrial techniques would never have come into existence. All this seems a rather heavy burden of history to place upon a simple fire mark, but as we have seen, it was created by the same artisans and craftsmen who laid the foundations of modern industrial techniques.

The record which Mr. Bulau has compiled of what he has aptly termed the footprints of assurance is valuable not only to those who are interested in the history of fire insurance in this country and abroad, but also to collectors of fire marks, students of American history and craftsmanship, and to the general public. He follows the footprints of assurance as they have gone along with the progress of enterprise, responding to the influences of commerce, politics and war, tells the story of the great collectors with special emphasis on the H. V. Smith Museum, with some excursions into the related fields of coin and stamp collecting. His book is a welcome addition to the growing body of knowledge concerning Americana and its relationship to similar developments abroad.

HOLGER CAHILL

XIII

FOOTPRINTS OF ASSURANCE

.

PART ONE

A foreman and members of the fire brigade of the Sun Fire Office, circa 1808. The emblem of the Sun appeared on the badges worn on the left arm of the watermen as well as on their fire caps. The machine in the background is a Newsham engine which was popular in London from the middle of the 18th century to the first quarter of the 19th. The illustration was engraved and colored by hand in 1806 by W. H. Tyne of London.

COLLECTORS AND THE PARALLELS

The instinct that leads men to collect and preserve things of beauty, value, or interest is as old as the race itself and expresses itself in many ways. Some collect early parchments or ancient carvings; many more acquire old books or paintings. The variety is infinite, but by far the largest groups are those who collect coins and stamps. The newer and much more limited fraternity collects fire marks.

To the uninitiated, collecting is merely a hobby. In actual fact, however, it is much more than that, inasmuch as collectors are the real historians. Their medium is the stuff of which history is made, and their efforts have preserved down to this day the creations of the passing ages which would otherwise have been lost forever. Thousands, through collecting, have become experts and genuine antiquarians; many have made important contributions to history since in their zeal they are constantly turning up the previously undiscovered or unrecorded item. When the sum of these findings has been assimilated and coordinated into a definite picture the result is a new facet, a new known fact of history. Historians have followed this very procedure for centuries.

Collectors and other students of history are well aware of the fact that in reality there is little or nothing new under the sun, almost no situation that has not had a multitude of parallels in the past. Creative minds either knowingly or subconsciously draw upon the past almost every waking moment, molding and re-creating it to fit a particular purpose. Without the many who seek knowledge of the past, both literary and material, even those who are content to live in the world of the moment would find themselves severely handicapped. Great advances in every field of endeavor have been based upon the sum of previous discoveries. This is the background, the powerful drive that motivates the true collector. His searching mind and ceaseless devotion result in many unselfish contributions to society.

In certain basic respects, many of the numerous hobbies which develop history are closely related. To outline more clearly the underlying principles of the acquisition, selection, and perpetuation of the marks of assurance, we shall, in Part One, draw parallels with similar situations in the better-known fields of coin and stamp collecting.

Coin collecting, or numismatics, is the oldest of the three activities. "Numismatist" is derived from the French *numismatique* (current coin—to have in use). A reference in 1799 describes a numismatist as "one who has a special interest in collecting coins."

Next, in point of age, come fire marks, or signs of insurance, which were variously known as "badges," "placques," and "house signs." Small collections of these were first made by certain fire insurance companies in the early nineteenth century. To this activity has been designated the term "signeviery" (from the Old French *signe*, denoting signs, as attached to buildings, and *vier*, the Flemish root from which our Anglo-Saxon word fire is derived). Thus, a collector of fire marks is a "signevierist."

Because postage stamps were not used until Great Britain issued the "Penny Black" on May 6, 1840, stamp collecting becomes the last of the three parallel endeavors. In 1864, M. Herkon, a postage stamp collector, proposed that the word "philatelist," derived from two Greek words (*philos*, loving, and *atelia*, exemption from tax), be used to denote a collector of stamps.

And, so, hereafter we will frequently refer to the three parallel designations: numismatics, signeviery, and philately.

DEVELOPMENT OF THE COIN, STAMP, AND FIRE MARK

We have observed that there are recognizable parallels among the coin, the stamp, and the fire mark as collector's items. Such parallels are evident in the history of each, for all were created to fill a specific need and perform a useful function.

1. THE COIN

From the earliest periods of history there are references to barter and trade among the first of the earth's citizens. Thus one can well imagine the exchange of a stone axe for a mortar and pestle in which could be ground the coarse grains of the age. In each of the ancient lands we find that some type of money, developing through an almost endless chain of materials, was used as a medium of exchange. In Angola in ancient Africa a flat, paddle-shaped piece of iron, twelve pieces of which bought a wife, was used. Egypt produced glass ring money, while Ethiopia favored its native ivory. Ancient China used jade, while the Incas, who had advanced far in the arts and culture of the early Americas, used gold, silver, and copper. As man evolved in his associations with other men he experienced the need to acquire by exchange items of unequal or varied value possessed by others.

Numismatists and archeologists have unearthed many unusual specimens of ancient moneys. Their discoveries include shells, bone, wood, stone, and odd mineral specimens which frequently took the form of implements, weapons, or ornaments. Later, the widely accepted means of exchange assumed the form of ingots or bars of precious and useful metals, usually gold, silver, or bronze. As the population grew and travel among the peoples and nations spread, the need of a more convenient method of barter developed.

The gold and silver ingot was an accepted means of exchange in ancient times. The unique silver specimen above is now in the H. V. Smith Museum.

The forerunner of the modern coin was brought into existence by the early mintage of silver, gold, and bronze undertaken by the Greeks, the Persians, and finally the Romans. Since that time there has been a constant succession of improvement in mintage and international exchange.

2. THE STAMP

In the first days of postal service, it was customary for the recipient, if he finally received the item, to pay the postage. Great Britain inaugurated the first prepaid postage system on May 6, 1840, when they issued the "Penny Black" stamp. The stamp was little different from those issued today and contained the likeness of Queen Victoria. At first there was considerable resentment over the prepaid postage system, and many British folk objected to "kissing the back of Queen Victoria's face." Resistance soon faded, however, as the value of the postage system was recognized. In 1842 the practice spread to America where a local "carrier stamp" was issued in New York City. Switzerland and Brazil followed in 1843. With other local issues in the interim, the first United States government general issue stamp was placed on sale in 1847. In the same year the small island of Mauritius, located on the main route from Britain to the East Indies, issued its first stamp. Now, practically every country in the world subscribes as a member to the regulations of the International Postal Union, and one can forward mail to the farthest point on the globe without difficulty.

3. THE FIRE MARK

Just as the coinage and postal systems evolved from crude beginnings, so, too, assurance of security from loss by fire has also run the gamut. Indemnity from loss by fire dates back more than twenty-five hundred years when "communes" of the towns and districts of Assyria were formed. After many incidental trials and tribulations, insurance finally reached a more refined status late in the seventeenth century when it, too, developed its own symbol of exchange and security.

Raging and destructive fires have rent the hearts of mankind since the first stirrings of civilization. There are many references to conflagrations during Biblical times, and the burning of Rome is a story familiar to most readers. The greatest holocaust of more recent centuries, however, was that which devastated London in 1666 A.D. At that time, methods of extinguishment and control were either unheard of or so rudimentary as to be of little help. Consequently, the fire swept unchecked through the city.

The work of rebuilding progressed during the following year, and we learn from the archives of the British Museum that in 1667 the citizens and officials of London finally gave serious thought to fire protection. The City and Liberties were divided into four parts and each of them was to provide eight hundred leather buckets. Every parish was to have two hand squirts of brass, a number of "pickax-sledges," and "shod shovels." Each quarter of the city was also to have fifty assorted ladders, and every householder was to provide buckets and be in readiness to pass them from hand to hand at the scene of the fire. Some sort of a fire-fighting organization had been established, for there is a reference to fire commissioners, engineers, and sentinels. History records that a fire insurance association, known as the *Feuer Casse*, had been established in Hamburg, Germany, in 1591, but no such plan or fire indemnity system was developed in England until 1667. In that year Dr. Nicholas Barbon organized the first recorded fire insurance scheme for insuring houses and buildings. The venture was known as The Fire Office. Even during the first year of its existence this office maintained a number of watermen with livery and badges. In 1683, The Friendly Society organized its own brigade, and in 1699 the Hand-in-Hand Fire and Life Insurance Society took similar action. The individual offices had their names prominently displayed on their engines which were painted a distinctive color and when the several brigades were proceeding to a fire they must have made quite an attractive picture. It is understood, of course, that these brigades were not formed for the protection of the public at large or for the mutual protection of the offices. For instance, if the brigade of office "A" arrived at the scene of a fire and found that the property was insured by office "B," it promptly returned home or merely stayed to watch the fire as a more or less disinterested spectator. At least this appears to have been the rule with the majority of offices.

It is obvious that when the fire brigade crews of all the different offices turned out at the alarm of fire and arrived at the scene of action, there had to be some means of revealing instantly whether the property was insured or not and, if insured, which office held the risk. The several offices, therefore, devised a metal sign which they fixed on the front of the property in which they were interested. In other words, these signs "marked" the property and are the signs which we know today as "fire marks." The fire mark was not originally evolved solely for the purpose of

marking the property insured for the guidance of the office fire brigade, however. It was also necessary because the original offices made it a condition that no property was "secure" until the mark had actually been fixed thereon.

From the early proposals of The Fire Office we learn that they used as their device the emblem of the phoenix. Because of the popular acceptance of this mark, the company adopted the name Phoenix in 1705 (this is not to be confused with the Phoenix of today, however, which was established in 1782).

There are many early references to the origin of the practice of affixing fire marks to insured buildings by British companies, and some of these will be referred to in later chapters.

A majority of the fire insurance offices established in London before 1833 organized their own brigades, but in that year they formed a single joint brigade for the whole of the city. This brigade was known as the London Fire Engine Establishment. As a result of a conflagration in 1861 there was enacted the Metropolitan Fire Brigade Act of 1865, a public authority established in the city to assume the responsibility for fire fighting. In 1866, all the private brigades' equipment was turned over to the Metropolitan Brigade by the insurance companies. Company-owned brigades lingered elsewhere in Britain until at least 1925. It is therefore apparent that the transition from the company-owned brigades to the municipal department was a gradual one consuming almost a century in passing.

It is generally conceded by collectors in Great Britain that the true fire mark passed when the brigades became a public responsibility. Subsequent to that time many collectors refer to the signs issued largely for advertising purposes as "plates." To a signevierist, however, they definitely pertain to an era in the progress of assurance and can well be admitted to the general classification of a fire mark.

Besides Great Britain and America, the fire mark was also used in many other countries for the same purposes as it was employed in these two areas. Probably a greater portion of the marks of other countries was used for advertising purposes, or to give assurance to the policyholder. Each of these countries or areas will be referred to in detail in the closing chapters of this book.

In America, the relationship between fire insurance concerns and brigades was the reverse of that established overseas. Almost as soon as the white man settled upon the eastern seaboard volunteer fire brigades were formed. From 1648 these volunteers operated as bucket brigades, but in 1731 New York received its first hand pumper from London. The number of volunteer brigades, with their many rivalries, spread throughout the larger centers of population very rapidly, and these organizations often had as their members the political and social leaders of the community.

The volunteer firemen were mostly responsible for the organization and establishment of the first fire insurance companies in America. While the first and somewhat short-lived fire insurance scheme was born in Charleston, South Carolina, the origin and use of the American fire mark is attributed to the next company of record which was organized at Philadelphia, Pennsylvania, on April 13, 1752, and known as the Philadelphia Contributionship for the Insurance of Houses from Loss by Fire. It is stated that at their meeting of May 20, 1752, a committee was to treat with John Stow about making the marks for insured houses. On July 22 an order was drawn on the Treasurer to pay John Stow the sum of twelve pounds, ten shillings for one hundred marks. It would, therefore, appear that the use of American fire marks began in the year 1752, a custom outlined in an excerpt from their minutes of October 3, 1755, wherein it is related that the Directors ". . . proceed to view the house of Edward Shippen in Walnut Street, No. 103, that was damaged by means of a fire which happen'd at the house of William Hodge, situate in that neighborhood; which house of E. Shippen having no badge put up. The Directors observing that much of the damage was done thro' indiscretion, which they think might have been prevented had it appear'd by the Badge being placed up to notify that the house was so immediately under their care; to prevent the like mischief for the future; it is now ordered that the clerk shall go round and examine who have not yet put up their Badges; and inform those that they are requested to fix them immediately, as the major part of the Contributors have done, or pay Nathaniel Goforth and William Rakestraw, who is appointed for that service."

Thereafter, most companies established in America issued a mark; some were of lead, others of cast iron or tin. From 1870 to about 1890, the more modern American offices made use of small metal plates, having the name of the company thereon, in their agency business. These plates were freely scattered throughout the smaller towns and villages more for advertisements, probably, than for any other special purpose, although insured parties were occasionally met with who did not consider themselves safe from fire unless this plate was affixed to their houses. While records of American fire marks and their usage have been fragmentary, an amazing amount of new material has been brought to light during the last half century by the ever-increasing number of signevierists. They have cleared up many inaccuracies previously extant and have arrived at a two-fold conclusion. First, the fire mark was used to mark insured buildings to indicate to volunteer firemen that their association, or one in which they had a special interest, carried the insurance. Second, there was a generally accepted theory and consciousness that evildoers would not molest an insured building for which the owner would receive reimbursement in the event of loss. It is quite apparent that in our less populated days personal feelings ran high and arson was not an infrequent instrument of malice.

In America, the period of transition from the volunteer brigades to the paid fire department was a slow one, and records indicate that the change extended from 1865 to as late as 1910. Step by step the fire fighters and the insurance companies have forged ahead in their service to the public. Of course, even today there is an abundance of volunteer fire brigades, but since these operate for the benefit of the general public and since insurance is so widely recognized as a necessity by all property owners, the need for an identifying fire mark has ceased to exist. Indeed, the necessity for the use of the mark disappeared when the old volunteer brigades gave way to the paid, municipally owned fire departments. Thus we see that the parallels among the three collectors' fields of numismatics, philately, and signeviery exist even in their creation and development. Each has developed its own emblematic art form, and each has contributed materially to the expansion of trade, industry, and economics throughout the world. The fire mark is that important sign which played a definite role in the beginnings and progress of fire extinguishment. It is that device, now used only in remote places, which symbolizes the great fire insurance business without which commerce and industry could not have reached their present heights.

MATERIALS OF MANUFACTURE

Tracing the development of the three parallels—coins, stamps, and fire marks—through their materials of manufacture, the most dissimilar are the stamps. Most of these have been made from line-engraved plates though some were hand-stamped from a single die. Only the most discerning philatelist differentiated between the kinds and grades of paper on which they are printed.

The uninitiated may also be interested in the methods used in manufacturing coins. Two methods have been employed since the very beginning; the process of casting and the process of striking. In making a casting a mold was shaped with a design or type to be impressed in the negative form. Molten metal was poured into the mold which was then closed, and the metal was left to cool. This was obviously a somewhat slow and crude process, although many artistically superior coins were produced. The second method, destined to survive to the present day, was that of striking. First, a plain mold was placed upon a hard object, preferably an anvil, and then hit with a hammer containing the punch design of the coin on one end. Later, this method was supplemented by having a mold in the anvil itself, thereby producing a design on both the obverse and reverse sides of the coin with a single stroke.

In 1547, the Italians invented the screw press, and that appurtenance produced an even pressure and consequently a better grade of coin. The greatest perfection in the striking or press style of manufacture came about a quarter of a century later when in 1573 a metal collar was devised and placed around a planchet. In this manner, the metal was restrained to form a perfect circle when the blow was struck or pressure applied, and in consequence there was born the style of coin which we are using today. Not until 1800 did Boulton and Watts invent the steam coining press in Britain. That type of modernized machine is still employed in the mints of the twentieth century.

Materials and method of manufacture were also considered when the need arose for the use of a fire mark. The first of these were made of lead, some of which were cast while others were stamped, depending largely upon their design. Extracts from the minutes of the oldest English fire insurance plans refer to the fact that an order for the manufacture of marks was placed with a plumber. This use of the term plumber does not precisely agree with the common American concept of the word, although, according to Webster, a plumber is: "a worker in lead" and also, "an artisan who works in lead."

The practice of placing the policy number upon the mark predates 1708 and prevailed almost as long as the lead mark was used in Britain. Most of these policy numbers were stamped into a panel appearing at the base of the mark. Some of the numbers were pierced while others were painted in gold numerals. Many of these signs of assurance were painted in brilliant colors. In many instances records indicate that when an order was awarded to a plumber he was reimbursed additionally to do the painting; in other cases a regular painter was employed to complete the mark. The company also employed individuals to remove these marks when the policy was not renewed. Before they were used again it was the custom to stamp one or more additional digits upon the number plate so that there would be no confusion as to the exact property covered. This practice accounts for the many high policy numbers upon marks of early vintage. In some cases in which the assured had paid for his mark and did not desire to have it removed from the building it became the duty of the person designated by the company to stamp out and obliterate the old policy number.

Some British collectors conclude that genuine fire marks all contained a policy number and that they were made of lead. Marks made of copper, brass, and tinned iron were considered "plates" and were not classed as marks in the original sense of the word by some collectors. It is gratifying to have Fothergill, an early British authority, comment as early as 1911 that in many cases marks of any of these materials were used as genuine ones while in other cases, after the brigades became a public responsibility, the same materials were used for the signs employed for advertising purposes. A like position has been taken by Bertram Williams, another authority, so that as far as the British collectors are concerned they seem to be generally of one mind upon the subject. In other countries outside Britain and America the same materials were used. The far more recent modern plate, however, is usually of enamel or porcelain upon iron.

When the Philadelphia Contributionship issued the first American mark it consisted of a wooden shield upon which was mounted a lead casting of four clasped hands. The same material was used by several of the other early American concerns. Later, in New York State, Pennsylvania, Ohio, West Virginia, Maryland, South Carolina, Louisiana and a few other points, iron castings were employed as fire marks. On these earlier signs of assurance the policy number was usually affixed with gold leaf. Because of the many stamping mills in the New England states most of the companies domiciled there had their marks made of heavy tin, though some were of brass or copper. Obviously because of the proximity of the zinc mines, practically all fire marks in Missouri were heavy zinc castings. A majority of these were manu-factured at the same time that those of cast iron were adopted and in the same period that the volunteer brigades were so active.

Regardless of the material or method of manufacture or whether the mark was used before or after the paid fire departments were established, it is true that each one reflected a distinct era of development. Each of these marks, by whatever name known, has perpetuated a record of those firms which provided the guarantee of a new economy for the entire world.

ART AND CHARACTER

Design has played a most important part in numismatics, signeviery, and philately. A review of the coins of the world since several centuries before Christ would give the student a liberal education in the history of the world. Such a study gives one of the most comprehensive portrayals of the arts to be found in any form of record. On the most ancient coins we find the likeness of animals. During a later period grains were portrayed, while the Roman coins first depicted such gods as Hercules, Janus, Minerva, and Mercury and later bore the images of the emperors and their families.

The forerunner of the present commemorative coin then made its appearance, and soon each form of civilization and segment of culture was being portrayed by the best artists of the period. In their many thousands of forms these coins are still among our best evidences of the peoples and their customs. Their ambitions and their attainments are probably best depicted upon those coins employing heraldry, of which there is a great abundance.

Heraldry in itself is a major study, but since it is the basis of "signs" and is used freely in all three of our parallels it will be well to discuss its origin briefly. Ancient history tells us that in the early ages various communities or geographical groups deemed it wise to adopt some distinguishing sign or mark to use upon their standard. Most of these devices were somewhat symbolical of the group they represented. Because of confusion in battle it was important that the warriors' standards be clearly marked; at first these applied to nationalistic groups, but then they were adopted separately by leaders and lastly by individuals. Ancient writers gave detailed descriptions of these early devices. Heraldry as we know it today was not systematized until somewhere between 1216 A.D. and 1272 A.D.; its earliest trace was recorded in 1180 A.D.

Individual armorial bearings originated in the tournaments of Germany, France, and England. The English monarchs approved of these events since they encouraged the nobles to greater chivalry. For his mark of distinction, a combatant would adopt an outstanding figure which often became an hereditary sign. Single devices constitute the most ancient and honorable arms, while at a later date it became necessary to display several charges so as to produce a mark of distinction. To be a genuine hereditary possessor, a knight used a plain shield, but upon attainment of heroic distinction he became entitled to a charge of his own choice. Before the College of Heralds came into existence many nobles chose the same sign. If arbitration then failed to determine which individual was entitled to the device, the dispute was settled in combat. A knight was also entitled to bear the arms of a vanquished enemy; thus the design of armorial bearings became more and more complex. For us in this century, the record of these devices is still to be seen upon the various arms of a community, a group, or an individual.

In Britain, where the fire mark originated, many of the signs of assurance contain heraldic devices. The first fire insurance scheme adopted as its device that mythical bird from the religion of Egypt, the phoenix, which was fabled to live for five hundred years, to be consumed in fire by its own act, and to rise once again from its own ashes. Thus it is often an emblem of immortality. Other devices used principally in

In the nineteenth century, coins were often used by insurance companies to pay Board of Directors' fees. At the year's end, the collective annual fee given to the Board was distributed amongst the individual Directors according to the number of coins they had received at each meeting. This particular system of distributing Directors' fees is no longer utilized by private companies though still employed by institutions such as the Académie Française. Coins are illustrated here on both inverse and obverse sides.

Britain were the crown, Britannia (which appeared frequently), birds, animals, but especially crests and heraldic devices.

As the arts advanced so also did the style of design. In America, however, the fire mark came into use during a period of strife and readjustment. Thus while many of the earlier marks, especially those of cast iron, depicted in an artistic manner the vehicles and appurtenances of fire extinguishment during their specific period, the majority of American marks were limited to displaying the name of the insurance company. It was only after their general use was suspended that the arts of this new nation began to take real form and assert themselves with distinction. Of the other nations of the world it can be said that the fire marks clearly indicated their more advanced posi-

tion in the development of design. Country after country tried to outdo themselves in production of their marks of assurance. Illustrations of these endeavors will be portrayed in the pages to follow.

Since the earliest days, however, the most extensive exposition of art can be found upon postage stamps. There every imaginable subject has been depicted. Year after year issuing agencies of each nation seem to try to expand the art of the engraver and the printer, and one need only look at the size of a catalog of stamps, for any given country, to get some idea of the vastness of that enterprise. It remains a fact, however, that the art, the character of design and form to be found on coins, fire marks, and stamps, quite clearly defines the progress of design throughout the period which they represent.

CONDITION AND GRADING

Because we believe that all these visual signs of the past and the present ought to be well preserved for posterity, we must naturally consider their condition and grading, since there is frequent barter among the myriad collectors throughout the world. One authority on the collection of coins classifies them as: proof, uncirculated, very fine, fine, very good, fair, and poor. Another authority classes his coins: rare, scarce, desirable, and common. "Rarities," obviously, are usually small in number, and if many were issued at first only a few are known to survive. Sometimes when a new lot of a given type are found and unearthed, the market value at once goes down. In other instances, when it becomes known that existing rarities have been accidentally destroyed, the appraisal figure goes up. Obviously a rarity is a coin which has been well preserved in first-rate condition, and naturally such a coin will bring the highest price.

The "scarce" variety of coins does not show up often, but a sufficient number exists to supply the wants of numismatists. Since they are found only in a few collections, those which are available demand a better price. A coin referred to as "desirable" usually has beauty of style or workmanship. Sometimes, too, there is excellence of preservation. Then again, such a coin may be an item that is important to history. If an unusual story goes with the item, it ranks in the desired group. The term "common" speaks for itself; these coins are usually easy to obtain, and they have

few of the other desirable qualifications previously listed.

Most of these same principles pertain to the appraisal and acquisition of stamp collections. Because there are so many stamp groupings, however, the method of distinction is far more complex. Nevertheless, after a stamp is placed in its normal class as to rarity and availability the item which authorities stress is its condition. The highest value is placed upon a stamp with "full original gum" which retains the finest original color and is undamaged by stains, tears, or discolorations. The placing of perforations is also an important item. In a final analysis, that same practice which prevails in the evaluation of stamps and coins applies also to the acquisition of any type of antique.

Although little has been written about the grading and condition of fire marks, one can readily conclude that the application of the same methods which are employed in the other parallels applies here also. There are, of course, far fewer fire marks than either coins or stamps and in consequence the grading should be comparatively easy. One British authority has grouped them into four classifications: those having in "the field" some object connected with fire, those emblematic of the name of the company, those heraldic, and a fourth miscellaneous class.

Unlike coin and stamp collections there is a large number of unique fire marks, which designation implies that only one specimen of each has been uncovered. Naturally, from a value standpoint, such signs would head the list, for the market value of each is limited only by whatever sum a collector would spend to acquire it. Next in value come those marks, mostly of the earliest type, of which only a few specimens are known to exist. Of these the few marks issued late in the seventeenth century bring the highest prices. The marks which were in use during the first quarter of the eighteenth century are also very rare and in most instances have a high value. Those employed during the ensuing seventy-five years grade downward in price chronologically.

Marks became more numerous during the nineteenth century, and those used until 1866, when the Metropolitan Brigade was established in Britain and the paid fire department became the order in America, naturally have a greater value than others issued in later years. Rarity has the greatest influence upon desirability and value with condition ranking second as the most important consideration, though an unused mark from the archives of a company or its representatives would have a greater value than one damaged by the ravages of the elements, by careless removal from a building, or by shipment. The old lead marks of European countries and America, together with the cast-iron badges used in the United States, have top rank. Copper marks of all countries and the later tin plates continue to grade down in price. Those containing a policy number definitely "date" the item and that, too, would enhance the value. Collectors themselves are responsible for the prices paid for these marks, and it is hoped that in the not too distant future an organization of signevierists will list and establish average values for all the known marks.

In numismatics as well as philately no collection is complete until it contains a specimen of every known item. For instance, there are sixty different die varieties of the United States 1794 one-cent piece. So, in signeviery, the ultimate goal of the serious collector is to continue his search until he has a mark of every known kind. Since there are many unique signs, that goal may appear to be beyond attainment. With diligent and intensive search, however, many of these will be duplicated in the "finds" from some remote or hidden structures. Each style, each changed die or casting, each change in original coloring and each change in policy number constitutes a variant. Some collectors of fire marks would not carry the differentiation to that point, but it seems reasonable to apply the practices of the parallels. When one does that every point of differentiation constitutes a variant. Only when the activity is carried out to that extent does a collection or a group of collections form a complete history of the fire insurance industry.

COUNTERFEITS

As soon as some material item becomes a rarity and has real value in trade, someone usually takes it upon himself to profit by manufacturing fakes or counterfeits. In coins the common counterfeiter is only interested in circulating his reproductions at their current value, and he usually has on his heels some agent of the exchequer or treasury. He soon finds that his genius has gotten him into difficulty, and customarily he has an opportunity to repent at hard labor or in enforced confinement. These fake coins seldom annoy the numismatist. The ones that do perplex the unwary are coins of older mintage in which some feature has been altered so that the coin appears to be a specimen of a rare type. This is usually done by altering a digit on a common variety to "date" a very rare one. The uninitiated individual is cautioned to buy only from dealers or collectors known to be reliable. Postage stamp counterfeiters often take two stamps of ordinary value, cut out the center of one, and replace it with the center of the second stamp; the result is a fake of a variety said to be of considerable worth. Fortunately the number of fire mark collectors has not yet grown to such an extent that it is profitable to make counterfeits in any large numbers.

In Britain some specimens of the faker's art appear, and some of these will be illustrated later. Many of the early American marks were so ornate that they have been copied and sold as ornamentations for the outside of modern houses. A few, mostly of the cast-iron variety, have found their way into the hands of newer collectors. Philadelphia and Baltimore foundries have specialized in these copies and several purveyors of antique reproductions in the New England states now list these marks in their catalogs as house decorations. It is unfortunate that they are being circulated because in a few years' time, when the elements have obliterated the original finish and pitted the surface, it will be increasingly difficult to differentiate between the counterfeits and the originals.

Most original iron castings made in America were produced by the charcoal process which produced a very fine finish on both sides of the casting. Most of the fakes, however, have imperfections on the reverse side of the casting as well as air bubbles which were not to be found in the original marks. While a few of the early marks had rare imperfections, an experienced collector can readily distinguish a genuine mark from a counterfeit by the appearance and feel of the material. Such a test is as reliable in coin and stamp collecting as it is in fire mark collecting. Observances of the earlier admonition to trade only with collectors and dealers of known integrity, however, is the best safeguard.

COLLECTORS AND THEIR MUSEUMS

Probably the greatest impetus given to the urge to collect has come as a result of wars. Soldiers going to foreign lands, even in ancient times, have brought home with them tokens or coins of exchange. The Roman Emperor Augustus owned a coin cabinet in the days of Christ, and during the reign of Emperor Hadrian (about 100 A.D.) many scholars had Greek and Roman coin collections. The Crusades and another succession of foreign wars were responsible for a widespread distribution of new coins among the warriors and the populace as well. Interest in such acquisitions seems to rise to a peak and then recede before it takes on a new impetus. Numismatics was almost forgotten in the Dark Ages during the period of war conducted by the robber barons who had little intercourse with other nations. Then during the Renaissance there was a revival which later spread to France and Central Europe. By the seventeenth century hardly a European prince or dignitary who did not own a coin collection could be found.

There has been a natural exchange of wanted coins among collectors, and occasionally established museums will sell duplicates in their possession. In more recent years there have appeared a large number of reliable dealers who have established somewhat uniform prices which provide one of the most convenient forms of acquisition.

Because stamps are far more recent in origin they are also exceedingly more numerous. Stamps of late issue can be purchased from postal sources, and among the millions of collectors throughout the world there is free exchange and sale of the different types. For a beginner the responsible dealer is still the best source of a basic packet.

Signeviery provides for a more interesting and unique method of acquisition, even though the objects of its search were spread over more than two centuries in their usage. The reason for this difference is occasioned by the fact that fire marks can still be found posted upon the premises to which they were originally attached. As the process of collecting is continued and the number of those so engaged increased, so will the number of marks found at source rapidly decrease. Three decades ago writers upon the subject deplored the fact that soon marks would no longer be found, but it does remain that a diligent search frequently uncovers a mark of rarity in some secluded nook. To the finder there usually goes a thrill seldom experienced in any other line of endeavor. The experience of the writer in his contacts with collectors over a long period of years has proved that they are persons of the greatest integrity and with few exceptions are persons with whom one can confidently trade.

Because of our own experiences it is with incredulity that we read in *British Fire Marks* by Fothergill: "A word now as to how some collectors have come by their treasures. I shall be divulging no secrets, for the parties in question have amusingly recorded some of their experiences fire-mark hunting in the pages of certain magazines and newspapers, and have made a most candid confession of their crimes; so much so that it is a wonder they were allowed to be where they were to tell the tales! A gentleman in the north of England appears to have had many escapades in 'the dangerous hobby of collecting marks.' He even insinuates that for a while he lost his 'respectability,' when he offered a short-haired *stranger* who had 'done time' some financial inducements to obtain the objects of his love. He felt, somehow, that he was an accomplice, and that he, too, if the *stranger* was caught, might be brought before the Bench, and would run a poor chance of regaining his liberty for a month or two. If he could not himself get a tenant of a house, where he had spotted a rare 'mark,' to give him the 'ugly old bit of lead or copper spoiling the look of the house,' he would offer five shillings for it. The tenant would hand him on to the landlord, who, ten to one, cared nothing about the thing, but, when he found it was worth five shillings to the collector, declared it should be worth more to him, the owner. Our friend, rightly enough, would put such a fellow down as a curmudgeon, and would at once set the *stranger* on the track of the mark. Of course next morning the tenant would get up to find his landlord's 'ugly bit of lead or copper' no longer 'spoiling the look of the house.' But the collector and his accomplice were far away by that time." Needless to say, such acts were very uncommon and a majority of collectors proceeded in an honorable manner.

Other collectors in Britain also employed workmen with ladders to remove old marks from buildings, with permission, and then to replace the old sign with one of new and modern issuance. An impetus was given to collecting in Great Britain during the 1930's, and a number of auctions were held in London by a very reliable and established firm. By maintaining a careful record of the prices brought at these sales, an established value for marks having their origin in the British Empire was thereby developed. Trading and sale among collectors followed the same price pattern, so that in his writings Bertram Williams was able to list prices which were generally accepted. In other countries values were advanced by adding the cost of transportation and duty or other delivery expenses.

In America only a very few small groups of marks had been collected prior to 1900. As this avocation developed abroad, however, the idea took root here also. Since that time there has been a steady increase in the number of American collectors. Because this country was considerably younger than those across the sea, the marks found here were in a finer state of preservation. At first the property owners readily agreed to the removal of these old signs. As the news of their value spread, however, and interest in them expanded, the property owners advanced their prices. Thus many rare and unique marks have brought sums ranging far beyond one thousand dollars. Some collectors have traveled from village to city throughout a given state, while others have visited every state in the Union and made a systematic search for marks, traveling from street to street scanning each old structure for a possible "find." One of the characteristics soon developed by the collector is a sort of sense of detection. The occupant or owner, or those who pass the building daily, may never have noticed a mark affixed to the structure. One having developed the art of espial, however, can instantly spot such a sign and from that time on, until he is the proud possessor of his "find," the process of acquisition is usually one of shrewd trading.

In Philadelphia, Pittsburgh, Washington, and Baltimore the placing of marks was localized and common to all sections of the old cities. However, as the use of the mark spread westward and to the north and south a most unusual practice became prevalent and it, too, left its imprint upon history. After public transportation was inaugurated, fire insurance companies employed state and special agents to appoint local agents in each city and town of their territory. These company representatives of the last quarter of the nineteenth century would frequently sell a number of insurance policies in the locality prior to seeking out a prospective agent. Since in most cases the railroad station was centrally located, solicitation took place in close proximity to that station. In the inland river town that was also true in the section close to the steamboat landing. When the policy was sold by this itinerant agent he placed the customary fire mark upon the newly insured building. When a number of policies were dispensed the fieldman would then seek an agent for his company and offer to him, as a nucleus for his agency, this newly sold business. In most cases his endeavors were successful. In this manner a company's agency organization expanded, aided by the ingenuity of its fieldmen.

The steady increase of a community's population closed up a majority of the older rail depots and boat landings, but for the fire mark collector who sought out the sites of these old stations there was often a generous reward, for in those neighborhoods were found some of the finest and rarest fire marks in this country. A sharp eye, a generally inquisitive nature, and diligent search in these old city sections, even behind signs and other obstructions, still produce new and unheard of specimens.

Fire marks were also posted upon rural buildings, and many of these represent companies who discontinued business prior to 1865. It must be concluded, therefore, that they are marks in the truest sense of the word. Customarily marks were placed between the first and second floors of a building, out of the reach of vandals. In St. Louis and other river towns, however, marks were often found as high up as six stories, the idea being that they would be well above any possible high water level when floods, which were common, inundated the properties.

In the entrance foyer to the H. V. Smith Museum can be seen a large portion of fire marks issued by American insurance companies.

While that great thrill which comes to one who finds a new mark upon a building nourishes the urge to seek further, there are others, not as nomadic-minded, who also derive a genuine pleasure from the art of collecting. It is these individuals or groups who comprise the staffs of the great museums of the world. In London, England, the fire mark collection of the Chartered Insurance Institute is outstanding, while in America the most comprehensive collection of fire marks in the world is to be found in the H. V. Smith Museum of The Home Insurance Company in New York City. In Philadelphia there is the museum of the Insurance Company of North America, and in Baltimore the Baltimore Equitable Society has many early American marks on display.

In midsummer, 1934, a group of signevierists began the formation of The Fire Mark Circle under the guidance of the international authority, Bertram Williams, of London, England. There were seventy-five original members who resided in Britain, Canada, Australia, Spain, and the United States. The membership later extended to South Africa and Germany. The group got off to a fine start, and considerable new information came to light. The war with Germany soon forced them to disperse, however, and many passed away or dropped out of sight during the period of hostilities. With the cessation of active combat there appeared a small number of former members and a larger group of those now interested, so that in 1951 a new Fire Mark Circle was organized. The individual who gave impetus to this association of signevierists was Douglas Lawson, also of London. Much of the material contained in the British section of this publication has been made available or has been authenticated by members of this new Circle.

To any collector, be he an amateur or an ardent, advanced historian, it must be evident that membership in a collectors' group will be of extreme interest. Mu-

On the northwest wall of the present H. V. Smith Museum of The Home Insurance Company may be seen many specimens of early British marks, with other foreign marks displayed on the band at the top. In the foreground is one of the several early, hand-drawn, hand-pump fire engines on display in the collection.

seums in themselves are inanimate except as they record the story of the past. To endow them with a sense of spirituality, one must become acquainted with the individuals who have made these museums possible.

While the Roman Emperor Augustus collected coins, the turning point for real numismatists came with Joseph Eckel's *Doctrine of Ancient Coins.* It was he who started the first modern type of museum in Vienna in the 1760's by the order of Empress Maria Theresa who transferred her own collection to form the nucleus of the new exhibit. In America the late William H. Woodin, Secretary of the Treasury, had a very large collection, and one of the most famous numismatists was the late Virgil Brand of Chicago. Another famous collector was King Victor Emanuel of Italy.

Philately has had much wider publicity regarding its great. The greatest stamp collector of the ages was Count Phillipe la Renotiere von Ferrari. No collection

before or since has ever equalled his. He was an eccentric and very few people ever saw him. Employing two full-time stamp secretaries, his average stamp collecting expenses were reputed to be in excess of ten thousand dollars per week. He acquired many of his rare items from Baron Rothschild and the Thornhill collection of Australia. As a collector he was a "stamp miser" who never permitted anyone to see his acquisitions nor would he sell or trade with others. Of French descent, he was an Austrian by adoption and since, when World War I broke out, his collection was in Paris, it was promptly seized by the French government under a wartime act and locked in a vault. Ferrari fled from Austria to Switzerland where he died in 1917. When the French government auctioned off his stamp collection for over two million dollars it was discovered that the aggregation included the very rarest specimens to be found anywhere. Other greats among philatelists were Arthur

Hind of Utica, New York, King George of England, Alfred Lichtenstein of New York, Senator Frelinghuysen of New Jersey, Jackie Coogan of cinema fame, and Franklin D. Roosevelt. The well-established clubs and societies of numismatists and philatelists have well recorded the outstanding individuals in their respective endeavors.

Among the important signevierists of Britain were A. Bashall Dawson, G. W. Bain, Percy Collins, C. T. Davies, H. J. Stevenson, and A. Pordage. There were also E. Stroud, A. S. Pratten, and Cecil E. Faulkner who contributed materially to the record and knowledge of British and Irish fire marks. Many of the rare items from all of these collections may now be viewed in the Chartered Insurance Institute's Museum in London and also in the H. V. Smith Museum in New York. Collections of fire marks in America were begun in 1880, when Louis C. Madeira of Philadelphia gathered a number of them, and to him may be given the credit of having formed the first collection in the United States. Daniel Newhall, of McKean, Newhall & Borie, a company engaged in the sugar trade in Philadelphia, also was a connoisseur of these marks. In 1888, he turned over his collection to Mr. Alexander W. Wister who added materially to it.

In the first decade of this century the more important collectors were John Williams, George C. Gillespie, Stevenson H. Walsh, Gale T. Forbush, and Coates Walton. In the decade following 1910 there were John Longacre, Harrold Gillingham, Harold V. Smith, Joseph Sill, and Linden T. Harris, while in the 1920's Clarence Palmer, representing the Insurance Company of North America, David Pye, and Samuel Zinsman entered the lists of signevierists. Collections were started in the early 1930's by James Stroud of Philadelphia, Emmett Swigart of Huntingdon, Pennsylvania, and by the author.

Much has been said about collectors in general as well as the use of fire marks and the technical details pertaining to them. It has been stated, too, that America's most outstanding exhibit is the H. V. Smith collection of The Home Insurance Company, situated with the company's executive offices at 59 Maiden Lane, New York City. It is open to the public during the customary office hours. Because of its importance to signevierists, this unique exhibit is worthy of a more detailed description.

A frieze containing a specimen of each fire mark once used by The Home Insurance Company and its affiliates is immediately apparent on entering the Museum proper. With this display are marks used in oriental countries by various American institutions. There are also smaller types of American plates and a reconstruction of the 1790 firehouse of Manhattan's Eagle Engine Company 13. Glass and bronze en-

cased shelves contain some of the Museum's rarities, including the fabulous silver service once presented to retiring Chief Isaac N. Marks of the New Orleans Fire Department. British companies, too, are represented by very old and rare marks, the oldest being a mark of the Sun Fire Office issued in 1715. The exhibit contains the oldest and rarest American marks, including that of the Hope Mutual of Philadelphia which Mr. Smith secured from Ted Madeira. A large number of very old and semi-modern British marks as well as plates of companies with home offices in sixty-one different countries are also represented. On display, too, are early hand-pump engines, models of them with patent papers, toy fire equipment of a bygone day, and dozens of fire prints and woodcuts. Other features are ornate silver and brass trumpets, helmets, hat fronts, watchmen's alarms, buckets, salvage bags, ancient syringes, and extinguishers—in fact, practically every item pertaining to the early fire-fighting days and the insurance industry. Authorities consider this to be one of the most complete and well-appointed private museums in the country.

The background of both the collection and the man who made it possible is an interesting one. Even as a very young man in the employ of the Victor Talking Machine Company, Mr. Smith displayed his collecting proclivities by accumulating a number of unusual recordings. In 1910, after joining the Franklin Fire Insurance Company of his home city, Philadelphia, his interest was directed toward fire marks when the secretary of the company, Edgar P. Luce, explained to him the historical import of a fire mark on display in his office.

Starting to collect for himself from houses in South Philadelphia, Mr. Smith soon developed the basis for the present major exhibit. When Secretary Luce heard of Mr. Smith's interest he gave him the few British marks he owned and so, with only one interruption, Mr. Smith continued to build a master museum. Besides his own "finds," he purchased the most valuable marks from Robert R. Dearden, Jr.'s collection, most of Joe Sills' collection, those of his choice from the Madeira group, and most of the marks of Henry I. Brown of Brown & Crosby. This original collection was loaned to the Insurance Society of Philadelphia, an organization with which Mr. Smith was well acquainted.

Mr. Smith has developed a natural urge to collect into a great art. From his start as an office boy to his present place as head of a leading fire insurance company, collecting has provided one of his chief diversions. At one time he collected miniature elephants, coins, and some old books; even now he derives pleasure from finding some rare miniature jewel for Mrs. Smith. The kindly generosity for which he is known to all who are associated with him has evidenced itself throughout his collecting activities. As would be expected from a leading executive, he has been a shrewd trader, but there have also been many instances in which he has paid to some needy seller more than the price asked.

Subsequent to December, 1913, when he became a special agent for the Franklin Fire Insurance Company in eastern Pennsylvania, Mr. Smith started his second collection of fire marks. The H. V. Smith Museum's collection could not have reached its present size, however, without many acquisitions from other collections. It represents years of effort and includes entire exhibits formerly owned by James P. Stroud of Philadelphia; E. Stroud of Surrey, England; this writer; Alfred Chitty of Australia; and A. S. Pratten, Chief Officer of the London, England, Salvage Corps. Recently the Museum has acquired from Cecil E. Faulkner of County Wicklow, Ireland, a vast collection containing some of Britain's rarest specimens.

Each of these collectors has been of immeasurable assistance to Mr. Smith in building such a representative exhibit. The writer himself has traveled over forty thousand miles throughout the United States in search of marks and has written over twenty-six thousand letters to every country in the world in an effort to establish the usage of fire marks in the far corners of the earth. Conversely, it would have been impossible to gather such acquisitions in one place of record without the intense enthusiasm and business acumen of Mr. Smith. As insurance history is written much of the credit for research and visual background must be attributed to Mr. Smith.

In 1939 Mr. Smith and The Home Insurance Company sponsored the publication of Kenneth H. Dunshee's *Enjine! Enjine!* This publication constituted a milestone in the recording of early American firefighting equipment and illustrated many additional items of fire memorabilia to be found in the Museum. In 1952 the same author published *As You Pass By,* a vivid account of early New York history as seen through the eyes of the volunteer firemen. Year after year the guiding hand of Mr. Smith has enabled students and writers to provide posterity with a record of what has gone before in this joint enterprise of fire safety, fire extinguishment, and indemnity from loss. Even *Footprints of Assurance* is the culmination of an ambition which has inspired Mr. Smith for several decades. It is he who is responsible for the perpetuation and recording of all this material.

The following pages show the various fire marks displayed in the H. V. Smith Museum as well as over three hundred additional marks and their variations found elsewhere in the world. With these illustrations, the record of the founding of individual companies and the influence of military, political, and economic events in each decade or era should provide the proper background for the use and design of fire marks which are so indelibly engraved into the history of the fire insurance business.

PART TWO

American Fire Marks

AN ERA OF COLONIZATION

1736-1783

Signeviery would seem to be an important subject in its own right. Regardless of the angle of direct approach attempted, however, one always collides with the obstacles and influences of wars, politics, and economics. These were all factors from which sprang the American beginnings of those concerns that left behind their marks—some very faint and hardly discernible, others indelibly etched into the story of American progress. To understand more fully the conditions leading to the organization of America's first fire insurance scheme, let us review the background and history which will eventually lead us to Charleston, South Carolina.

The Old World countries had been reaching out toward new territories for colonization purposes. Landings and discoveries had been made in the New World by the Portuguese, Italian, Spanish, French, and English adventurers. Through varied and devious methods of elimination the great areas of land on the eastern seaboard were acquired by the English who promptly established companies and proprietorships under which the land was to be sold. To transplant any great numbers of people for colonization was a giant task, even though the rewards were glittering and tempting. First, the extraordinarily hazardous crossing of the high seas, and second, residence in a new, wild, and entirely undeveloped country were barriers which no ordinary people could easily surmount. But despite all obstacles colonization, with its resultant spread of business and enterprise, was rapid and successful. Therefore, it is well to recall something more about the background of the people who laid this foundation for the progress which is America's.

Until the great migration began those who lived in the Old World were emerging from barbarism to civilization and since most of Europe was a feudal state, few could call themselves free. The struggle of the masses had been long and disheartening, the future looked uncertain and desolate, and there had been almost a century of seemingly endless wars which discouraged the populace.

The people of Bohemia, Denmark, France, the German Principalities, Spain, Sweden, and lesser population groups had engaged in the Thirty Years' War which began in 1618 and extended almost without interruption for a thirty-year period. The wars were fought for supremacy on the continent or in behalf of their colonies. While these were major wars, there were also many local conflicts. The people of the Old World had little to look forward to except military servitude and poverty. With the discovery of the New World, however, the masses of Europe sensed the dawn of a new light upon the western horizon.

The new land was rough, and life was primitive and hazardous, but to the early colonists it held the light of freedom and hope. The land companies and proprietors of the vast estates were primarily interested in profit from the sale of land, but they soon realized that the immigrants had to be self-sustaining to develop a colony or group of colonies which would thrive and perpetuate their own prosperity. Thus, a very large percentage of those coming to America did so of their own free will, many being selected by the proprietors for their abilities as merchants, scientists, agrarians, and artisans of all the trades. As a result business and commerce developed rapidly. Inspired first by the zeal for freedom, then influenced by a knowledge of their respective crafts, these peoples found the need for self-sufficiency vital in a land where only natural resources existed, and consequently they became an inventive as well as an industrious people. There was a need for agricultural tools and implements, so they devised and invented their own. They needed to build homes, make utensils, and weave clothing, so they utilized new time-saving methods. As colonization spread, business property and residences were built in increasing numbers in the new centers of population. Merchants thrived as well as the land owners. With an abundance of lumber in their great forests the colonists built ships, and their commerce with the Old World expanded rapidly. Such was the fiber of the people who gave America its start.

One of the most important colonies in the New World was South Carolina in which Charleston (Charles Town) was founded in 1672, that community growing so rapidly that by 1690 it boasted a population of eleven hundred. It was here that America's first fire insurance concern had its beginning on

CHARLES C. PINCKNEY
Courtesy of Mr. Julian Mitchell and the Frick Art Reference Library

JACOB MOTTE
Courtesy of Mr. Langdon C. Quinn

The prime movers in the organization of America's first fire insurance establishment, both Charles Pinckney and Jacob Motte were also leading citizens of their times. Pinckney, attorney and legislator, later became Chief Justice of South Carolina while Motte, one of Charleston's foremost financiers was Public Treasurer of the Province from 1743 until his death in 1770.

January 18, 1732. The newly founded *South Carolina Gazette* published a notice which read in part: "At a meeting of sundry of the Freeholders of this Town at the House of Mr. Giguilliat, Proposals were offered for establishing an Insurance office against FIRE; . . ." This was to become the Friendly Society about which the same journal published other items in the following years.

Since agriculture, industry, the military, and politics seem always to be interwoven with insurance and banking, let us consider, as we go along, the personalities connected with each of these so as to gain a better understanding of the resultant economy. One such personality was Charles Pinckney, a native Carolinian, who was educated in England and returned to Charleston as a lawyer. Within a short time this young man distinguished himself both as an attorney and as a member of the Colonial Legislature of South Carolina. At that time acting Governor Thomas Broughton asked the lawmakers to add the sum of ten thousand dollars to the public expenses, for like some of his modern successors he had spent this amount of the citizens' money without asking for

approval in advance. Pinckney, feeling that such unauthorized expenditures should be halted, gained the floor in the Colonial Legislature on March 28, 1735, and offered the following resolution: "That the commons' House of Assembly in the Province . . . have the same rights and privileges in regard to introducing and passing laws for imposing taxes on the people of this Province as the House of Commons of Great Britain have in introducing and passing laws on the people of England." This resolution was adopted by the Carolinians, and thereby that Province was placed on a par with the citizens of the motherland and set forth a principle identical to that which caused the colonies collectively to make war with England in 1776.

Charles Pinckney was again mentioned when the Articles of Agreement of the Friendly Society were published in the *South Carolina Gazette* on January 3, 1736. They read as follows: "ARTICLES OF AGREEMENT, indented, had, made, concluded and agreed upon, by and between the several Persons, Freeholders and Owners of Houses, Messuages and Tenements in Charles-Town in Berkeley County in the Province of South Carolina, whose Names are hereunto subscribed, for a mutual Insurance of their Houses and Tenements from Loss of Fire.

"Whereas the Insurance of Houses against Fire hath by experience been found to be of very great service, to many Persons, who would otherwise have been reduced to Poverty and Want. And whereas, by reason of our Distance from Great-Britain, no Insurance Office there, will upon any Terms or Conditions, Insure any House in this Town from Loss by Fire; and it being natural for Men to form themselves into Companies and Societies, in order to guard against those Evils and Mischiefs, which separately and in their distinct capacities they would not be able to avoid.

"We Therefore, whose names are hereunto subscribed, Freeholders and Owners of Houses, Messuages and Tenements in Charles Town taking the Premises into Consideration, Do by these presents freely and voluntarily, and for our mutual Benefit and Advantage, covenant, promise, conclude and agree, for ourselves and our respective Heirs, Executors and Administrators, to and with each the other of us, in manner and form following, that is to say, Imprimis, We do covenant, promise, conclude and agree, That we will, and we do by these Presents form ourselves (as far as by Law we may) into a Society for the mutual Insurance of our respective Messuages and Tenements in Charles Town (which shall be entered in Books of the Directors of the Society to be insured) from Losses by Fire, and do name and call ourselves the Friendly Society."

And later, in the same journal: "On Tuesday, February 1, 1736, the subscribers met at the house of Captain William Pinckney and the Articles of Association having been approved, elected the following officers: Directors: John Fenwick, Joseph Wragg and Charles Pinckney esquires and James Crockatt and Henry Peronneau, Jr., merchants; Treasurer, Gabriel Manigault, Esq.; Clerk, Jacob Motte; Appraisers, Capt. Edward Croft, Capt. Isaac Holmes and Mr. Archibald Young; Fire Masters, Capt. Gerrit Van Valsen and Mr. John Laurens."

History also records items pertaining to the life story of Jacob Motte who as the first clerk held a position which is comparable today to a corporation's secretary. Motte became Justice of the Peace in 1737 and Public Treasurer of the Province in 1743 which office he held until his death in 1770. It is interesting to note that two centuries later some of the descendants of this early fire insurance clerk are prominently engaged in the fire insurance business in the southern states.

Family records indicate that Motte was one of the heaviest losers in the Charleston conflagration which on Tuesday, November 18, 1740, "consumed the Houses from Broad Street and Church Street down to Granville's Bastion." A contemporary account states that the number of houses burned in this conflagration exceeded three hundred besides storehouses, stables, and several wharves. This fire was responsible for the financial ruin of the Friendly Society, America's first fire insurance venture.

On February 19, 1741, the following notice was recorded in the *South Carolina Gazette:* "Pursuant to the Directions given at a General Meeting of the Friendly Society in Charles Town on Tuesday, the Third Instant. These are to give Notice to the Several Persons indebted to the said Society, that unless they discharge their respective Debts on or before the 25th Day of March next, they must expect to have their Bonds put in Suit; and as the Necessity the Society are under for calling in their Money, must be apparent to every one, it is hoped that no Person will fail of punctually paying off their Bonds within the Time above limited, or take it amiss if they do, if they are then sued without further notice by Charles Pinckney."

The people of England sent a large sum of money to aid the sufferers from this fire and Governor Bull led his people in the project of reconstruction. Modern building codes have been brought about largely by "hindsight" resulting from a disastrous fire, and Charleston, an early example, was no exception, since subsequent to the fire a law was passed prohibiting construction of houses of any material other than brick or stone. One of the most imposing of these was the handsome mansion built by Charles Pinckney which was to add to the beauty of this quaint and attractive city. The development of Charleston, and of the entire South, was so profoundly affected by the Pinckney family, and the story of Mrs. Pinckney and her own endeavors which had such a great effect upon the economy of the South is so intriguing that to neglect to give them brief mention would render this narrative incomplete. It was such building and economic advances which created a need for fire insurance, yet foreign companies were not inclined to venture into this new country. It required still further agricultural and business development to stimulate action to form another insurance concern.

Among the pioneers who contributed in this development was Colonel George Lucas, an English army officer, who later became Governor of Antigua. He brought his wife and daughter to South Carolina about 1737, bought three plantations, and built his home on Wappoo Creek, some five miles from Charleston. As he soon had to return to his duties in the West Indies, he left his plantations in charge of his eldest daughter, Elizabeth Lucas, who was then but sixteen years old, though extraordinarily self-sufficient and even at that age a competent administrator. Besides supervising the workmen upon the farms, she also spent time in educating the Negroes to read, write, and weave and still found time to spend on the study of plant life which seemed to intrigue her. Rice and tobacco had long been the chief products of South Carolina and had given that province a leading economic role in the early colonial development. "Eliza" Lucas, as she was fondly referred to, had been born on the West Indies island of Antigua where the French had grown indigo, a brilliant blue dye much in demand by the British textile industry.

Native wild indigo in South Carolina produced only a very inferior dye and could not compete with the product from the Indies. Because of her interest in plant life her father sent her indigo, ginger, cotton, lucerne, and cassava seeds and roots from the tropical beds in Antigua. She first planted the indigo seeds in March, but the plants were withered by a killing frost. She tried again in April, but this time the plants fell victim to a worm which quickly cut them to the ground. Undaunted, this young lady made a third planting in April, and the last proved to be a success. In the face of a further succession of obstacles, including a disloyal servant who tried to sabotage the dye, she developed a superior quality of indigo and distributed the seed to other Carolina growers. Soon indigo became a major product of this province and in each three to four years doubled the capital of the planters. Just before the Revolution, South Carolina exported over one million pounds annually, and during the period of the war for independence when all forms of paper money became worthless, small cubes of indigo were used as a valuable medium of exchange.

This same persistent woman greatly expanded the use of alfalfa, a major crop today. Grown from the plant sent to her by her father, the crop was introduced under its former name "lucerne." This woman was also influential in the development of cotton and silk, though neither was as important in that period as the indigo dye. In 1744 when Eliza married Charles Pinckney, then Chief Justice of the Province, her wedding dower was indigo grown upon one of her plantations on the Wappoo. As Mrs. Pinckney she moved to her husband's home which was known as Belmont and was located on the Cooper River just above Charleston. However, it was in the mansion which the Justice built in the city after the great fire that two sons were born to Charles Pinckney and Elizabeth Lucas, his wife. Both of these men, Charles Cotesworth Pinckney and Thomas Pinckney, became outstanding figures in the forward march of

their country. Charles C. became American envoy to France in 1797 and later made an unsuccessful campaign for the vice presidency and two times for the presidency of this new Republic. In 1792 his brother, Thomas, was appointed by Washington as Minister and Ambassador to England and four years later was also a candidate for the vice presidency. At the turn of the eighteenth century he served a four-year term as representative of South Carolina in the Congress. Such was the progeny of the man who so early in this history of America left the first faint footprint of assurance and of his spouse who for over a half century influenced the economy of an important segment of this new land.

The terrain of the country also had a definite influence upon the habits and industry of the day. Traversing northward from Charleston, through the early colonies, crossing lowlands, swamps, and low bush country one finally comes upon that land through which flows the Schuylkill and Delaware Rivers. It was along these two streams that the Swedes first established their settlements on land upon which the city of Philadelphia later grew. This area was dominated by dense forests which were of great benefit to the settlers because they afforded protection from hostile sources, while at the same time they provided excellent timber for housing construction. Because of the height of the forests there was little undergrowth, a factor which resulted in rich soil and lush grasses upon which cattle could graze. These conditions appealed to the settlers who had purchased large tracts of land from the Indians.

With the coming of William Penn in 1699 control of this area was solidified and under his able leadership the community expanded and thrived. The population along the Delaware was more cosmopolitan than elsewhere in the colonies, and undoubtedly that early admixture of peoples greatly influenced the rapid growth of Philadelphia which soon became the largest city in the colonies. In this expanding community and under the administration of Governor Gookin, Mayor George Roach notified the corporation board: "he had frequently had in his Consideration the many Providences this City had Mett with in that ffires that have so often happened have done So little Damage, And thinks it is our Duty to Use all possible means to prevent and Extinguish ffires for the ffuture by providing of Bucketts, Hooks, Engines, &c., which being Considered, it is the opinion of this Board that Such Instruments Should be provided." In August, 1713, and in succeeding years fire prevention ordinances were passed and on December 8, 1718, the council purchased its first fire engine and other equipment. In January, 1731, additional fire engines and buckets arrived from England.

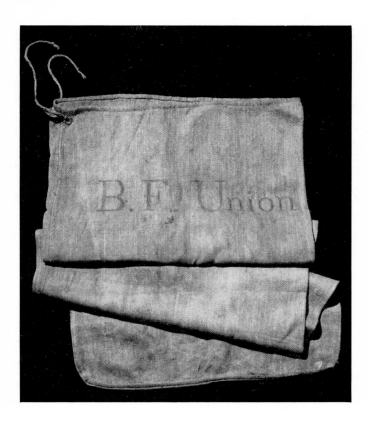

Salvage bag believed to have been owned by Benjamin Franklin whose published efforts in the Pennsylvania Gazette *were instrumental in the organization of the Union Fire Company, the first fire-fighting brigade in Philadelphia.*

Here again there was evidence that in the expanding community, fire prevention and extinguishment constituted a public responsibility. Benjamin Franklin, a native of Boston, who was later to become very active in such matters, moved to Philadelphia in 1723. Having learned the printing and newspaper business at Boston, he at once applied to Andrew Bradford, the printer and son of William Bradford, for employment. Bradford's paper, the *American Weekly Mercury,* had already gone on record in behalf of freedom of the press, and this connection afforded Franklin the opportunity to expand his theories and ideas for the advancement of the colonies. As a very young man he made valuable contacts with the leaders in the provinces and rapidly extended his ideas to such a point that he became the most influential figure in Pennsylvania. On September 25, 1729, he and Hugh Meridith began publishing the *Pennsylvania Gazette,* and three years later Franklin also published his first *Poor Richard's Almanac.* In 1736, Franklin officially entered public life by becoming clerk of the Assembly, thereafter holding a succession of public offices and being identified with practically every community interest. In the same year he repeatedly used the pages of his *Pennsylvania Gazette* to call atten-

tion to the necessity of adopting some effective method for the extinguishment of fires and the establishment of fire-fighting companies. Because of his efforts the Union Fire Company, an association for mutual assistance in fire fighting, was organized on December 7, 1736, the members furnishing the equipment at their own expense. As membership in the Union was limited to thirty individuals, thirty-five other individuals bound themselves together before the end of the year under the name of the Fellowship Fire Company. Then followed the Hand-in-Hand, the Heart-in-Hand, the Friendship Fire Company—all names symbolic of the spirit prevailing in the City of Brotherly Love—and the Britannia. These six companies carried on until 1750, after which time numerous other brigades were organized.

At this time relations between the colonies and Great Britain were going through a succession of increasing strains. There were conflicts between the royal governors, the proprietors, and the separate assemblies of the people in each province. Taxation was becoming so burdensome that little incentive remained for individual enterprise. Through his *Gazette* and other papers in the separate colonies Franklin used the printed medium to inform and encourage the citizens in their desire to administer their own affairs. Nothing illustrates more vividly the sentiment of the times than the article printed in the *Pennsylvania Gazette* in April, 1751, which complained of the treatment meted out to the colonies by the Home Government. We quote in part: "These are some of thy favors, Britain! Thou art called the mother-country; but what good mother ever sent thieves and villains to accompany her children, to corrupt some with infectious vices and murder the rest?"

In this same year the Assembly issued an order to the superintendent of the State House to provide a bell of such weight and dimensions as they deemed suitable. "Isaac Norris, Thomas Leech, and Edward Warner, the superintendents, wrote Nov. 1, 1751, to Robert Charles, of London, stating their order and authority, and applying to him to get them 'a good bell of about two thousand pounds weight,' the cost of which, they fancy, may be two hundred pounds or more, including charges. 'Let the bell be cast by the best workmen, and examined carefully before it is shipped, with the following words well shaped in large letters around it, viz.: 'By order of the Assembly of the Province of Pennsylvania, for the State House in the City of Philadelphia, 1752.' And underneath: 'PROCLAIM LIBERTY THROUGH ALL THE LAND UNTO ALL THE INHABITANTS THEREOF.—Levit. XXV. 10.'"

Norris wrote on March 10, 1753: "In that letter I gave information that our bell was generally liked

One of the thirty-one milestones leading from Philadelphia to Trenton, erected in May, 1764, by the Philadelphia Contributionship. Both sides of the stone are illustrated here — one side carrying the mileage to Philadelphia and the other, the seal of the Philadelphia Contributionship.

and approved of, but in a few days after my writing, I had the mortification to hear that it was cracked by a stroke of the clapper without any other violence." And again on April 14, 1753, he wrote: "A native of the Isle of Malta and a son of Charles Stow were the persons who undertook to cast our bell." The inscription on the Liberty Bell gives good evidence of the sentiments of the Assembly and the inhabitants at the turn of the half century.

Historians have made vague allusions to individual underwriters in the colonies prior to 1750, yet there seems to be no written record of how or by what authority they operated. While fire insurance concerns had been established for almost a century in Great Britain none of these seemed interested in properties in the colonies. *The Insurance Blue Book of 1876* states that until 1752 not a single building in Philadelphia was protected by a policy of insurance, and with the exception of the short-lived Friendly Society of Charleston this was also true elsewhere in the colonies.

Having started his career in public office as a councilman, an alderman, and a justice of the peace for Philadelphia County, Franklin was again appointed to that office in 1752, the year that marks the advent of the Gregorian system of calendar computation. Without question he was the man of the year, the leader of thought during this entire era, and a greater influence on public opinion than any other individual in the colony. While he was directly interested in several fields of endeavor he soon became convinced by the citizens that merely to lend his name to a project assured its success, while without it a new venture failed to gain the public confidence.

A great patriot, he often used his publications to urge constitutional freedom and to "proclaim liberty through all the land."

On February 18, 1752, Franklin's *Pennsylvania Gazette* published a notice that "all persons inclined to subscribe to the articles of insurance of houses from fire, in and near the city, are desired to appear at the court-house, where attendance will be given to take in their subscriptions every seventh day of the week, in the afternoon, until the 13th of April next, being the day appointed by said articles for electing twelve directors and a treasurer." On the appointed day the subscribers convened and signed the articles of agreement which were called "a deed of settlement" and so was established The Philadelphia Contributionship for the Insurance of Houses from Loss by Fire, the second known concern for the insuring of such property to originate in the colonies and also the last prior to the years of independence.

The name first subscribed to this deed of settlement was that of James Hamilton, the Lieutenant Governor of the Province under the Proprietaries, and as a public officer he evidenced the approval of the government. The first private name was that of Benjamin Franklin who was also elected a director at this first meeting. The Contributionship was not incorporated until February 20, 1768. It adopted as its seal the Hand-in-Hand, originally patterned after the Amicable Contributionship of London and apparently they at once set out to design a mark of distinction. This consisted of four leaden hands, clasped and crossed, and mounted on a wooden shield.

Five weeks after the original subscriptions were made, Hugh Roberts, one of the directors, was ordered "to treat with John Stow (the same one who the next year recast the Liberty Bell) about making the marks for Houses Insured," while on July 22 of this same year "An Order was drawn on the Treasurer to pay John Stow, for One hundred Marks, the Sum of Twelve pounds, ten Shillings." The wooden shields upon which these castings were mounted were of varied sizes and shapes, and the policy number was painted upon the badge in gold. The older marks which have been collected show the effect of the elements which have worn away the wood surface. Only where the hands were mounted and the policy number affixed was the wood protected, and now these places appear somewhat raised over the background. This gives a sort of carved effect to the numerals and that is fortunate, since it has preserved the identity of the mark. Because of this we are able to show building descriptions and locations for a number of the rarer plaques.

These same directors who authorized the issuance of the fire badge agreed "to pay a forfeiture of one shilling for not meeting precisely at the hour appointed, and two shillings for total absence." This early fire insurance concern which remains successful to this day was not only responsible for America's first visual footprints of assurance but also was the first to implant the milestone on the highways of this continent. The directors' fines having accumulated to a considerable sum, at the meeting of February 17, 1761, the directors then agreed "to apply their fines in purchasing Stones to be erected on the Road leading from Philadelphia towards Trenton, the distance of a mile One from another with the Number of Miles from Philadelphia, to be cut in each Stone, and Tho. Wharton and Jacob Lewis are requested to Contract for the same.

"The committee, being so directed, caused to be cut some thirty-one mile-stones. On the fifteenth of May, 1764, at five o'clock in the morning, they started at Front and Market Streets, taking with them the Surveyor General of the Province, and at the distance of every mile planted one of the stones. Within four chains from the edge of the Delaware River, they planted the twenty-ninth mile-stone, and having gained by accurate measurement two miles in the estimated distance, they gave the two additional stones, numbered 30 and 31, to be planted on the Jersey side of the road to New York."

The Hand-in-Hand, as it was commonly referred to, occupied a unique position in that it was born in a period when the colonists felt the first pangs of a new oppression. It witnessed the growing pains of a populace bent upon attaining a genuine freedom and it weathered the storms of a bloody revolution to emerge stronger and healthier than before.

For three decades there had been an undercurrent of sentiment throughout the colonies against the alleged injustices meted out by the government. The main issue, as is well known, was taxation without representation. The colonists were British subjects, and the principle for which they contended was, in fact, the very basis of British constitutional government. It was an Englishman's birthright and the treatment accorded to the colonists violated the very principles upon which the empire was founded. Volumes have been written upon the details of the struggle for independence. Let it suffice to say that on July 4, 1776, the Continental Congress adopted the Declaration of Independence, and during the next several months it was signed by members of the Congress. Regarding the atmosphere of fear which prevailed in this period, the Philadelphia Contributionship quotes in its minutes: "The assets have been twice in danger of confiscation by enemies of the country. On July 2, 1776, the clerk was ordered to have made a chest in which to deposit the books, papers and other valuable property belonging to the Company for hasty removal to a place of safety in the event of danger." Also in a booklet published by this company we find that: "One of the interesting traditions of the Company is that during the War of the Revolution, the scarcity of lead becoming of some moment, the Directors temporarily discontinued the practice of affixing the marks to insured houses and those on hand were melted and recast into bullets for the Continental Army."

The necessity for this eighteenth century "scrap drive" ended when Cornwallis ran up the white flag and surrendered on October 19, 1781. Though the war was over, the final treaty between the United States and Great Britain was not signed until September 3, 1783, nor was it ratified by Congress until January, 1784.

In preceding pages much was said about the abundance of trees within the city of Philadelphia. There are numerous records of the difficulty which early firemen experienced in fighting and extinguishing fires because of the obstructions created by the many trees in the community. Even before the surrender at Yorktown the Philadelphia Contributionship took one last step during the era of colonization when on April 9, 1781, at a general meeting of the contributors it was resolved that "no houses having a tree or trees planted before them shall be insured or reinsured." Coming at a time when the citizens were aroused by a multitude of problems of readjustment, this embargo naturally was met with indignation, and though subsequently removed in 1810 it nevertheless resulted in the organization of the first fire insurance concern in the new Republic.

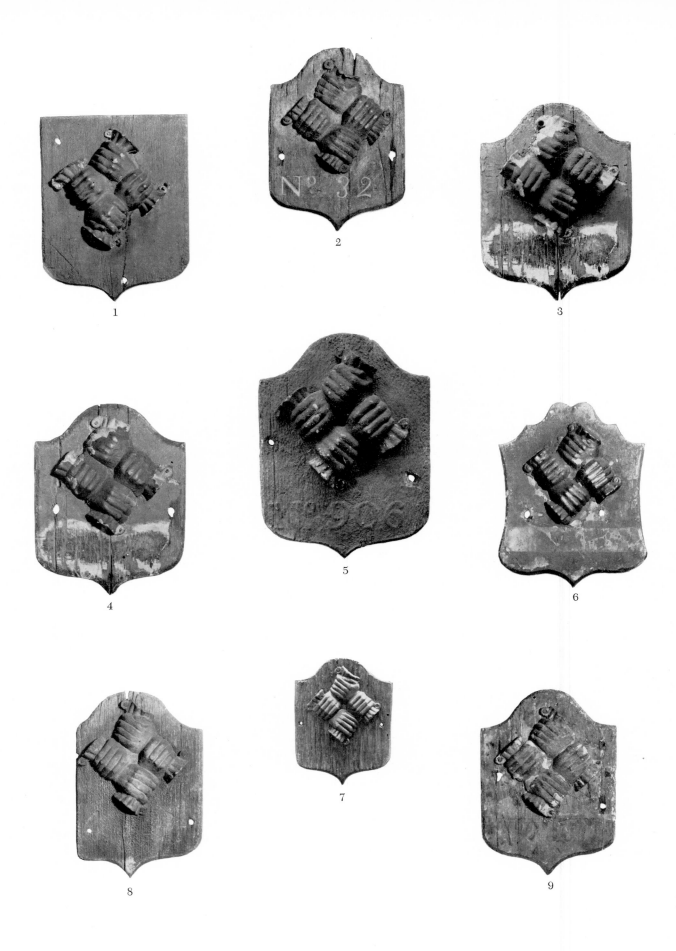

1
2
3
4
5
6
7
8
9

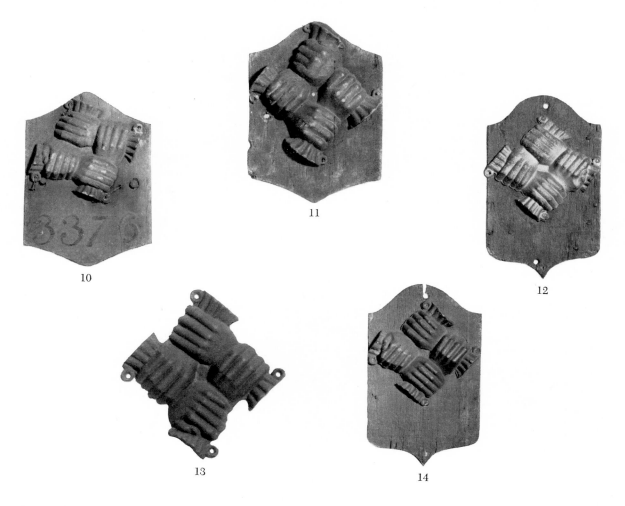

10

11

12

13

14

(1-21) THE PHILADELPHIA CONTRIBUTIONSHIP FOR THE INSURANCE OF HOUSES FROM LOSS BY FIRE. PHILADELPHIA, PENNSYLVANIA. 1752-

1. Wood. Shield shape. 12″ x 15⅞″. Four lead clasped hands of very large size, measuring 9″ x 10¼″ from point to point. Thumb up originally. Undoubtedly a mark which was issued early in the company's existence between 1752 and 1761. Contained a policy number, but only the "N" is now distinguishable.

2. Wood. Shield shape. 10½″ x 14½″. Four lead clasped hands. Thumb points up. Policy number 232 was issued in 1754 and covered upon a house on the south side of High Street (now Market) in Philadelphia.

3. Wood. Shield shape. 12″ x 15½″. Four lead clasped hands of the large variety having thumb up. Issued about 1758.

4. Wood. Shield shape. 11⅛″ x 14¾″. Four lead clasped hands with thumb up. Issued about 1759.

5. Wood. Shield shape. 11¼″ x 15½″. Four lead clasped hands, large size; thumb up. Policy number 906 was issued to John Beeker in 1764 and covered "in house, kitchen and piaza," located on west side of Front Street in the Northern Liberties near the Shuger house, Philadelphia, Pa.

6. Wood. Shield shape, very odd. 12⅜″ x 16″. Four lead clasped hands with slender fingers and thumb up. Very rare. Issued about 1765.

7. Wood. Shield shape. 10½″ x 14½″. Four lead clasped hands, thumb up. Board has beveled edges. Originally on building on Third Street, Philadelphia, Pa. Issued 1774.

8. Wood. Shield shape. 12″ x 15¼″. Four lead clasped hands, large size; thumb up. Left side broken. Original size probably as given. Issued about 1774.

9. Wood. Shield shape. 10⅜″ x 14½″. Four lead clasped hands with thumb up. Policy number 2370 was issued in 1789 to John Cats and covered house and kitchen located on north side of Sassafras Street and third door below Third Street, Philadelphia, Pa.

10. Wood. Shield shape. 9¼″ x 13″. Four lead clasped hands mounted with thumb down on left side. Board 1⅛″ thick. Policy number 3376 was issued in 1810 to Peter Thouron and covered house situated on south side of Powell Street, about halfway between Fifth and Sixth Streets, Philadelphia, Pa.

11. Wood. Shield shape. 9¼″ x 13″. Four lead clasped hands, large size; thumb up, large cuffs. Policy number 3437 was issued to Peter Bob in 1811 and covered house on southwest corner of Ninth and Filbert Streets, Philadelphia, Pa. Numbers barely discernible on board.

12. Wood. Shield shape. 8⅝″ x 12½″. Four lead clasped hands mounted with thumb up on right side. Issued about 1811.

13. Lead. 8⅛″ x 8¾″. Unmounted lead clasped hands of the type appearing on marks issued about 1815.

14. Wood. Shield shape. 8½″ x 14½″. Four lead clasped hands mounted with thumb down on left side. Issued about 1817.

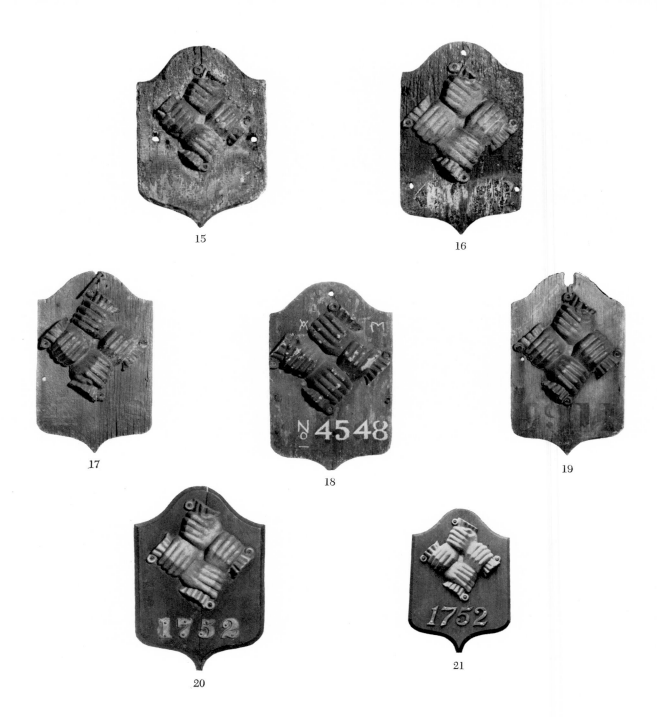

15   16

17   18   19

20   21

15. Wood. Shield shape. 10½″ x 15½″. Four lead clasped hands with thumb up. Issued about 1819.

16. Wood. Shield shape. 8¾″ x 14⅛″. Four lead clasped hands with thumb up. Policy number 4059 was issued in 1822 to Adam Reigart and covered four adjoining houses located on the west side of Ann Street and south corner of Brewers Alley, Philadelphia, Pa.

17. Wood. Shield shape. 8⅞″ x 14⅜″. Four lead clasped hands, small size; mounted with thumb down. Policy number 4198 was issued to John Warder in 1823 and covered "on house located on east side of Third Street, between Callowhill and Noble Streets, number 245, Philadelphia, Pa."

18. Wood. Shield shape. 8¾″ x 13¾″. Four lead clasped hands mounted with thumb down on left side. Policy number 4548 was issued to James Furlong in 1827 and covered on house located on the northwest corner of Cherry and Seventh Streets, Philadelphia, Pa.

19. Wood. Shield shape. 8¾″ x 12½″. Four lead clasped hands with thumb up. Policy number 4911 was issued to Daniel B. Smith in 1832 and covered his printing office on the south side of Hartungs Alley, number 2, Philadelphia, Pa.

20. Wood. Shield shape. 10″ x 14⅞″. Four lead clasped hands with thumb up. Lead date of organization, "1752." Modern type mark issued by this organization about 1920 for advertising purposes.

21. Wood. Shield shape. 10″ x 15″. Four lead clasped hands with thumb up. Lead date of organization, "1752." Modern type mark issued by this organization in 1935 for advertising purposes.

IN THE NEW REPUBLIC
1784-1800

Gillespie and Walsh in their valuable and informative *Fire Insurance House Marks of the United States*, give a comprehensive account of the establishment of the Mutual Assurance Company for the Insuring of Houses from Loss by Fire. According to the authors: "This Company was formed under rather peculiar circumstances. A claim was made on the Philadelphia Contributionship for a loss by fire, which fire was communicated to the building they insured from another house which was on fire, by means of some trees upon the sidewalk, which caught and carried the flames to the insured dwelling house. And no doubt another reason was that the proximity of trees to houses hampered the work of the firemen. The consequence was a prejudice against insuring houses which had trees near them. The Contributionship made it a condition precedent that they would insure no house before which trees were planted on the sidewalk. This caused the cutting down of some trees and occasioned much dissatisfaction among many citizens who took pride in the trees which shaded the sidewalks. The consequence was the formation of an association for insuring houses whether trees were near them or not.

"The subscribers were composed of forty members of the Contributionship, who had trees before their houses, and they were willing to pay an extra premium for the privilege of retaining them, but the Directors of the Contributionship refused to sanction the retention of the trees on any terms.

"Consequently, the friends of the trees formed the new Company in 1784, which was to go into effect as soon as so many persons as had property in houses to the value of £100,000, collectively, should join it. Notice was given the old Company and two months from the 5th of July, 1784, given them to reconsider, but they would do nothing. The new Company was therefore formed on the 29th of September, 1784, officers were duly elected and the members adopted as the badge of the Corporation the representation of a Green Tree. Being, however, somewhat prejudiced by the action of the Contributionship, the Mutual Assurance Company required, according to an article in the Deed of Settlement, that an additional deposit should be made upon insurance of all houses having

trees planted before them or in the yards near the houses, to be charged in proportion to the risk such trees may occasion.

"The Deed of Settlement was made on the 21st of October, 1784; and the advantages resulting from their association having been confirmed by experience, the members were incorporated by an act of the Legislature of Pennsylvania passed the 27th day of February 1786."

Thus was established the first fire insurance company in the new era of independence. The fire mark of the Mutual Assurance of Philadelphia first consisted of a wooden shield and oval plaque upon which was mounted a lead casting of a tree, painted green. The policy number was painted upon the shield. As in the case of the marks of the Philadelphia Contributionship the shields have become worn and reduced in thickness, so that the portions covered by the casting and the painted numerals now stand out in relief. Later the entire mark, both background and trees, was made of cast iron. It is a matter of record that the brass founder, Samuel Parker, who was located on Arch Street, between Fourth and Fifth Streets, in Philadelphia, made the brass die for the casting of the lead trees.

Many of the marks of the Green Tree are depicted upon these pages, one of which, issued in 1790 to represent policy number 484, appeared on a building once situated on the southwest corner of Seventh and High (Market) Streets in Philadelphia. It was in this house, owned by Jacob Graff, Jr., that Thomas Jefferson wrote the first draft of the Declaration of Independence. Green Tree marks can also be viewed today upon buildings of historic significance in the city of Philadelphia.

Even though Congress had ratified the Peace Treaty the financial situation was alarming. With a national debt of sixty million dollars and three hundred million of practically worthless currency the populace was distraught and in doubt. Differences and disputes prevailed among the newly formed states and it was not until 1787 that the thirteen sovereignties decided to resolve their differences and effect a union under our Constitution. While the entire banking capital of the country was only about two million dollars, venture money came out of hiding, and between 1787 and the close of the century as many as eighteen fire insurance concerns were established. With the exception of the first fire insurance carrier born in South Carolina, our story must be confined to those companies whose fire marks remain as a visual reminder of their existence.

Among the first measures of the government of the new Republic was the placing of its seal of approval upon the establishment of corporations. There was no general legislation on the subject, however, and they were permitted to organize only under the general powers granted by the state legislatures. As the doctrines of English law were adopted in this as in other respects, early enactments by the states were limited to special charters. Patterned after the old English custom, a group of individuals signed a Deed of Settlement on April 3, 1787, and formed the Mutual Assurance Company for Insuring Houses from Loss by Fire in New York. At a meeting held October 9 the same year it was moved: "That the Treasurer and Secretary prepare a Badge, viz: 'An oval tin plate, painted black, with the words Mutual Assurance, and the number, in gilt letters and figures.'" These marks are now extremely rare, almost unique, because most of them were obliterated in the early New York fires and only one or two are known to be in existence today. An interesting point in this case is that the directors specifically instructed that this "badge" be placed above the door of the insured building. In 1798, the legislature authorized the company to write insurance on property other than buildings, thus providing for indemnity for loss to household goods as well as structures. In 1809, this old mutual was chartered into a stock company, finally becoming The Knickerbocker Fire Insurance Company in 1846.

Once again our attention is focused upon the birthplace of our national government, where early in the year 1791 the Bank of North America abandoned the method of keeping accounts on the old British basis of pounds, shillings, and pence to substitute the plan of dollars and cents. At this time also the citizens of Philadelphia were seeking the permission of the legislature to demolish wooden buildings and dilapidated structures, there having been two serious fires that year. But this request was refused as was the petition seeking additional power to regulate building construction.

These were the years of change from a monarchal basis of government to a representative republic. One might think that under such conditions chaos would prevail. Instead, there was a somewhat orderly endeavor to frame legislative acts and policies which would eventually benefit the many and still permit the free advance of trade and industry. During that period a kind of gambling or lottery in the form of tontines had been popular, and in Philadelphia as well as Boston a project was begun which was known as the Universal Tontine, a form of life insurance lottery. Before anticipated subscriptions were completed, however, these plans had come into disfavor, and their many subscribers were faced with the problem of the disposition of their funds. After several meetings the subscribers voted to convert their objectives into a society to be known as the Insurance Company of North America, whose name was probably inspired by that of the Bank of North America already formed in Philadelphia.

The subscribers agreed on November 19, 1792, with the plan calling for a general insurance company empowered to write marine, fire, and life insurance. Because the public was skeptical of life insurance, as evidenced by their attitude towards tontines, the directors decided not to enter that field. They also decided to pass up fire insurance for the time being, concentrating all of their early endeavors in the marine field which was very lucrative at that time. That their judgment was sound—Philadelphia merchants and businessmen have had such reputation from the earliest times—was proved in 1797 when the company's marine premiums amounted to over seven hundred thousand dollars and in 1798 reached nearly one million five hundred thousand dollars, a phenomenal production for such a young concern.

On December 18, 1792, a petition was filed with the state legislature for incorporation as a stock company, yet it was not until April 14, 1794, that the act was signed by the Governor. There had been a succession of obstacles, mostly in the opposition of individual marine underwriters who feared competition, which delayed the approval of the lawmakers who failed to act until the company threatened to incorporate in Delaware. On July 11, 1794, the committee of the Board finally decided to write fire insurance on a basis new to Philadelphia property owners who were subsequently enabled to cover goods as well as houses. Not to be outdone by the custom of the two other local fire concerns, the Insurance Company of North America employed Robert Haydock, a plumber at 38 South Second Street, to manufacture one hundred fire marks or badges. The sign consisted of a star with six wavy points formed of lead and mounted upon a wooden shield. In 1796 the company also adopted a metal fire mark depicting an eagle taking flight from a rock, the first being of copper, while in 1828 a cast-iron variety came into use. Since the American bald eagle had been adopted by Congress in 1782 for the Great Seal of the United States a great many enterprises and organizations utilized this patriotic symbol, particularly after the War of 1812.

These sentiments undoubtedly also influenced the adoption of our national bird by the Insurance Company of North America over whose destinies he has watched as zealously as those of the nation itself. Of American companies this is one of the few that employed a heraldic device, one which is recognized as emblematic of a stalwart in the fire insurance business today.

During the early 1790's a great deal of time and money were expended in building roads from Philadelphia to Baltimore and Washington where the new national government was to be established. Population centers in Maryland were taking on a new importance, while their legislators and commissioners were making an attempt to liberalize their restrictive laws. Maryland and Virginia made a pact which permitted vessels entering Chesapeake Bay to enter the shores of either state free of toll or duty when seeking shelter or safety against an enemy. An early act affecting the economy of Maryland came about when Oliver Evans, a miller, represented to the legislature in 1787 that he had "invented, discovered and introduced into exercise" two new machines. These were for use in merchant mills. One was called an "elevator," and was intended to hoist grain from the lower level, remove the flour or meal from the burs, and carry the product to the upper level or place of storage. His second machine, known as a "hopper boy," was built to spread the meal or flour on an upper floor to cool after which it was gathered up and taken to the bolting hopper, all without the aid of manual labor. Because flour was one of the principal staples of the state, the legislators, feeling that the inventions would lower the cost of manufacture and consequently improve local economy, gave Evans the sole right to make and sell these machines in Maryland for a period of fourteen years. The same principles are still used in milling today.

In 1792 the area contiguous to Baltimore was plagued by many fires, mostly in the brush or wooded lands. The resulting damage became so severe and its effect upon the economy was so disastrous that the legislature enacted a law which held that any person responsible for such a fire was to be fined £50. It was in this fire-conscious community that the Baltimore Equitable Society opened its office at the house of Joseph Townsend on April 9, 1794, to insure properties in "Baltimore Town" and for five miles around. They organized under a Deed of Settlement similar to that of the Hand-in-Hand of London and adopted a house mark utilizing the two clasped hands of that British concern. The earliest types had cast-iron hands mounted upon a wood panel; the later ones were entirely of cast iron. The Baltimore Equitable is still thriving in its limited bailiwick.

Into a nation which was struggling for its existence even after it had gained its independence there also came the strife of party politics. Washington had refused to run for a third term as President. The bitterly fought campaign between Adams and Jefferson was close—seventy-one against sixty-eight electoral votes —leaving Adams with a very small majority which resulted in the weakening of his leadership. Amid these conditions in that same year the Mutual Insurance Company was founded in Charleston, South Carolina, the date of incorporation being December 16, 1797. There is little written evidence of this company's activity except that in 1806 it had an office at No. 131 Broad Street. It is believed that they discontinued business shortly thereafter. However, they did leave behind a number of their marks as evidence of their liability. These consisted of an oval cast-iron mark containing the raised image of an angel in flight over a burning city. This guardian of the skies held a cornucopia in hand from which water was pouring onto the flames below. Charleston was settled largely by French Huguenots and undoubtedly the vivid imagination exhibited by the early American artist who designed this mark was influenced by an Old World religious background. As indicated in a pamphlet published by the Charleston Museum in 1923 marks of this company could still be seen on buildings in Charleston, some of which were located at 94 Church Street, 14 Water Street, 284 Meeting Street, 47 Laurens Street, and 117 Calhoun Street.

While Charleston remained a great seaport, Newport, Rhode Island, became the fourth largest port in the colonies by the end of the eighteenth century. This little state, at first made up of outcasts and refugees, had developed a tremendous trade with the West Indies and as a result of its import of sugar and allied products it became a center for the manufacture of rum. In 1765 there were twenty-two distilleries operating in Newport as well as a number in Providence. This product was the lubricant of trade in the New England states. Such "stimulation" caused the expansion of many lines of manufacture so that at the close of the eighteenth century Providence was a thriving city of seven thousand inhabitants. In 1791 the Providence Bank was founded and John Brown, a leader in the community and active in most of its enterprises, became its president. This frugal New Englander took an unusual interest in the formation of the Providence Insurance Company which opened its doors for business on January 14, 1799. To the organizers he suggested that he favored low salaries for the officers of the insurance company fearing that "if the Salleries (were) fixed too high it (would) have a bad effect—in Respect (to) our other Institutions allready Astablished." Brown was referring to his pet project, the Providence Bank. He suggested total salaries of not more than one thousand dollars split seven to three between the "Conductor & Clark or President & Secretary if You please So to call them." His advice on salaries was followed: eight hundred dollars for the president and two hundred dollars for the secretary were deemed sufficient. Early in 1800, the Washington Insurance Company was organized and approved by the legislature, and in March, 1820, a merger and final incorporation as the Providence Washington Insurance Company was consummated. These companies started out principally as marine underwriters, but they had many corporate contingencies to meet and finally decided to expand into the fire insurance field in 1844.

With the conservatism of a Brown one can well understand why this company failed to issue a fire mark in America. Gillingham states, however, that they did issue a mark for use in Puerto Rico where the natives would not accept insurance on their property unless the issuing company furnished them with a fire mark. That was true also in the Orient. Consequently, specimens of both types of Providence Washington marks have been found to form a part of this story of signeviery.

At the close of one era and the beginning of another, in a period when commerce and industry were torn with indecision, it is reassuring to record the beginning of this sound and conservative underwriting concern which has progressed successfully in our American free enterprise system for over one hundred and fifty years.

22

23

24

25

26

27

28

29

30

31

32

33

(22-42) THE MUTUAL ASSURANCE COMPANY FOR IN-SURING HOUSES FROM LOSS BY FIRE. PHILADELPHIA, PENNSYLVANIA. 1784-

22. Wood. Shield shape. 12¼″ x 15⅝″. Green tree of cast lead. Policy number 149 was issued in 1786 and covered at 224 North Front Street, Philadelphia, Pa.

23. Wood. Shield shape. 12¼″ x 15½″. Green tree of cast lead. Policy number 153 was issued in 1786 and covered at 237 Lombard Street, Philadelphia, Pa.

24. Wood. Shield shape. 12¼″ x 15⅝″. Green tree of cast lead. Policy number 445 was issued in 1790 and covered at 224 Vine Street, Philadelphia, Pa.

25. Wood. Shield shape. 12½″ x 15½″. Green tree of cast lead. Shield has broken sides but originally was about size shown above. Policy number 484 was issued in 1790 and covered property on the southwest corner of Seventh and High (Market) Streets, Philadelphia, Pa. Here Thomas Jefferson wrote the first draft of the Declaration of Independence.

26. Wood. Shield shape. 12½″ x 15¾″. Green tree of cast lead. Policy number 562 was issued in 1792 and covered the property of Frederick Heisz at 610 Race Street, Philadelphia, Pa.

27. Wood. Shield shape. 12⅛″ x 15⅞″. Green tree of cast

lead. Policy number 670 was issued in 1794 and covered on the west side of Fourth Street, between Spruce and Pine Streets, Philadelphia, Pa.

28. Wood. Shield shape. 11¾″ x 15½″. Green tree of cast lead. From a three-story house located on Fifth Street, Philadelphia, Pa. Issued about 1797.

29. Wood. Oval. 10″ x 15″. Green tree of cast lead. Policy number 978 was issued in 1799 and covered at 165 North Front Street, Philadelphia, Pa.

30. Wood. Oval. 10½″ x 15″. Green tree of cast lead. Policy number 1025 was issued in 1800 and covered "in a court" at 831 Cherry Street, Philadelphia, Pa.

31. Wood. Oval. 10½″ x 14⅝″. Green tree of cast lead. Policy number 1095 was issued in 1800 and covered at 312 South Fifth Street, Philadelphia, Pa.

32. Wood. Oval. 10⅛″ x 14¾″. Green tree of cast lead. Mark is of 1800 issue while policy number 1131 was issued February 12, 1801, and covered at 737 Walnut Street, Philadelphia, Pa., the original street number being "199, situated on the north side of Walnut Street, between Seventh and Eighth Streets, Philadelphia."

33. Wood. Oval. 10½″ x 14¾″. Green tree of cast lead. Policy number 1195 was issued in 1801 and covered at 263 North Fifth Street, Philadelphia, Pa.

34

34

35

36

37

38

39

40

41

42

MUTUAL
ASSURANCE
3617

43

44

45

46

47

48

49

50

51

52

53

34. Wood. Oval. 10½″ x 14¾″. Green tree of cast lead. Policy number 1348 was issued in 1803 and covered at 419 South Second Street, Philadelphia, Pa.

35. Wood. Oval. 9½″ x 14″. Green tree of cast lead. Policy number 1644 was issued in 1803 and covered at 155 Green Street, Philadelphia, Pa.

36. Cast iron. Oval. 9⅜″ x 13⅝″. Raised green tree and flat back. Largest size iron mark of this company. Issued about 1805.

37. Cast iron. Oval. 8¾″ x 12¾″. Raised green tree and flat back. Somewhat smaller type. Rare. Issued in 1806.

38. Cast iron. Oval. 8⅜″ x 12¼″. Raised green tree and hollow back. Issue of 1810.

39. Cast iron. Oval. 8⅛″ x 11⅞″. Raised green tree and hollow back. Evidently a variant of issue of 1810.

40. Cast iron. Squatty oval. 8″ x 8⅜″. Raised green tree and flat back. Very rare. Issued about 1827.

41. Wood. Shield shape. 7½″ x 13″. Green tree of cast lead. Issued about 1890 but used principally for advertising purposes. Very rare. Authenticity of this mark questioned.

42. Cast iron. Oval. 8¼″ x 12″. Raised green tree and hollow back. Raised date of organization, "1784." This is last type of mark issued by this company, about 1930 and was used for advertising purposes.

(43) MUTUAL ASSURANCE COMPANY FOR INSURING HOUSES FROM LOSS BY FIRE IN NEW YORK, NEW YORK. 1787-1846.

Tin. Oval. Black with gold letters and figures. Very rare. *(Courtesy of Insurance Company of North America.)*

(44-53) INSURANCE COMPANY OF NORTH AMERICA. PHILADELPHIA, PENNSYLVANIA. 1792-

44. Wood. Shield shape. Lead star, six wavy points, mounted on shield. Unique. *(Courtesy of Insurance Company of North America.)*

45. Wood. Oval. Lead eagle mounted on oval board. Painted policy number 447. Unique. *(Courtesy of Insurance Company of North America.)*

46. Copper. Oval. 8⅝″ x 11½″. Gilded eagle rising from cloud. Design raised. Mark has rolled edge. Issued after 1800.

47. Cast iron. Oval. 8⅝″ x 11⅜″. Eagle rising from cloud. Design raised. Mark has beaded edge. Nail holes at top and bottom. Very rare. Issued about 1830.

48. Heavy tin. Rectangular. 8⅜″ x 4⅞″. "North America—Philadelphia, A.D. 1794" raised. From building, south side of National Road, Old Washington, Ohio. Very rare. Used inland. Issued about 1865.

49. Heavy tin. Rectangular. 7⅜″ x 3⅞″. "A.D. 1794—Insurance Co. of North America." and border raised. From brick dwelling in Delaware, Ohio. Rare. Issued about 1870.

50. Tin. Rectangular. 6⅞″ x 2½″. Gold background with black border and "Insured North America, Philadelphia, Pa." Rare. Issued about 1880.

51. Copper. Oval. 8⅜″ x 11¼″. Eagle rising from cloud, "I.N.A." and date "1792." Design, lettering and numerals raised. Issued in 1920 as an advertising medium.

52. Tin. Diamond shape, slightly convexed. 5¾″ x 5¾″. "North America" and Chinese characters in dark blue on speckled light blue enamel background. Mark used in China.

53. Tin. Circular. 6¾″ in diameter. Raised gold eagle on red center. Border and company name with Chinese characters in raised gold on black background. Modern mark used in Far East.

54

55

56

57

58

59

60

61

62

63

64

36

(54-61) BALTIMORE EQUITABLE SOCIETY. BALTIMORE, MARYLAND. 1794-

54. Wood. Rectangular. 13¼″ x 9⅜″. Pair of cast iron clasped hands mounted on wood plaque. From old building in Baltimore, Md. Issued 1794. Exceedingly rare.

55. Wood. Rectangular. 14¼″ x 11⅜″. Pair of heavy cast iron clasped hands mounted on wood plaque containing molding on all four sides. Issued about 1795.

56. Wood. Rectangular. 14″ x 9¾″. Pair of cast iron clasped hands with unusually lacy cuffs, mounted on wood plaque. Issued about 1820.

57. Cast iron. Rectangular. 10½″ x 9⅞″. Heavy rolled border and raised clasped hands. Cuffs lacier than later types. Issued about 1837.

58. Cast iron. Rectangular. 10⅜″ x 9⅝″. Heavy rolled border. Raised clasped hands are gold on black background. Date of organization, 1794, in gold numerals. Roped cuff. Issued about 1845.

59. Cast iron. Rectangular. 10⅛″ x 9½″. Heavy rolled border and raised clasped hands. Casting varies slightly in size and relief of hands and is a variant of the 1845 issue.

60. Cast iron. Odd shape. 8″ x 5″. Pair of clasped hands.

These appear to have been broken from a regular fire mark of this company. They contain customary hole at top for hanging.

61. Heavy cast iron. Rectangular. 10⅜″ x 9¾″. Clasped hands and "1794" in raised gold on black background. Modern type issued 1927.

(62) MUTUAL INSURANCE COMPANY. CHARLESTON, SOUTH CAROLINA. 1797-1806.

Cast iron. Oval. 9⅝″ x 7⅝″. Depicts guardian angel hovering over burning city, sprinkling water onto fire. Also contains company name on convexed margin. From property on Laurens Street, Charleston, South Carolina.

(63-64) PROVIDENCE WASHINGTON INSURANCE COMPANY. PROVIDENCE, RHODE ISLAND. 1799-

63. Tin. Rectangular. 7″ x 4″. Lithographed light blue border and "Incorporada 1799, Providence Washington Compania De Seguros. Providence, R. I., U. S. A." Dark blue background. Rare, old mark used in Latin America.

64. Iron. Diamond shape, slightly convexed. 5¾″ x 5¾″. "Providence Washington" and Chinese characters in dark blue on speckled light blue enamel. Mark used in China.

THE DECADE OF RECONSTRUCTION

1801-1810

One indication of the transition of the economy from its crude beginning to the system adopted by the new Republic is substantiated by the fact that there were only seven million dollars in exports in 1803 but these were increased to eleven million in one year. By 1805, they had expanded to thirteen million dollars. As further evidence of the progress made during this decade it is recorded that by 1810 American securities were listed on the Exchange at London at higher rates than those quoted in the homeland.

Philadelphia, retaining the lead in almost every line of endeavor, remained a great center of this early development, for its manufactures, banking, and insurance were geared to the new freedom of action implemented by the impulses of those who so successfully weathered the storms of the Revolution. Near this early capital city, plants were founded to print calico. One of these was Stewart's, located at Germantown, another was Hewson's at Kensington, and a third at Darby was known as Thorburn's. In 1803, these three factories employed seventy hands who turned out two hundred thousand yards of goods; it is little wonder that the ladies of this era used an abundance of material for their crisply starched finery. It is related that the dress of "m'lady" during the post-Revolution days in America far exceeded in styles and elegance the costumes produced both in London and in Paris.

Cotton machinery manufacturing was also begun in Philadelphia by a Mr. Eltonhead, who provided mules equipped with one hundred and forty-four spindles for the sum of three hundred dollars each. He also produced a carding engine for four hundred dollars, while a drawing and roving frame could be secured for two hundred dollars. As an impetus to the promotion of industry there was organized The Association of Artists and Manufacturers, their original activity being the gathering of statistics of domestic industry. Throughout Philadelphia County the seeds of industrial enterprise were taking root, and while to us in this century these efforts may seem minor, the advance was a gigantic one with each step beset by obstacles not now encountered.

This progress was not achieved without imagination in overcoming obstacles. A notable example of such imagination was the work of Oliver Evans, who in 1804 commenced to manufacture steam engines in Philadelphia. In *Poulson's Advertiser* he wrote some ten years later that he had advocated the use of steam-propelled motors for land vehicles in 1773 and that in 1778 he recommended them for boats, ending his dissertation with this quotation:

"In the year 1804 I constructed at Philadelphia a machine (of my own invention) for cleaning docks,—a heavy mud flat, with a steam-engine of the power of five horses in it to work the machinery. And, to show that both steam-carriages and steamboats were practicable (with my steam engines), I first put wheels to it and propelled it by the engine a mile and a half, and then into the Schuylkill, although its weight was equal to that of two hundred barrels of flour. I then fixed a paddle-wheel at the stem and propelled it by the engine down the Schuylkill and up the Delaware, sixteen miles, leaving all the vessels that were under sail full half way behind me (the wind being ahead), although the application was so temporary as to produce great friction, and the flat was most illy formed for sailing, done in the presence of thousands."

Evans was not only a genius who certainly had a greater understanding of steam engines and their adaptability to locomotion than any of his contemporaries, but, as is evidenced by the quotation from a letter he addressed to the New York *Commercial Advertiser*, he was also a man of remarkable foresight. In an amazing glimpse into the future Evans said: "The time will come when people will travel in stages moved by steam-engines at fifteen to twenty miles an hour. A carriage will leave Washington in the morning, breakfast at Baltimore, dine at Philadelphia, and sup at New York on the same day. Railways will be laid of wood or iron, or on smooth paths of broken stone or gravel, to travel as well by night as by day. A steam-engine will drive a carriage one hundred and eighty miles in twelve hours, or engines will drive boats ten or twelve miles an hour and hundreds of boats will so run on the Mississippi and other waters, as was prophesied thirty years ago (by Fitch); but the velocity of boats can never be made equal to that of carriages upon rails, because the resistance in water is eight hundred times more than that in air. Posterity will not be able to discover why the Legislature or Congress did not grant the inventor such protection as might have enabled him to put in operation those great improvements sooner, he having neither asked money nor a monopoly of any existing thing." As we progress from decade to decade, we in this twentieth century must pause to marvel at the spirit born of American independence which filled the souls of our citizens with an urge to persist against all odds.

During this decade of reconstruction fifty-seven new insurance charters were granted throughout the various states. While prior to this period there was no real basis for a policy contract and crudities prevailed, there now arose a demand for improvement and stabilization. For the first time fire insurance risks were classified somewhat after the old English system, they being listed and rated as Common Insurances, Hazardous Insurances, Doubly Hazardous Insurances, and Special or Extraordinary Risks. When a policy was written for over ten thousand dollars the companies secured an extra premium, as they did also for contingent increases in hazards. A proposal and application for coverage as well as the requirement of a legal or corporate seal were all set forth as conditions of the policy, although there remained a lack of uniformity among the various underwriters.

Into such an atmosphere and without any apparent opposition came a new fire, marine, life, and inland transportation insurance concern known as The Philadelphia Insurance Company. This concern was incorporated on March 26, 1804, and established its office on the southwest corner of Dock and Second Streets in Philadelphia. On January 11, 1804, they published their proposals for fire insurance. Among the numerous stipulations we find that "a badge of moderate cost shall be fixed on every store, warehouse and shop insured, at the expense of the insured, but to be procured and put up by the officer of the company." That this underwriter had no difficulty in its formation and the success attendant upon its operations may be due to the device adopted which consisted of a dove cast in lead and affixed upon a wooden shield. In its bill this bird of peace and tranquility carried an olive branch and the hand upon which it rested was undoubtedly intended as a symbol of friendliness. In the only example which has come to our attention of an underwriter leaving the table of chance and taking all his chips with him, this concern finally dissolved in 1844 solely because it had enjoyed such a successful career.

The post-Revolution prosperity which prevailed in Philadelphia then spread to Charleston, South Carolina, where the economy had undergone a forced change because of the war. Prior to the war the British bounty on indigo brought large returns, but now, as an independent sovereignty, the citizens began to produce cotton and rice. Because quick profits were harder to obtain and small planters could not bear the cost of slave labor, the consolidation of pioneer homesteads into large estates resulted.

Where production expands, so also does insurance, another example being the establishment of the Union Insurance Company in Charleston on June 17, 1807. The subsequent incorporation of this venture by the General Assembly of South Carolina authorized it to write policies upon marine risks and against fire upon buildings, wares, and goods as well as upon merchandise both within the state and elsewhere. The Union was the first American fire insurance company to own its own building which was located on State Street just behind the People's Office Building.

The fire marks of concerns in this community were of cast iron, and all were emblematic of their endeavor. The Union oval, besides the corporate name, contained the word "Restored" above the symbolic imprint of city buildings on the left; on the right the structures were a mass of flames. Beneath this scene there was boldly embossed a pair of clasped hands, indicative of the friendship and assistance between the owners of the undamaged properties and those lost in the conflagration. As late as 1923, marks of this concern could be seen on properties.

In the capital city of Philadelphia during the closing days of this decade of reconstruction a radical change took place as the fear of a new war and economic instability grew. James Madison was President, and the new congressman from South Carolina, John C. Calhoun, was lending his prestige and energy to the cause of the "War Hawks." The political atmosphere was one of bitterness and conflict, and a decade which had seen great progress was ending in a note of chaos and unrest. Almost washed away in this uproar were the hard-earned fruits of our early independence.

Despite the unfavorable aspects of the times new concerns appeared, venturesome and enterprising, a spirit which also characterized those entrusted with the protection of property from loss by fire. One of these was the American Fire Insurance Company of Philadelphia, organized on February 28, 1810, and headed by Captain William Jones who had distinguished himself in both the army and navy. Jones must have had an excellent opportunity to display the attributes responsible for his naval honors, since there was considerable question in the legislative chambers as to the granting of a charter. The obstacle was the intimation that the American was to be organized to take over the Philadelphia business of the Phoenix (London, 1780) Fire Office. Israel

Whelen, the agent for the Phoenix, was one of the prime organizers and one of the first directors of the new company. Through him most of the business of the London company in Philadelphia was taken over by the new concern.

The American was probably formed in anticipation of the passing of an act by the legislature on March 10, 1810, prohibiting foreign concerns or underwriters from issuing any contract of insurance in Pennsylvania, all such policies being considered as void. For a person to act as a foreign company agent the fine was five thousand dollars, while an individual who became a part of such an illegal policy transaction was also to be fined five hundred dollars. When President Madison took office, Captain William Jones resigned from the American Fire to become Secretary of the Navy. He held that position throughout the new war, later assuming the presidency of the Bank of the United States. Through its celebrities in state and national life, fire insurance has taken a leading position in the social, political, military, and economic welfare of America.

The closing year of the decade also brought the fire insurance industry to Hartford, Connecticut, a community which was destined to be entirely absorbed by this enterprise of indemnity. One of the town's important meeting places during that period was Ransom's Inn, a tavern where the socially elite and the leaders of commerce in the community gathered to exchange the news of the day, discussing numerous activities which would benefit their village. At a meeting held here on June 27, 1810, a group of men decided to incorporate The Hartford Fire Insurance Company, authority having been granted for the charter by the legislature during the previous month. Though times were perilous and these men were without knowledge of the dangers of their venture, they invested fifteen thousand dollars in cash capital at the outset and subscribed the balance of one hundred thirty-five thousand dollars by giving notes and real estate mortgages as security. Nathaniel Terry was elected as its first president, and Walter Mitchell was the secretary. Like so many other insurance executives Terry was also a public servant who had served both in Congress and the legislature. From the outset this company was a financial success. In its forward march it left behind many varied specimens of its house marks, twelve known varieties being recorded on these pages. In addition to these there may be others still to be found upon a building in some secluded byway.

Many fire insurance companies introduced and strongly advocated fire safety measures, but the average citizens also contributed since every householder was expected to be ready, in case of necessity, to assist in fire fighting.

Fire engines—the hand-pump variety—were still somewhat crude, but in 1808 a genuine advancement was made when the riveted hose was invented in Philadelphia, and it was no longer necessary for the engine to be brought too close to a burning building. This produced the hose carriage, first a supplementary attachment to the engine and later an independent unit, operated by separate companies. The innovation completely altered the method of fighting fires in the larger cities. There are records that long hose lines were used in Holland in the late 1600's, but the beginning of the nineteenth century seems to have brought their introduction into this country.

66

67

69

68

70

71

72

(65) PHILADELPHIA INSURANCE COMPANY. PHILA-
DELPHIA, PENNSYLVANIA. 1804-1844.

Wood. Shield shape. 9" x 16½". Cast lead design of dove
resting on a hand, olive branch in its beak. Only known mark.
From 29-31 Old Saint Mary's Street, Philadelphia, Pa. (now Rod-
man Street, near Sixth). *(Courtesy of Insurance Company of
North America.)*

(66) UNION INSURANCE COMPANY. CHARLESTON,
SOUTH CAROLINA. 1807-1839.

Cast iron. Oval. 7⅞" x 9¾". Depicts building in flames, a new
building, two clasped hands and the word "Restored" in center
oval. Company name raised on the outer border. From building at
156 East Bay, Charleston, South Carolina. Very rare.

(67-68) AMERICAN FIRE INSURANCE COMPANY.
PHILADELPHIA, PENNSYLVANIA. 1810-1906.

67. Tin. Rectangular. 7" x 3¼". "Insured American A. D.

1810—Philadelphia" black on green-gold background. First mark
issued by this company.

68. Tin. Rectangular. 6⅞" x 3¼". "American Fire 1810,
Philadelphia." black on light green background.

(69-80) HARTFORD FIRE INSURANCE COMPANY.
HARTFORD, CONNECTICUT. 1810-

69. Tin. Rectangular. 6½" x 2¼". Border and "Hartford"
gold on black background. Issued 1840. Very rare.

70. Tin. Rectangular. 6½" x 2⁵⁄₁₆". Border and "Hartford"
gold on black background. Type of letters varies from those of
mark #69.

71. Tin. Rectangular. 9⅛" x 4¹³⁄₁₆". Raised border and
"Hartford Fire Ins. Co.—Chartered 1810." Lettering had been
gold on black background.

72. Heavy tin. Rectangular. 8⅛" x 3¼". Wide raised border, and "Hartford," in semi-circle. A very rare type of this company's mark, issued about 1850.

74

73

75

77

76

78

79

80

73. Tin. Rectangular. 7⅞" x 4". Raised border and "Hartford Fire Ins. Co." From frame cabin in Xenia, Ohio. Rare. Issued about 1850.

74. Tin. Rectangular. 7⅞" x 3⅞". Raised border and "Hartford Fire Ins. Co.," strictly horizontal, gold on black background. Issued about 1860.

75. Tin. Rectangular. 6¾" x 3⅛". Raised border and "Hartford Fire. Ins, Co." gold on black background.

76. Tin. Rectangular. 6⅞" x 3⅛". "Hartford," and border black on gold background.

77. Tin. Rectangular. 6⅞" x 3¼". "Hartford — Chartered 1810" silver on black background. Type mark used in Kentucky and Tennessee about 1895.

78. Tin. Rectangular. 9¾" x 6". Raised border and "Hartford Fire Ins. Co. Chartered 1810." Semi-modern.

79. Aluminum. Rectangular. 7" x 3½". Company trademark and "Insured in Hartford Fire Insurance Company, Hartford, Conn." black. Modern type mark.

80. Tin. Diamond shape, slightly convexed. 5¾" x 5¾". "Hartford 1810" and Chinese characters in white on dark blue enamel background. Mark used in China.

THE DECADE OF DESPAIR

1811-1820

The second decade of the century began under the continuing threat of war which filled the hearts of the citizens of the new Republic with apprehension. In Congress the war party, a group of young men including Henry Clay of Kentucky and led by John C. Calhoun of South Carolina, demanded war with France or Britain. A considerable majority insisted upon war with both countries.

Down in Calhoun's home in Charleston the prosperity of commerce and agriculture had carried over from the previous decade, at the close of which two new banks were incorporated. When the expansion of business brought increased demand for such banking facilities, the need for added fire insurance protection grew correspondingly.

On December 21, 1811, the Charleston Fire Insurance Company was incorporated, the charter providing for insurance against fire on buildings, goods, wares, merchandise, and other property. The charter also contained a unique clause authorizing it to "Engage in their service such persons, and to procure such apparatus, implements or other articles . . . as may appear necessary . . . to preserve buildings or other property by them insured from destruction or damaged by fire or from depredation." The designer of this company's mark of assurance could well have been the same one who originated the sign of the Union Fire, since it is of the same size and style. It, too, has the name of the company upon an outer band with the word, "Restored," above a group of new buildings, while at the right is a house in flames. Superimposing all is the figure of a woman with a protective shield in one hand, while the other hand points to the restored property.

The young Charlestonians and their friends in the war party of Congress seemed to prevail over the wishes of President Madison and in June of 1812 war was declared on Great Britain. While Madison ascribed the reasons for the quarrel to the seizure of American sailors, the raiding of our ships at sea, and the support which the English were giving to the Indians on our frontiers, it is strongly suspected that the underlying reasons were the ambitions of the young politicians to take over Florida and Canada. As a result of this war, property values and business generally began to collapse. Banks to the north and to the south suspended specie payment shortly after the declaration of war and as a result of the distress among even the wealthy planters of South Carolina, that State as an emergency measure created on December 12, 1812, a bank which was wholly state owned. The war was exceedingly unpopular throughout the states, and as far north as the city of Poughkeepsie, New York, there were rumblings of dissatisfaction. The *Journal* in that city vigorously denounced the draft as "tearing men away from the support of their families" to support a war brought on by Jefferson and Madison. Their representative in Congress, James Emott, was equally outspoken.

It was in 1814 that the New York Legislature enacted some regulatory laws for insurance companies, the first of these making provision for dissolution in case of insolvency or impairment of capital. At the same session and as a result of the war, foreign companies were prohibited from transacting business in New York State. On one occasion the banking situation at Poughkeepsie became quite acute and as a result the postmaster, who was also a private banker, was faced with a run on his bank. This shrewd individual, Levi McKeen, announced that a boat was coming to port with a wagonload of specie from New York. When the vessel arrived at the boat landing, the wagon was at hand. With considerable effort the vehicle was loaded with small kegs. These were transported to the bank which was surrounded by anxious depositors and holders of notes. Two men proceeded to carry in the kegs, one of them inadvertently dropping a keg which broke open and scattered coins among the expectant customers. Satisfied with this unexpected exhibit of wealth, the depositors soon dispersed and the run was stopped. Not until some time later was it disclosed that only one keg contained specie, while the remainder was filled with nails.

Undaunted by the war, confident of their native instinct for success in commerce and business, other citizens of Poughkeepsie set out on a new venture in 1814 when they organized the Dutchess County Fire, Marine and Life Insurance Company. James Talmadge, Jr. and James Emott, who were so vehemently opposed to Madison's policy in Congress, were among the first directors. The bust of the Indian chieftain upon the company's fire badge bears witness to the abundance of Indian lore which this city upon the Hudson contains. It is interesting to note that despite the distressed situation thirty-six charters were granted to insurance concerns throughout the states during this decade.

On Christmas Eve, 1814, a treaty of peace was signed with Britain, thus ending a war which at least to that day was one of the most unpopular in which America engaged. It was referred to as "Mr. Madison's War" and in the treaty nothing was stated about the raiding of our vessels, the capture of our sailors, or the support given to the Indians. None of the war aims was realized and as a result of the action the country found itself deeply in debt. The federal obligations which totalled seventy-five million dollars on the date of independence had reached the vast sum of one hundred and twenty-five million dollars at the conclusion of the war. As a result of an inrush of cheaply made British goods which gave a staggering blow to the American economy, a very high protective tariff was passed in 1816. Considering the chaotic state of affairs it was with relief that Madison turned over the reins of government to James Monroe in 1817. On February 20 of that year, the banks in Philadelphia resumed specie payments.

Banking and fire insurance were interdependent, but the physical safety of any community lay in the hands of an efficient fire-fighting force. Nowhere else in this new Republic had fire fighting reached such an advanced stage as that attained by the many volunteer brigades in Philadelphia. At the close of the war there were both engine companies and hose companies. A controversy raged amongst the "hose" companies about the correct spelling of that word. In the minutes of these old companies some of the secretaries wrote "Hoose," others "Hooze," one persisted in spelling it, "Hoase," though the prominent Philadelphia Hose Company insisted that it remain as we now so commonly use the term. It was not until August, 1824, that by special resolution of the volunteers the current version of the word was adopted.

A unique insurance organization was founded during this decade when several of the volunteer fire companies in Philadelphia banded together "to establish such relations as were proper among volunteer firemen, whose views were sympathetic with each other, and to more effectively perform their duties." The fire-fighting companies in attendance at the initial meeting of this association which met at the northwest corner of Third and Tammany Streets, September 17, 1817, were the Diligent, Hand-in-Hand, Relief, and United States Fire Companies and the Good Intent, Perseverance, and Southwark Hose Companies.

Insurance upon properties was really a secondary object at this meeting, although it was pointed out that each member could effect insurance with the Association at 5 per cent less premium than non-members. At first there was no paid-in capital, but the volunteer companies did pledge their apparatus and property as security, while the trustees made themselves individually liable for all losses. Profits were to be paid to the volunteer company members, but such payments were to be limited to 30 per cent of the total profits until a permanent capital stock of two hundred thousand dollars was established. As soon as the organization of the Association was completed it applied for a charter but encountered a most effective opposition promoted by the older established fire concerns which, of course, feared such organized competition. The legislature refused the charter on the grounds that no capital funds were being provided. The action caused indignation and consternation among the members of these volunteer companies. In consequence when the opportunity to vote was provided in 1819, these men established a Firemen's Ticket. Of the five candidates elected to the Assembly from Philadelphia, four were from the firemen's slate. When the next legislature convened the Fire Association was granted a charter which was signed by the governor on March 27, 1820.

So that these firemen might better identify the properties insured by their association, a fire mark was devised consisting of a convexed oval whose center contained an old-fashioned fire plug with a length of hose and the letter "F" to the left of it and "A" to the right. Some of the early marks were of lead, others of brass, but the majority were made of cast iron. One antiquarian, after considerable research, concluded that each of the volunteer companies had their own mark struck, which would undoubtedly account for the slight variations in the design and mold. It is recorded that in one period alone over forty thousand of these marks were posted upon buildings in Philadelphia. Such a figure is reasonable, since every one of the volunteer firemen of the forty-five engine and hose companies were solicitors for insurance. Little wonder that the older established companies opposed the original petition for a charter! Until 1838 the Association insured nothing but buildings, but in that year they were authorized to conduct a general fire insurance business. When the volunteer department was taken over by the city and converted into a paid unit in 1881, the Association was reincorporated upon a basis comparable to other similar concerns.

While this had been largely a decade of despair,

business was once more on the upgrade, judging from the support given to this new insurance plan organized in the city of Philadelphia. The financial disorders of the War of 1812 were beginning to disappear, but it looked as though the Indian uprisings on the Florida boundary might lead to war with Spain. However, Monroe persuaded the King of Spain to cede his Florida lands to the United States in 1819, the purchase price being mostly offset by claims of the Americans for damages against his government.

Recovery and development progressed upon a local level as may be noted in Hartford, Connecticut, which had attained a population of about seven thousand people. Not all of the citizens gathered at Ransom's Inn, which was mentioned in the preceding chapter, since we find that another gathering place of the merchants and business men was Morgan's Exchange Coffee House, established in November, 1816, and located on the north side of State Street. Joseph Morgan, the proprietor, was one of the important men of the community. A man of fine character and judgment, he was also a financial genius, a family characteristic which his son Junius Spencer Morgan, the noted London banker, inherited. The trait was particularly evident in his grandson, J. Pierpont Morgan, and his successors. Little wonder is it that in these closing days of the decade, the most important of those engaged in commerce, banking, and affairs of state would gather at his coffee house to quench their thirst and discuss problems of moment.

One of these habitués was Thomas K. Brace who headed the wholesale grocery and commission firm of Thomas K. Brace & Co. and served as a director and vice president of the Phoenix Bank. Brace was also a member of the Common Council, Justice of the Peace, director of the United States Branch Bank, and a member of the Committee to Abate Taxes. He was a founder of the Society for Savings which was incorporated in 1819 and was also a prime mover, in company with President Terry of the Hartford Fire Insurance Company, in the promotion of the American Asylum for the Deaf and Dumb, the first successful institute of its kind in the country. When such an important character as Thomas K. Brace announced to his friends and associates at Morgan's Exchange Coffee House that Hartford needed another fire insurance company, he at once received a sympathetic ear. Brace had been a director of the Hartford Fire and knew something of the problems of the business. At his suggestion, therefore, one hundred and thirty-

seven men of Hartford signed a petition for a charter which was granted by the legislature, during its current session, on June 5, 1819, the incorporated concern to be known as the Aetna Insurance Company. Thomas K. Brace became the first president and his enthusiasm vitalized the management to conduct its affairs with shrewdness, efficiency, and honesty. It progressed rapidly and successfully and the best evidence of its success is that which it left in its footprints of assurance, since over a dozen different types of these marks have been discovered. All of them bear evidence of the business acumen of founder Brace and his successors.

In this year of 1819 business was regaining its health in all of the states of the Union and there was progress and an internal peace to bridge the decades. Down in Baltimore, Maryland, however, the populace was not so healthy in this year, for an epidemic of yellow fever had visited the city, resulting in many deaths and untold distress. It was in Baltimore that same year that a new fraternal or secret society was organized—the Independent Order of Odd Fellows. Always ready to assist in times of sickness and disaster the newly founded organization undoubtedly lent a helping hand to many of the citizens during this plague. So far as can be learned this order has never engaged in a fire insurance endeavor but members did use a house plate of bronze which is depicted upon these pages in the hope that if a fraternal aid movement for fire indemnity ever did exist, the plate will be made a matter of record.

The Northwest Ordinance had been adopted as far back as 1787 and the Ohio Land Company, under the guiding hand of Rufus Putnam, took over the sale and development in the new Northwest Territory. An act of Congress authorized surveys in this new country dividing townships six miles square. These again were divided into sections containing six hundred and forty acres each, all providing a new type of measuring stick for the cartography of the future. At the close of the decade in 1820 the value of this land was officially fixed at one dollar and a quarter per acre. Ohio had been admitted to the Union in 1803 and in 1820 had a population of 581,400; Indiana came in during 1816 and its 1820 census was 147,100, while Illinois did not "arrive" until 1818 with a count of 55,200 souls.

This emigration to the west was soon to provide more footprints to record the expansion of the fire insurance industry.

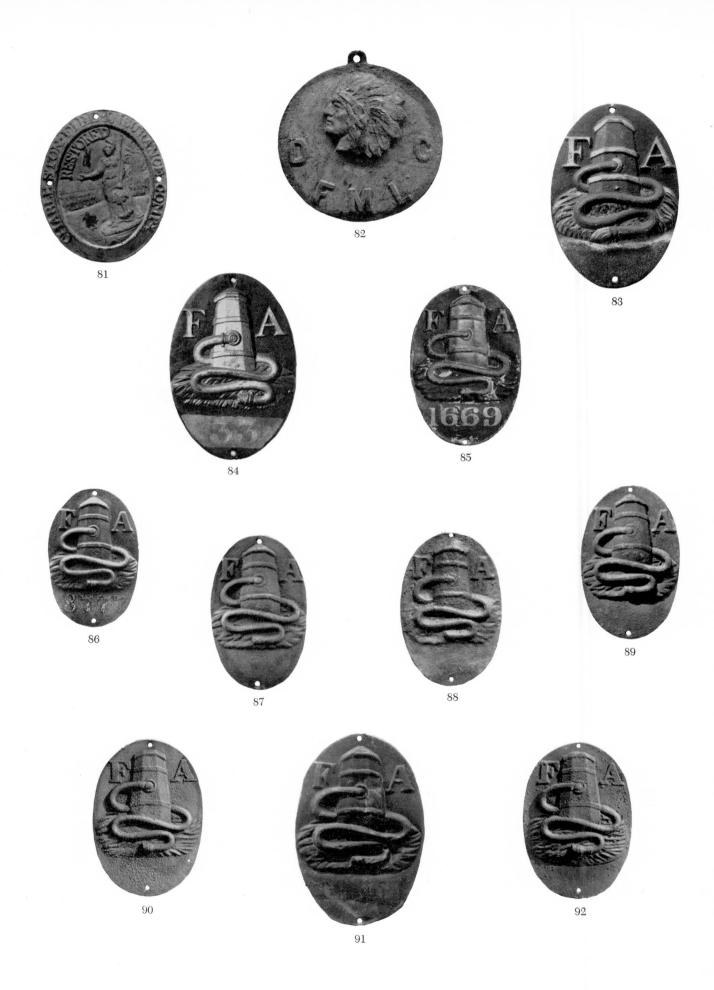

81

82

83

84

85

86

87

88

89

90

91

92

93

94

95

(81) CHARLESTON FIRE INSURANCE COMPANY. CHARLESTON, SOUTH CAROLINA. 1811-1896.

Cast iron. Convexed oval. 7⅜" x 9½". Design in relief shows the figure of a woman holding a shield, pointing towards the "Restored" with a burning building in the background. Company name raised around the mark. Very rare.

(82) DUTCHESS COUNTY FIRE, MARINE AND LIFE INSURANCE COMPANY. POUGHKEEPSIE, NEW YORK. 1814-1906.

Heavy cast iron. Circular. 10½" x 11½". Bust of American Indian in high relief and "D.F.M.L.C." in raised letters around lower half of mark. Loop at top. Very rare.

(83-95) FIRE ASSOCIATION OF PHILADELPHIA. PHILADELPHIA, PENNSYLVANIA. 1817-

83. Cast iron. Oval. 8⅜" x 11½". Raised "F.A.," and fire hydrant with water gushing from hose. Flat back. First mark issued by this company, 1817.

84. Cast iron. Oval. 7¾" x 11⅝". Raised "F.A.," and fire hydrant with short end of hose ending to the right of center of hydrant. Flat back. Second mark issued by company. Policy number 33 (painted on mark) was issued on April 13, 1820, to Joel Atkinson and covered, "on his brick messuage or tenement and piazza adjoining thereto situate on the east side of Ninth Street between Walnut and Locust Streets in the city of Philadelphia."

85. Lead. Oval. 7⅝" x 11¼". Raised "F.A.," and fire hydrant. Hollow back. Policy number 1669 (painted on mark) was issued to Benjamin S. Janney on May 22, 1827, and covered on a three-story brick building situated on the south side of a court opening into Dillwyn (now North Orianna Street) between Tamaney and Green Streets, Philadelphia, Pa.

86. Cast iron. Oval. 7⅝" x 11⅝". Raised "F.A.," and fire hydrant. Hollow back. Policy number 8777 (painted on mark)

was issued February 17, 1844, to "the mayor, alderman and citizens of Philadelphia," and covered the two-story building (known as the "State House") and situated on the south side of Chestnut Street between Fifth and Sixth Streets.

87. Cast iron. Oval. 6⅝" x 10¾". Raised "F.A.," and fire hydrant. Hollow back. This is the smallest of the convex iron marks and the first to have a drainage knob in back. Issued in 1860.

88. Cast iron. Oval. 7½" x 11⅛". Raised "F.A.," and fire hydrant. Slightly convex. Hollow back. No drainage knob. Issued in 1863.

89. Cast iron. Oval. 7⅛" x 11⅜". Raised "F.A.," and fire hydrant. Medium convex type. Hollow back. Drainage knob in back. Issued in 1863.

90. Cast iron. Oval. 7⅝" x 10¾". Raised "F.A.," and fire hydrant. Flat type. Hollow back. Drainage knob in back. From building at 232 South Front Street, Philadelphia, Pa. Very rare. Issued in 1865.

91. Brass. Oval. 7½" x 11¼". Raised "F.A.," and fire hydrant. Hollow back. No drainage knob. Policy number 44551 (painted on mark) was issued on June 23, 1868, to Benjamin Levy and covered a three-story brick dwelling situated at 533 North Orianna Street, Philadelphia, Pa.

92. Cast iron. Oval. 7⅝" x 10¾". Raised "F.A.," and fire hydrant. Wide convex type. Hollow back. Drainage knob in back. Very fine, thin casting. Very rare. Issued 1869.

93. Cast iron. Oval. 7½" x 11". Raised "F.A.," and fire hydrant. Extremely convex. Hollow back. Drainage knob in back. Last cast iron type of mark of this company. Issued about 1870.

94. Tin. Rectangle. 6" x 8". Black background with gold and black design of hydrant and "Fire Association—Philadelphia— F. A. 1820." Latest mark of company for use at home. Very rare. Issued about 1875.

95. Tin. Diamond shape, slightly convexed. 5¾" x 5¾". "Fire Association" and Chinese characters in dark blue on speckled light blue enamel background. Mark used in China.

97

96

98

100

99

101

103

104

102

106

107

105

108

109

(96-108) AETNA INSURANCE COMPANY. HARTFORD, CONNECTICUT. 1819-

96. Tin. Oval. 9¾″ x 4⅜″. Slightly curved "Insured—Aetna," and border in gold on black background. Very rare type. Issued about 1825.

97. Heavy tin. Rectangular. 9½″ x 4½″. Raised border and "Insured Aetna Co." Issued about 1835.

98. Heavy tin. Rectangular. 6½″ x 2½″. Raised border and raised gold "Aetna" on black background. Very rare. Issued about 1835.

99. Heavy tin. Rectangular. 9¾″ x 4½″. Border and "Aetna" raised. From old brick residence on south side of Main Street, Tarlton, Ohio. Issued 1840.

100. Tin. Rectangular. 6½″ x 2⅜″. Border and "Aetna" gold on black background. Issued about 1850.

101. Heavy tin. Rectangular. 7¼″ x 3⅞″. Border and "Aetna" raised. Issued 1853.

102. Tin. Rectangular. 6⅞″ x 3⅜″. Border and "Aetna" black on silver background. Issued about 1860.

103. Tin. Rectangular. 6¾″ x 3¼″. Border and lettering gold on black background. "Aetna" slightly curved; "of Hartford" strictly horizontal. Issued about 1860.

104. Tin. Rectangular. 6⅞″ x 3⅜″. Border and "Aetna" black on silver background. Issued about 1860. A variant of #102; lettering differs slightly.

105. Tin. Rectangular. 7¼″ x 3¹³⁄₁₆″. Border and "Insured Aetna Hartford" raised. From building in Rockford, Illinois. Rare variant of mark issued about 1862.

106. Tin. Rectangular. 7⅜″ x 4″. Border and "Insured Aetna Hartford" raised. From old frame residence at Piketon, Ohio. Issued about 1862.

107. Heavy tin. Rectangular. 6½″ x 2½″. Border and "Aetna" raised; lettering gold on black background. Issued about 1865.

108. Tin. Rectangular. 6⅞″ x 3″. Border and "Aetna—Incorporated 1819." black on silver background. Last mark of this company. Issued about 1895.

(109) INDEPENDENT ORDER OF ODD FELLOWS. BALTIMORE, MARYLAND. 1819-

Heavy bronze. Horeshoe shape. 4⁵⁄₁₆″ x 6⅝″. Spread eagle at top. Three links, clasped hands and "Luck" across center. House plate used by members of this fraternal organization. From building in northern New York State. Questionable as fire mark.

PRESIDENT MONROE'S DECADE OR
"ERA OF GOOD FEELING"
1821-1830

Economically this period commenced as one of stability and prosperity, and it generally became known as Monroe's "Era of Good Feeling." Savings institutions had been started in several cities, including New York, and the people had taken a new lease on life and were filled with optimism. The Island of Manhattan was taking on a new look which challenged the economic and industrial leadership of Philadelphia. With the increase in immigration, the housing situation became so acute that in 1822 over twenty-five hundred new houses were constructed in New York City. Many immigrants moved into the framework long before the building itself was completed. The new concentrated masses in New York were visited by a series of yellow fever plagues and as a result those who could afford to do so moved out in "the country," to Greenwich Village, to form a community which was destined to become famous as the home of the Rhinelanders and the Astors. When the fever subsided, business maintained its stride at such a pace that in this year alone New York collected two-thirds of the total import duties of all states.

Over on the west side of the Island, in 1821, the North River Bank was established and, as was customary in so many instances, it was also deemed desirable to have a fire insurance company nearby. Thus, on February 6, 1822, the legislature chartered the North River Insurance Company with a capital of $350,000. When one learns that William C. Rhinelander and William B. Astor were among the first directors, it can easily be understood how it was possible for all of the capital stock to be paid-in immediately—a unique feature in these early insurance days.

Captain Richard Whiley, formerly Commandant on Governor's Island, was the prime organizer of this company and its first president. A conservative underwriter, he at once declared that the company would not insure any building over eighty feet in height, probably because very few of the hand-pump engines of the era could extinguish a fire beyond that distance. Whiley was also responsible for the grading of risks into eight classes of hazards, another innovation in these early days of taking risks. The North River established its offices in a building at 202 Greenwich Street, with offices on the lower floor and the residences of the company's officials on the upper floors.

Director William C. Rhinelander, of course, became famous in the mercantile business, while Astor was the heir apparent to the fortunes of John Jacob Astor who had established the American Fur Company which, over a period of years, secured a monopoly in the fur market for all of North America. The business acumen of these men who figured so prominently in the business history of the country added materially to the success of this new fire insurance company.

New York State commenced to tax insurance companies along with other state corporations in 1823 and also obliged agents of companies of other states to pay a tax of 10 per cent of premiums collected. So started a succession of taxes upon capital stock insurance companies, a practice which has multiplied during the succeeding one hundred and thirty years.

On April 22, 1824, Timothy Dewey, as agent of the Gas Light Company in New York City, first exhibited gas light in a residence at 286 Water Street. The next day the *New York Post*, endorsing this progressive step, stated: "All doubt as to its practicability was at once removed. In point of economy, safety, and cleanliness, it appeared perfectly obvious that this mode of lighting our streets, public buildings, manufactories, and dwelling houses, surpasses everything of the kind that has hitherto been attempted by oil or candles." The same paper on June 12 published: "The New York Gas Light Company, having erected in Franklin Square, an iron lamp post, of the kind in use in London, for the purpose of showing the corporation and citizens of New York the superiority of this description of light over any other, it is lighted this evening to the gratification of hundreds." And on June 23: "The building for manufacturing gas from oil, is going on rapidly under the immediate inspection of Timothy Dewey, Esquire, the agent and manager of the company. The pipes having now arrived, and all arrangements completed, the laying of them will be commenced immediately, and there is no reason to doubt that a part of Broadway, and probably, of Pearl Street, will be lighted with gas the ensuing winter."

There were reasons, however, for fire insurance underwriters to doubt the effects of this new-fangled innovation on fire safety. They were skeptical, and rightly so, until proper safeguards were provided, but in the face of all this agitation one group of investors retained their optimism. The friends of John L. Bowne were so anxious to offer him the presidency of an insurance company at an annual salary of fifteen hundred dollars that, for that purpose alone, they subscribed to and established the United States Fire Insurance Company. Bowne opened the company's first office at 34 Fulton Street in New York on April 8, 1824, after having received the charter on the first day of that month. Both this company and the North River, together with two other New York fire insurance concerns stood alone as survivors of the great conflagration in New York in 1835. While the United States Fire issued a fire mark in its early period, its other footprints, together with that of the North River, were not implanted until it trod soil in the Orient.

Fire insurance was gradually becoming established on an even sounder basis. Proof of this fact was contained in a general act passed in 1825 by the New York Legislature. The act stated, in part, "that it should not be lawful for the directors or managers of any incorporated company in this state to make dividends except from the surplus profits of the corporation." As a result of this action dividends dropped from an average of 10 per cent down to 3 per cent.

The "era of good feeling" prevailed even when John Quincy Adams took over as the sixth President of the United States in 1825. The country continued to prosper with a banking capital of one hundred and twenty-seven million dollars and a national debt which had been reduced from one hundred and thirty million in 1816 to less than eighty million.

The Pennsylvania Legislature during this period was a conservative group, as evidenced by their objection to the application made to incorporate the Philadelphia Gas Light Company. This company, like the progressive Manhattanites, wanted to manufacture gas, lay pipes in the streets, and furnish gas to the public. When objections arose on the grounds that gas was "unsafe, unsure, a trouble and a nuisance with an intolerable stench," the petition was denied, and Philadelphians had to wait for their gas.

The same legislature, however, was more generous to the Pennsylvania Fire Insurance Company, granting it a charter in January, 1825. This company, which left an early footprint, is still advancing in our American procession.

The transportation system between Philadelphia and Baltimore during this decade was approaching a state of comparative luxury. The vehicles used were tremendous blue conestoga wagons covered with white canvas and drawn by blooded Pennsylvania horses. Ornate stage coaches, serviced and driven by men in frock coats and high hats, were also "making the run." Along the way there was an abundance of taverns patterned after those in old England with their quaint signs and appellations. When one stopped at a hostelry the fare was unsurpassed, for each strived to out-do the other.

Baltimoreans had probably made more profit from wartime business than any other community. In the reconstruction period, however, all enterprise gradually settled down to a slower, sounder, but still profitable basis, and those who conducted business and commerce in that city promptly changed their methods to conform to the new order. In this atmosphere during December, 1825 a charter was granted to the Firemen's Insurance Company of Baltimore, an institution organized by the active and honorary members of the Volunteer Fire Department of the city with a provision that the original stock could be held only by those brigades or their individual members. The office of the newly formed company was located on the north side of Second Street, adjoining the Savings Bank.

This company used a fire mark consisting of a round, flat, cast-iron plate which had a hand pumper and the letters "F.I.Co." in raised form. At the top there was a loop by which the plate could be suspended on a hook. Barker's Iron Foundry on North Calvert Street cast these marks. A reference to the design of the mark may be found in a resolution made by the firemen on July 27 which ordered that "the badge used by this company be a cast iron plate of circular form with the gilt figure of an engine in relief, bordered by a plain cast iron head and without numbers." And later, on September 5 of the same year "that the badge be charged at $1.25 for its use and that no new or second charge be made to the same persons so long as they continue to insure, and when they discontinue their insurance, the badge to be returnable as the property of the company." Once again on September 18, 1826, an order was issued stating that "the various proposals for painting and gilding the badges was this day acted on, when it was determined to contract with Daniel Pope for painting and gilding one hundred badges at thirty cents each, including the nails or hooks for putting them up." In size these marks outdid any others made in America, a fact which seems symbolic of the optimism of the period.

In the year 1826 it is also recorded that individual fire insurance underwriters had just about totally disappeared and that this insurance was now being dispensed exclusively by incorporated companies. It has been indicated that a preponderance of shipping had been transferred to the city of Father Knickerbocker during this decade; otherwise Philadelphia was rapidly progressing in other directions. The major factor contributing to the transfer of coastwise and seagoing commerce from Philadelphia to New York was the fact that the city in Pennsylvania was located some one hundred and thirty miles from the ocean and that often in winter months the streams were closed to navigation for as many as ninety days a year. Because of her geographic location, however, Philadelphia became a sort of hub for early transportation to the South and to the West; those were the sections which were being steadily developed by constant immigration from the Old World. Stagecoaches went daily to Baltimore and Washington and in 1828 a new line inaugurated daily service to Pittsburgh.

To accommodate this ever-growing influx of travel the city of Philadelphia abounded with taverns, coffee houses, and inns which had long been frequented by the local citizenry. These taverns bore the imprint and atmosphere of the intimate hostelries of old England. They were usually located in regular houses which had been appropriately altered to make them more suitable for public use. From the beginning, descriptive signs, which in the majority of cases contained the most discriminating work of the resident artists, were displayed on the taverns. There was Clark's Inn, "The Coach and Horses" in Chestnut Street opposite the State House; Enoch Story's Inn, at the sign of "The Pewter Platter"; the "Golden Lion," "Yellow Cat," "The Conestoga Stage-Wagon," "Bottle and Glass," and the "Green Tree." For the curious there is written evidence of several hundred additional places of refreshment which are equally as colorful and distinctive as those mentioned.

One of these gathering places was the house of Daniel Rubicam, located at number 20 South Sixth Street and known in 1829 as Rubicam's Tavern. Many of the Community notables assembled there, for Rubicam's provided such food as would delight the fastidious epicure and such ales, wines, and liquors as would please the real connoisseur. Thus it comes as no surprise that the tavern, so conveniently situated near Independence Hall, was frequented by men of greatness and leaders of the nation.

During the winter evenings of early 1829 there gathered at Rubicam's a group of men, already fa-mous, who were destined to band themselves together again to form an association whose influence would be a contributing factor to the economy of the nation. It is easy to visualize the mayor of this City of Brotherly Love, Benjamin W. Richards, toasting his toes at the hearthside and discussing with Elihu Chauncey, noted and respected lawyer, the legal problems of the growing metropolis. There was Thomas I. Wharton, another leading lawyer, and Frederick Brown, a prosperous druggist, who were probably conversing over mugs of Rubicam's famous ale with Erskine Hazard (who in 1808 had built a rolling mill and wire factory and had also demonstrated the value of anthracite coal) on the possible success of the first forthcoming issue of the *Philadelphia Inquirer*. At another table, John K. Kane, who was later to become Judge of the United State District Court, probably debated with his friend Robert Toland about the prospects for the projected Pennsylvania Railroad both of these men being active in securing a charter to provide for that mode of transportation.

Another important member of this group was Richard Willing who officiated in the first Fourth of July Parade in 1788 and became chairman, in 1813, of an association to plan for the defense of the Port of Philadelphia against the enemy. Willing was one of the original members of the Washington Guards formed in the same year, as was Henry C. Carey, the well-known author and authority on economics. Another original member of the Guards, also known as "State Fencibles," was Clement C. Biddle, one of the incorporators of the Philadelphia Saving Fund Society. Others were John Cadwallader, considered dean of the group, who was famous for his leadership and achievements throughout the war; William Rawle, who played a prominent part in attempting to memorialize General Lafayette for his achievements in the French Revolution; and the popular Charles N. Bancker, an individual of great ability and energy who was greatly admired by the entire aggregation at Rubicam's. About 1808, Bancker was the largest importer of merchandise in the United States, but speculation by others had depleted his assets. He, too, was one of the originators of the Philadelphia Saving Fund. Bancker also devised the idea of forming another fire insurance company in Philadelphia and after considerable effort, against almost hopeless odds, he secured a perpetual charter for The Franklin Fire Insurance Company. The charter was granted by the legislature in 1829 and approved by Governor J. Andrew Shulze on April 22 of that year. Subscription books were opened in Rubicam's Tavern and taken up the first day, the company having a paid-in capital of four hundred thousand dollars. Further testimony of the esteem in which Bancker was held was presented by the fact that all his distinguished associates, mentioned above, became original stockholders and directors of the company.

The company leased offices from Stephen Girard at No. 163½ Chestnut Street and began business on June 25, 1829, with Richard Willing as its president and director and Charles N. Bancker as its Secretary. Then in 1837, Bancker succeeded as president and director of the company. As evidence of their interest in this famous institution, the few important men who are listed as gathering at Rubicam's served in various capacities for the company they helped to organize. Henry C. Carey and Clement C. Biddle both became presidents and directors, while Thomas I. Wharton and Frederick Brown became directors. At first the Franklin Fire was famous for its issuance of perpetual policies, but as changes were wrought in the business, it changed its policies to keep in step with the leading underwriters. The company had a distinguished and successful career and left its imprint in the form of a mark of assurance. This black rectangular plate with the company's name affixed in

gold soon became known throughout the cities and villages of the country as a symbol of sound fire insurance management and while many other newly developed companies in the various states adopted the same name, this was the only "Franklin" to survive.

It is singular that the Franklin's first New York agent was Charles J. Martin who later became president of The Home Insurance Company of New York. The latter concern merged the Franklin Fire into its own institution in 1948, at the very height of the Franklin's success. The career of Harold V. Smith began with the old Franklin, and he distinguished himself in directing this merger of interests which effected an economy for policyholders and stockholders alike.

The year of the Franklin's organization, 1829, was a fateful one, for it brought the end of a decade of good feeling and the approach of another period of uncertainty. On March 4, 1829, Andrew Jackson became President of the United States and at once launched an attack upon the Bank of the United States, intimating that it was unconstitutional. His position fermented much hostility and bitterness which closed an era of otherwise domestic tranquility.

110

111

112

(110) NORTH RIVER INSURANCE COMPANY. NEW YORK, NEW YORK. 1822-

Tin. Diamond shape. 6⅜" x 6⅜". "North River U. S. A." and Chinese characters in gold on bright red background. Mark used in China.

(111-112) UNITED STATES FIRE INSURANCE COMPANY. NEW YORK, NEW YORK. 1824-

111. Tin. Rectangular. 9⅛" x 2⁵⁄₁₆". Border and "United States." raised. From building in Illinois. Rare.

112. Tin. Diamond shape. 6" x 6". "United States" and Chinese characters in raised gold on light green background. Gold border. Mark used in China.

113

114

115

116

117

118

(113) THE PENNSYLVANIA FIRE INSURANCE COMPANY. PHILADELPHIA, PENNSYLVANIA. 1825-

Brass. Rectangular. 7" x 4". Slightly raised brass lettering, "The Pennsylvania Insurance Company, Philadelphia"; black background.

(114-117) FIREMEN'S INSURANCE COMPANY. BALTIMORE, MARYLAND. 1825-1904.

114. Cast iron. Circular. 13" x 14". Old double-decker hand pump and "F. I. Co.," in high relief. Wheels have twelve spokes. Issued about 1840.

115. Cast iron. Circular. 12¾" x 14¼". Old double-decker hand pump and "F. I. Co.," in high relief; raised date, "1789." Wheels have twelve spokes. Since no other company is known to have issued this type of mark and the numerals on the plate do not correspond with date of organization, the numerals were un-

doubtedly cast in error. There is some question as to the source and authenticity of the mark.

116. Cast iron. Circular. 13⅛" x 14". Old double-decker hand pump and "F. I. Co.," in high relief. Wheels have six spokes. Loop at top is plain and round. Issued about 1855.

117. Cast iron. Circular. 12½" x 14⅛". Old double-decker hand pump and "F. I. Co.," in high relief. Wheels have six spokes. Loop at top is fluted. Smallest type mark of this company. Issued 1835.

(118) FRANKLIN FIRE INSURANCE COMPANY. PHILADELPHIA, PENNSYLVANIA. 1829-1948 (Merged with The Home Insurance Co.).

Tin. Rectangular. 6⅞" x 3¼". Border and "Franklin Fire Philadelphia," in gold on black background. Only type mark issued by this company. Issued 1835.

A DECADE OF DEVASTATION
1831-1840

The years from 1831 to 1840 constitute one of those complex periods in American history when prosperity reigned for a few years only to be followed by a season of failure and despair after which a hardy people once again forged ahead into a new era of gain and progress. During the previous decades, when there was such vacillation in our economy, there occurred a gradual but steady improvement in laws and such safeguards as would make a repetition of loss or unfavorable conditions unlikely. While new problems constantly presented themselves, the ingenuity of free action and enterprise always resulted in a better and more progressive society than had existed before. In 1833, President Jackson's position with reference to the unconstitutionality of the Bank of the United States was upheld, and as a result there was a tremendous multiplication of state banks. Because of this development, money became readily accessible. Though protective tariffs had been tightened earlier in the decade, they were again reduced by 1835 and speculation thrived.

There was also a substantial increase in the number of insurance concerns at this time. Twenty-six new companies appeared between 1832 and 1837; nineteen of these confined their writings to fire insurance. The growth of the industry naturally broadened its area of operation as the trail of the marks left behind undeniably shows. The marks had extended to Upper New York State, northward into Connecticut and Vermont, southward to Maryland, the District of Columbia, and Virginia, and westward through Pennsylvania, Ohio, Kentucky, and Illinois.

With the physical growth of concerns there also came into being a new type of carrier. The Philadelphia Contributionship, the Mutual Assurance (Philadelphia), the Mutual Assurance (New York), and the Baltimore Equitable Society, which were established on the basis of mutuality, nevertheless issued their policies on a perpetual basis, confining their writings to their own cities and environs. Up in Hartford County in Connecticut there had spread among the farmers a slogan: "Beware of Cities! Farmers, club together!" A group composed largely of agrarians became allied and on May 28, 1831, they received a charter to establish the Hartford County Mutual Fire

Insurance Company. The office was located in the city of Hartford, but the company granted insurance only on rural properties within the county itself. Later it accepted applications throughout the state except in cities. David Grant, of the same family stock which produced Ulysses S. Grant, was the first president. Charles Shepard, the first secretary, was directed in 1832 to procure "a suitable number of tin insurance plates, inscribed 'Insured Mutual Hartford,'" a sign which was familiar in the sections surrounding Hartford for many years.

Meanwhile, over in Winchester, Connecticut, the Greenwood Mutual Fire Insurance Company was established in that same month and year for the identical purpose. The Middlesex Mutual Fire Insurance Company had its beginnings in the village of Middletown, located in the beautiful Connecticut River Valley. Further upstream, at Bellows Falls in Vermont, the Windham County Mutual Fire Insurance Company was founded.

There is a similarity in the manner in which these insurers were organized as well as a definite resemblance among the fire marks which they adopted. Their standard tin plates were produced by the new stamping and lithographing plants of New England. In the establishment of these companies the northern farmers were beginning to seek a level of their own, and understandably so, for in the next few decades there was to come a new separation between agriculture and industry.

The directional finger now points to the South where the United States Insurance Company was established in Baltimore in 1833. That company used a heavy cast-iron plate to mark its insured properties. And down in Washington five fire engine companies of that new metropolis and two engine companies from Georgetown petitioned Congress for a charter and in 1837 this was granted under the name of The Firemen's Insurance Company of Washington and Georgetown, in the District of Columbia. Stock was restricted to members of these fire brigades who promptly adopted as a badge a round cast-iron mark containing the image of a hand pumper with the words: "Firemen's I. Co." On October 19, 1837, two hundred of these were ordered from W. R. Spalding and again on April 3, 1838, another hundred were ordered from Samuel S. Briggs, at a cost of $1.25 each including the expense of installation when needed.

In Richmond, Virginia, a great enterprise was launched on March 16, 1832, when the legislature authorized a charter for The James River and Kanawha Company, thus making it possible for that concern to connect the tidewater of the James River with the navigable waters of the Ohio, either by canal or rail. Just two days prior to that event the Virginia Marine Insurance Company, whose official title in later years became the Virginia Fire and Marine Insurance Company, was also organized in Richmond. After the change this company adopted at least two different types of fire marks.

This ten-year period also carried insurance progress westward from New York City first to Niagara Falls Village. There in 1835 Riddle and Company inaugurated the first bank and a year later the Niagara District Mutual Fire Insurance Company was formed, its mark containing the clasped hands of mutuality. The forward movement of organization provided fire underwriting establishments in four additional Pennsylvania communities. In Coatesville, the town named for Moses Coates, who contributed so materially to the early manufacture of farm implements, another mutual company was established, while in the agricultural area of Muncy the Lycoming County Mutual was developed under the guiding hand of its president, William Alexander Petrikin, who headed practically every business concern in this settlement.

Further west, in Chambersburg, paper mills began to produce, and in 1827 the first successful strawboard paper was originated in the Hollowell Paper Mill, who thereby established a standard which was enthusiastically accepted by manufacturers and users alike. William Heyser, owner of that mill; Alexander Calhoun of the Mammoth Paper Mill; Philip Berlin, a wagon maker and first director of the Cumberland Valley Railroad Company; and John King, president of the Chambersburg Bank; were all very active in the establishment of the Chambersburg Fire Insurance Company. T. G. McCulloh, its first president, was also the head of the new railroad company whose rails in 1837 were extended from Harrisburg to Chambersburg where they joined with a turnpike to Pittsburgh, challenging the old Baltimore and Ohio Railroad. It is obvious by now that the origin of most insurance companies can be accredited to the leaders in banking and industry, for simultaneous with the development and expansion of the nation and its need for insurance protection, these men of vision assumed the leadership in most of the nation's underwriting institutions.

The image of the Philadelphia-type of fire engine which appeared upon the fire mark of the Chambersburg Fire was similar to the type of engine depicted on the iron plate issued to the policyholders of the Firemen's Insurance Company of Pittsburgh. When the latter company came into being in 1834, Pittsburgh had already become the first ranking manufacturing town in the Union. Its commercial and manufacturing income for that year was estimated at fifteen million dollars, while the commission and jobbing business passing through wagon and boat was estimated at fifty million dollars—figures of gigantic size in that era. Surely, there was also room for the Pittsburgh Navigation and Fire Insurance Company, a concern which employed the heavy iron oval casting bearing its name as a mark of insurance.

Pittsburgh was a pivotal point for the North, South, and West with one daily packet line and four daily stages traveling westward. The area surrounding Lisbon along the stage route in Ohio became a great fruit raising section, populated largely by German and some Scotch-Irish immigrants. Here the Columbiana County Mutual Insurance Company was formed, while further to the south, in Mount Vernon, a similar community produced the Knox County Mutual Insurance Company. The Buckeye State mothered a third fire insurance concern which, prior to the close of 1840, left a heavy imprint along the banks of the Ohio River in the city of Cincinnati, a new western metropolis which was destined to play a very important part in the protection of this country. It had been a discouraging decade in this place which had so early been referred to as the Queen City. A severe flood had damaged and destroyed much property, and there had been repeated large fires and three successive years of cholera. A powder mill had exploded, taking its toll in lives. Slavery had become an issue and in 1836 there were mob killings of colored people and violence to the owners and property of sympathetic abolitionist newspapers such as the *Philanthropist*, the *Chronicle*, and *Gazette*. These were a persistent people, many of old German stock, and in the face of all of these obstacles as well as one of the severest monetary collapses in the early Union, they rebuilt rapidly. At the close of the decade they had re-established a tremendous number of enterprises headed by 227 woodworking establishments, 109 iron-work factories, 61 workshops in other metals, and 212 leather workshops. Pork, too, must have been plentiful for some twenty-four manufacturers of hair and bristle goods were listed.

Van Duzen and Tift had started the famous Buckeye Bell factory and in the jobbing industry Knost Brothers and Company became the first importers of toys and fancy goods west of the Allegheny Mountains; even today the quaint little shops of the "over the Rhine" section dispense for the youngsters items of joy which are all reminiscent of an era when *gemütlichkeit* prevailed. As early as 1836 this progressive populace had equipped the city with twenty-seven fire cisterns which were supplied with water from the new works through some fifty-five cast iron plugs, also an innovation. Into that development fitted the founding of The Fire Department Insurance Company which proudly displayed on its fire mark the same Philadelphia type of hand pumper which had adorned the plates of the eastern concerns.

Across the Ohio River, though not very far south, the city of Lexington crowned the lovely countryside known as the Blue Grass section of Kentucky. The Northern Bank of Kentucky had been organized in 1835 and it was only fitting that this community should give rise the following year to the Lexington Fire, Life and Marine Insurance Company. In a spirit of patriotic fervor, the company adopted as its insignia the image of the American eagle whose spread wings adorned the several rare specimens of fire marks which it left behind. Louisville, too, was experiencing growing pains and sprouted the Louisville and Kentucky Mutual Fire Insurance Company.

From here—downstream a short distance to the junction of the Ohio and Mississippi Rivers and thence northward a spell upon the latter—one comes to Alton, a young community in the state of Illinois where Abraham Lincoln had just been re-elected for the second time to the state legislature. Alton had been incorporated as a city in 1837 and, though geographically it lay just north of that section where slavery was favored, there were many repercussions of the issue there. Indeed so strong were the feelings that in the same year Elijah Lovejoy, a noted aboli-

tionist editor, was murdered while trying to protect his presses from the attacks of the pro-slavery mob. There must have been many citizens of more kindly nature in Alton, however, for the plates of the Illinois Mutual Fire Insurance Company, all displaying the clasped hands of friendliness, remain.

Into a decade of both progress and devastation came the greatest calamity of all—New York City's Great Fire of 1835, a disaster previously surpassed only by the burning of Moscow during the Russian campaign of Napoleon. Five hundred and twenty-nine stores and forty-one other buildings, comprising most of the business section of the city, were destroyed with a loss estimated at fifteen million dollars. Fire insurance concerns of Boston, Hartford, and other cities contributed some $2,000,000, but the New York companies' assets totalled only about $9,450,000, making it necessary to limit their payments to about 75 per cent. Every insurance company in the city was bankrupt except the North River, United States Fire, the Greenwich Fire, and the Bowery. The poverty and despair created by the property and investment losses shattered public confidence. As a result, the great industry of fire insurance faced a period of drastic re-adjustment. The lesson taught by this tragedy was the proverbial one of the danger in placing all your eggs into one basket. Thereafter it became sound practice to write coverages over a much wider space rather than to confine insurance underwriting to one congested area. Those concerns that have since thrived are mostly those who accept insurance in all centers of population. It was a decade of devastation, but, in a manner typical of the American scheme of things, the people and the insurance industry profited from their mistakes and rebuilt on a more solid foundation.

119

120

121

122

123

124

125

126

127

128

129

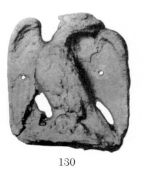

130

131

133

134

132

(119) GREENWOOD MUTUAL FIRE INSURANCE COMPANY. WINCHESTER, CONNECTICUT. 1831-1836.

Tin. Oval, somewhat convexed. 9¾" x 4¼". Border and "Insured Greenwoods Mutual," gold on black background.

(120-121) HARTFORD COUNTY MUTUAL FIRE INSURANCE COMPANY. HARTFORD, CONNECTICUT. 1831-

120. Tin. Convexed oval. 9¹³⁄₁₆" x 4⅜". Gold "Insured Mutual Hartford," on gray background. Rare.

121. Tin. Convexed oval. 9¾" x 4½". Gold "Insured Mutual Hartford," on black background. A variant both in color and size.

(122) PITTSBURGH NAVIGATION AND FIRE INSURANCE COMPANY. PITTSBURGH, PENNSYLVANIA. 1832-1845.

Heavy cast iron. Oval. 12½" x 9". Company name in high relief. Removed from a four-story building on Market Street, Pittsburgh, Pa.

(123-124) VIRGINIA FIRE AND MARINE INSURANCE COMPANY. RICHMOND, VIRGINIA. 1832-

123. Tin. Rectangular. 6⅞" x 3¼". Gold "Virginia Fire & Marine—Richmond," on black background. First mark of this company.

124. Tin. Rectangular. 8" x 4¼". "Virginia Fire and Marine. Richmond 1832." From an old, dovetailed log smokehouse in Pulaski, Va. Exceedingly rare.

(125) CHAMBERSBURG FIRE INSURANCE COMPANY. CHAMBERSBURG, PENNSYLVANIA. 1833-1872.

Cast iron. Oval. 9⅛" x 9¾". Old double-decker hand pump in high relief; border slightly raised; "C. F. I. Co.," raised.

(126) UNITED STATES INSURANCE COMPANY. BALTIMORE, MARYLAND. 1833-1845.

Heavy cast iron. Rectangular. 11¾" x 9⅝". Raised border.

Raised "Insured," in semi-circle above and "U. S. I. Co.," in semi-circle below. Very rare.

(127-129) FIREMEN'S INSURANCE COMPANY. PITTSBURGH, PENNSYLVANIA. 1834-1845.

127. Cast iron. Rectangular. 10¼" x 8¼". Border raised and beveled. Old double-decker hand pump raised. Does not have loops for fastening to building.

128. Cast iron. Rectangular. 10¼" x 8¼". Border raised and beveled. Old double-decker hand pump raised. Does not have loops for fastening to building. Differs slightly in border design from other marks.

129. Cast iron. Rectangular. 11⅝" x 8". Border raised and beveled. Old double-decker hand pump raised. Has loop at each side for fastening to building.

(130-132) LEXINGTON FIRE, LIFE AND MARINE INSURANCE COMPANY. LEXINGTON, KENTUCKY. 1836-Prior to 1872.

130. Lead. Cut out eagle. (Courtesy of Insurance Company of North America.)

131. Lead and tin. Rectangular. 7" x 8½". Small lead eagle mounted on tin.

132. Cast iron. Oval. 11¾" x 8¾". Beaded border, spread eagle and lettering raised. "Insured" above and "L.F.I." below. Very rare.

(133) MIDDLESEX MUTUAL ASSURANCE COMPANY. MIDDLETOWN, CONNECTICUT. 1836-

Tin. Oval, slightly convexed. 6½" x 3½". Gold "Mutual Middlesex," on black background.

(134) NIAGARA DISTRICT MUTUAL FIRE INSURANCE COMPANY. NIAGARA FALLS, NEW YORK. 1836-1896.

Heavy iron casting. Oval. 7¼" x 5⅜". Pair of clasped hands in high relief in center. Raised date, 1836, below. Company name raised on scalloped border. Very rare.

135

136

137

138

139

140

141

142

143

144

145

146

147

148

(135) COLUMBIANA COUNTY MUTUAL INSURANCE COMPANY. LISBON, OHIO. 1837-

Tin. Oblong. 6¾" x 3⅛". Lettering, "C.C.M." had been painted.

(136-138) FIRE DEPARTMENT INSURANCE COMPANY. CINCINNATI, OHIO. 1837 - About 1855.

136. Cast iron. Oblong. 7⅞" x 6⅛". Raised figure of old double-decker hand pump. Wheels have eight spokes. First and smallest mark issued by this company, 1837.

137. Cast iron. Oblong. 8¾" x 6⅞". Raised border and figure of old double-decker hand pump. Wheels have eight spokes. Larger than first type mark. Issued about 1841.

138. Cast iron. Oval. 11½" x 7¾". Raised figure of old double-decker hand pump in center with company name raised around edge of mark. Wheels have eight spokes. Third type mark of this company. Issued about 1850. Very rare.

(139) FIREMEN'S INSURANCE COMPANY OF THE DISTRICT OF COLUMBIA. GEORGETOWN, DISTRICT OF COLUMBIA. 1837-

Cast iron. Circular. 13¼" x 13½". Reproduction. Raised border, figure of old double-decker hand pump and "Firemen's I. Co." Loop for hanging at top.

(140) WINDHAM COUNTY MUTUAL FIRE INSURANCE COMPANY. BELLOWS FALLS, VERMONT. 1838-

Tin. Oval. 9¾" x 4½". Only "Mutual" can be discerned across center. Because found in Grafton, Vermont, which is near home city of this company, it is assumed that the mark represents this concern but the fact remains unverified.

(141-142) KNOX COUNTY MUTUAL INSURANCE COMPANY. MOUNT VERNON, OHIO. 1838-

141. Tin. Rectangular. 7" x 3½". Raised border. Raised gold "Knox," on black background. Rare.

142. Tin. Rectangular. 7" x 3½". Border and "Knox," raised. Border and lettering differ from No. 141.

(143-145) ILLINOIS MUTUAL FIRE INSURANCE COMPANY. ALTON, ILLINOIS. 1839-1871.

143. Tin. Shield shape. 4¾" x 4⅞". Border, two clasped hands and "Illinois Mutual," raised. From Central Hotel building in Troy, Illinois. First mark of this company. Very rare.

144. Heavy tin. Rectangular. 8¼" x 4⁵⁄₁₆". Border, two clasped hands and "Illinois Mutual," raised. Very rare type with strictly horizontal letters.

145. Heavy tin. Rectangular. 8½" x 4½". Border, two clasped hands and "Illinois Mutual," raised. From old frame residence on north side of East St. Louis Street, Lebanon, Illinois. Rare.

(146) KENTUCKY AND LOUISVILLE MUTUAL. LOUISVILLE, KENTUCKY. 1839-1947.

Tin. Oval. 5¼" x 3¾". Border and "K Y," in raised form. From a farm house near Milton, Trimble County, Kentucky.

(147) LYCOMING COUNTY MUTUAL INSURANCE COMPANY. MUNCY, PENNSYLVANIA. 1840-1880.

Tin. Rectangular. 7⅝" x 3¾". Border and company name raised. From old frame dwelling on Noblestown Road, Carnegie, Pa. Very rare.

(148) MUTUAL FIRE INSURANCE COMPANY OF CHESTER, PENNSYLVANIA. COATESVILLE, PENNSYLVANIA. 1840-

Tin. Rectangular. 7" x 2". "Mutual" had been painted. While it is not certain that this is the particular mark of this concern, it is similar to others known to have been issued by it, but it may also be the mark of any one of a large number of Mutuals operating throughout the country and using similar plates.

TEN YEARS OF REVOLUTION IN INDUSTRY

1841-1850

A great devastation had occurred, an economic panic had followed, and as business and commerce once again began a new march forward revolutionary developments which affected all segments of the population took place in industry. Until this time agriculture, industry, and commerce had been pretty much of an individualized matter. The farmer tilled the land and harvested his crops by hand. The people in industry and manufacturing performed a large portion of their work in their own homes, applying individual energy in such activities as weaving on hand looms. In many cases, artisans and workers lived on the same premises in which they produced their goods as did those engaged in commerce also.

Now came an era when inventors worked tirelessly to put out new machines and gadgets, some unique and others improvisations and improvements upon formerly patented items. Consequently, a large number of machines were being manufactured, machines which would eliminate much laborious hand labor and provide the first means for speedy mass production. Samuel Morse's electric telegraph line was opened in this decade; thus news could be spread throughout the Union almost immediately as soon as instruments could be made and lines strung. The invention which brought the greatest change in method of living, however, was the automatic reaper which Cyrus McCormick began to manufacture in Chicago.

Until this time farmers had utilized the hand labor of their entire families, but now with the aid of a fast-moving reaper a tremendous amount of hand work could be eliminated. Consequently, agrarians could handle increased acreage, and the grown children and former hired hands could migrate to the villages and cities. The changes and migratory feats throughout the land during this mass movement were equalled only by the shifting of displaced persons during our present generation. Corporations were being formed and businesses expanded in every town to utilize the newly invented machines. These plants quickly assimilated those who had deserted the farms along with the new millions of immigrants entering America which had been heralded abroad as the land of plenty with gold in the streets. Others of a more migratory nature pulled up stakes and moved to the

North, the South, and mostly to the West to set up anew in more virgin soil—hoping as always for more and quicker profits.

That basic urge for progress and profit combined with an innate restlessness which has characterized the American to the Old World was inherent in America's earliest citizens. It was a motivating influence in the hearts of those who migrated here in later years, and it has prevailed throughout the many decades minimizing the influence of the Old World ideologies upon the masses of the American populace.

In this decade of Industrial Revolution, in the year 1848, a man named Karl Marx issued a *Communist Manifesto* in Europe, and his German apostle, Joseph Weydemeyer, came to America where he founded a newspaper to spread the new doctrine. Through this propaganda he attempted to revolutionize the social order here. He is the General Weydemeyer of Civil War fame, but as a proponent of communism he seems to have met with little success.

Change was also the order in the fire insurance business since the devastation of the previous decade made necessary some new safeguards for stockholders and policyholders alike. The state of Pennsylvania began to scrutinize annual reports of companies in 1842, and these concerns themselves held their first convention in 1846 to develop comparative data for uniform treatment. These activities resulted in the ultimate establishment of the National Board of Fire Underwriters. In 1841 the General Bankruptcy Act was passed. Its operation greatly relieved the monetary stringency, restored public confidence, and enabled business to proceed upon a sounder basis. That no permanent cure was effected in the fire insurance industry is related by C. C. Hine, of New York, when he published his *Insurance Blue Book* in 1877. About our revolutionary decade he says in part: ". . . the New York Legislature found it necessary to curb her country mutuals.

"Nearly all the special charters granted to corporations in New York City after the beginning of 1840 were for mutuals. But notwithstanding the favor shown by successive legislatures, the demand for companies continued urgent until, in 1849, the celebrated bill was introduced and passed without a dissenting voice, entitled, 'An Act to provide for the Incorporation of Insurance Companies.' The Act was designed to facilitate and regulate their formation; that it accomplished the first no one will dispute; how far it was successful in the second part of its design we shall see presently. . . . The first general insurance law produced the same results that attended the previous introduction of the general banking, railroad and other systems. Framed without past experience it was impossible to anticipate the safeguards necessary to protect the community from fraud. Full freedom given to individuals to incorporate themselves, without individual liability, is pretty sure to develop all the ingenuity of men in abusing the public confidence so cheaply secured to them.

"Such was the case in the law under consideration. The first great mistake committed by its framers was in the method of creating mutual fire companies, without limiting the amount of each of the notes to be given. According to its terms, thirteen persons might furnish all the notes required, in the shape of capital outside of New York and Kings Counties, and the company immediately proceed to take risks without a single dollar of cash in its treasury. Another error was in allowing these original notes to be withdrawn as fast as risks could be obtained and secured by bona-fide premium notes. During the next four years after the passage of this law, about sixty mutual fire companies were organized throughout the state, a large proportion of them being scattered through the country districts. The notes of a few parties for large amounts were secured as a basis on which to start. These were rapidly replaced by the notes received as premiums.

"As the companies increased competition increased likewise. Both officers and agents were paid according to the number of policies that were issued. Risks were taken regardless of their character or value. The strife between the companies reduced the amount for which the premium notes should have been taken, and the proportion paid in cash was correspondingly reduced. But while the policies were thus passing out, and the paper capital pouring in, the cash continued low in the treasury. What was not needed for salaries and commissions was absorbed in the losses which soon began to follow.

"To add to the demoralization in store for these doomed corporations, they launched out from their legitimate sphere of business. Cash policies were issued for cash premiums in the same manner as they were stock companies, and the premium notes of the mutual insurers were thus made liable for the risks of parties who had no interest in the companies. Even here they did not rest in their reckless career. Originally intended to be merely local institutions, they

were totally unfitted to extend their risks far beyond the limits of their own counties, while in many cases they were actually pushing their agencies beyond the line of the state. 'Whom the Gods wish to destroy they first make mad.' Soon the receipts began to fall off, while the losses accumulated. Assessments one after another on the premium notes followed in quick succession. The companies passed into receivers' hands; and, in less than ten years from the passage of the law, five-sixths of them had disappeared, entailing losses of over $2,000,000 on the community."

Naturally, in the decade to follow, New York State began to correct its laws, and that action was followed by other states. Even in this ten-year span, however, many fire insurance companies had their beginning, and twenty-eight of them stretched out over an area of twelve states to leave their marks upon buildings. In Upper New York State, in Glens Falls, the Dividend Mutual Insurance Company was chartered in 1849, reorganizing in 1864 as a joint stock company and changing its name to the Glens Falls Insurance Company. It was one of the few companies in America to issue brass fire marks.

From this outpost it was still necessary to travel by stage, by packet, and by railroad to reach New York City where progress was the keynote. There in 1850 the citizens were concerned about the dissension tearing at the Union on the slavery issue. President Zachary Taylor had died and Millard Fillmore had become the thirteenth President of the United States. California had just been admitted to the Union. One bright note affecting only the morale of the citizens came with the arrival of Jenny Lind, the "Swedish Nightingale," who was introduced to New York by P. T. Barnum, the producer of her first show in Castle Garden. Tickets were sold at auction by her manager, and after deducting the large expenses of her first concert her net income amounted to $12,600, all of which she distributed among the charitable and benevolent institutions of New York City.

In this year the first platform elevator, a contrivance manufactured by Henry Waterman and installed for use in the premises of one Hecker at 201-203 Cherry Street, was built in Manhattan. In 1850 also the Common Council made a concession when they granted a permit to the Hudson River Railroad Company "to propel their cars from Chambers Street to Thirty-first Street by their street locomotive, or 'Dumb Engine' upon the condition that the same shall not be run at a greater speed than six miles an hour; and also, that they shall employ a proper person to precede the trains on horseback, to give necessary warning in a suitable manner of their approach." Out West in Chicago the first railroad running out of that city connected with Elgin, Illinois, while back in New

York the Hudson River Railroad also opened a line from that city to Albany.

The only fire insurance concern in Manhattan to leave its sign of indemnity as evidence of organization during this decade was the Niagara Fire Insurance Company which started business on August 1, 1850. In 1870 it began to issue participating policies. Over in Newark, New Jersey, the Newark Gas Light Company finally overcame prejudice, and in 1846 secured its charter. Almost simultaneously, the American Insurance Company was authorized to transact business. Both the Mutual Fire of Frederick County and Mutual Insurance Company of Washington County in Maryland used the token of clasped hands upon their trade emblems, while in Baltimore the Associated Firemens issued an ornate plate of a fireman in parade dress with a flambeau in one hand and a speaking trumpet in position to issue orders in the other.

The year 1847 saw the incorporation of the Magnetic Telegraph Company (Maryland) under contract with Morse to erect and maintain a telegraph line through the state of New York. Also in this year the Southern Mutual Fire Insurance Company, the second American fire insurance company to use a brass fire mark, began business in Griffin, Georgia, removing to Athens the following year. An American collector records the incorporation of the Insurance Company of Florida at Jacksonville on June 7, 1841, the year in which that city and all of Duval County were immersed in warfare with the Seminole Indians. The crude wooden fire mark accredited to this concern seems to indicate that it represents an extreme outpost of insurance development in this decade. There is no evidence, however, that it was issued by a Florida company.

The pivotal finger next points to New England where in the state of Connecticut the Litchfield Mutual Fire Insurance Company, the Connecticut Fire Insurance Company of Hartford, and the City Fire Insurance Company of New Haven all issued the traditional tin fire marks made in their own bailiwick. The Washington Mutual Insurance Company of Boston, Massachusetts, distinguished itself by the issuance of a brass mark of somewhat larger size than its competitors. In this decade when Elias Howe produced the first sewing machine in the Bay State, and when the plow, reaper, and thresher were invented in rapid succession, Edmund Freeman became the first president of the Springfield Fire and Marine Insurance Company. In that same year (1849) Freeman, who had served in the legislature as well as acting as financial agent for the builders of the Terra Haute and Alton Railroad, also became a director of the Western Bank, just incorporated at Springfield.

"Protection" became synonymous with fire insurance, there being one such concern in Boston, and the Protection Mutual Fire Insurance Company which put Maine upon the insurance map was established in 1848. One year later communities in West Buxton, Maine, came forth with the York County Mutual Fire Insurance Company.

The theme "go West" was generally accepted during these years. Residents of Pennsylvania migrated to Ohio, those from Kentucky and Ohio went to Indiana, and the Hoosiers pressed on into Illinois and Missouri, the more adventurous striking out for the glittering attraction of Sutter's Mill in California. Pennsylvania, Ohio, Indiana, and Missouri soil carried the imprints of fire insurance west of the Hudson.

Considering the more complex acts of a rapidly growing population, law and order became a major consideration. Until 1843, there had been no standardization of law or dissemination of decisions rendered. Most timely was the origin of the *Legal Intelligencer*, published in Philadelphia in that year as the first law journal in the United States. In this same locale, two new mutual fire insurance companies were established, one at Germantown and another, a bit further to the north, in Nazareth. Pittsburgh, which suffered a disastrous conflagration in 1845, witnessed the birth of two more companies, the Penn Fire Insurance Company and the Associated Firemen's Insurance Company. The origin of these concerns and the fire marks they used were instrumental in making the "Iron City's" history of this period so colorful. The Penn used a cast-iron, cutout bust of William Penn, while the Associated Firemen's Insurance Company utilized a delicate, cutout iron casting of a fireman standing near a fire hydrant and shouting orders through his trumpet. The many business and residence properties adorned with these marks added considerably to the interesting aspects of downtown Pittsburgh.

A stagecoach ride to the little village of LeRoy in Westfield Township, Medina County, Ohio, brings one to the home of "The Old Man on the Fence," the symbol of the Ohio Farmers Insurance Company which received its charter upon the petition of a group of local farmers in 1848. This company utilized fire marks in a greater variety than any other company in America until a later date. Traveling southward from this point one would pass through Mansfield, where the Richland County Mutual was organized, and on past Dayton, the home of the Montgomery County Mutual, both leading to the city of Cincinnati which had increased its population 250 per cent during this decade.

This was a turbulent era for the Queen City which suffered a series of disasters and civil uprisings as

A lithographed fireman's certificate issued in 1860 by the Weccacoe Volunteer Fire Company of Philadelphia. The various vignettes show the evolution of that company at three different stages of its career.

violent as any encountered in the nation during times of peace. Being an egress from the South, the citizens were bitterly divided on the slavery question. The underlying current was given expression in 1841 when a riot against Negroes broke out. In consequence the city was under mob rule for three full days. When the Bank of Cincinnati closed its doors in 1843, rioting again broke out, and in the following year the city was visited by a conflagration which took the lives of nine people and severely injured many others. The factory of Miles Greenwood, the inventor, was destroyed by a fire but quickly rebuilt. Just as Cincinnati was recovering from this series of blows, the city was submerged by a damaging flood. The citizens were a hardy lot, however, and despite these adversities they built eleven hundred new buildings and continued to expand their industries.

In 1845 the City Insurance Company was founded in Cincinnati, issuing a cast-iron fire mark which was the most ornate ever devised in this country. The image of a fully manned Vigo type of pumper, referred to as a rowing type, as well as the name of the company appearing on the mark, plus its artistically designed outline, made this plate unique. Since the concern was short-lived, the specimens are exceed-ingly rare. Near the close of the decade, the screech-ing eagle of the Eagle Insurance Company was to be seen on buildings throughout Ohio. That company carried on until 1894 when it disposed of its liability in an honorable manner.

Cincinnati kept its foot to the fore in this decade. It opened rail travel on a daily basis to Springfield, Ohio, by way of the Little Miami Railroad, and it sponsored a meeting of the Southern and Western Anti-Slavery Convention, preparing the foundation for a far different kind of a "railroad" bed.

Near the close of this decade the Equitable Insur-ance Company of Indiana was chartered in Indian-apolis. A little further to the west on the National Turnpike, St. Louis, Missouri, came forth with the Home Mutual and the Missouri State Mutual, both of which employed the typical zinc fire plates peculiar to that new center of outpost development.

The era which had started out so auspiciously with a multitude of new inventions ended in a like man-ner. America was finally on its way to the ultimate in industrial achievement. Fire insurance continued to march hand-in-hand with the progress of the country, but pitfalls were soon to be encountered in the ensu-ing decades.

149

150

151

152

153

154

155

156

157

158

160

161

159

162

163

(149) PENN FIRE INSURANCE COMPANY. PITTSBURGH, PENNSYLVANIA. 1841-1845.

Cast iron. Cut out bust of William Penn. 8¾" x 9". Lettering, "Insured," on panel below. Very rare.

(150) INSURANCE COMPANY OF FLORIDA. JACKSONVILLE, FLORIDA. 1841-(?).

Wood. Shield shape. Lettering, "I. F." in high relief. *(Courtesy of Insurance Company of North America.)*

(151) THE LITCHFIELD MUTUAL FIRE INSURANCE COMPANY. LITCHFIELD, CONNECTICUT. 1843-

Tin. Oval. 9¾" x 4⅜". Border and "Insured Mutual Litchfield," gold on black background.

(152) MUTUAL FIRE INSURANCE COMPANY OF FREDERICK COUNTY. FREDERICK, MARYLAND. 1843-1899.

Wood. Rectangular. 9¾" x 6¾". Two clasped hands, gold and umber, on black background. Plaque is ⅞" thick. It is believed that this mark was issued by the Mutual Fire of Frederick County and it bears the trade mark of that company although the source of the mark cannot be positively established.

(153) MUTUAL FIRE INSURANCE COMPANY OF GERMANTOWN AND VICINITY. PHILADELPHIA, PENNSYLVANIA. 1843-

Cast iron. Oblong. 11½" x 8½". Slightly raised clasped hands and "Germantown Mutual Fire—1843."

(154) WASHINGTON MUTUAL INSURANCE COMPANY. BOSTON, MASSACHUSETTS. 1844-1844.

Brass. Oblong. 8½" x 4½". Border and "Washington Mutual" raised. Very rare.

(155-156) MONTGOMERY COUNTY MUTUAL FIRE INSURANCE COMPANY. DAYTON, OHIO. 1844-

155. Cast iron. Rectangular. 7¾" x 4". Border and "Mont-

gomery Co. Mutual Ins.," raised. Center holes for mounting. Very rare.

156. Cast iron. Rectangular. 7¾" x 4". Ridged border and "Montgomery Co. Mutual Ins.," raised. Loop for hanging at top. Very rare.

(157) CITY INSURANCE COMPANY. CINCINNATI, OHIO. 1845-1849.

Heavy iron casting. Odd shape. 13" x 9½". Scroll border, rowing-type fire engine manned by six firemen, and lettering, "City Insurance Co. Cin.," raised. From building at Cutter Street and Carlisle Avenue, Cincinnati, O. Very rare. Issued 1846.

(158) FARMERS MUTUAL FIRE INSURANCE COMPANY OF NORTHAMPTON COUNTY, PA. NAZARETH, PENNSYLVANIA. 1845-

Tin. Rectangular. 7" x 3⁵⁄₁₆". "Farmers Mutual," black on silver background. Rare. Issued about 1850.

(159-162) HOME MUTUAL FIRE AND MARINE INSURANCE COMPANY. SAINT LOUIS, MISSOURI. 1845-1880.

159. Zinc. Oblong. 6⅞" x 5". Border, two clasped hands and "Home Mutual," raised. Thin, large type. First mark of this company. Issued 1845. From building on Sixth Street, St. Louis, Mo.

160. Zinc. Oblong. 6½" x 4¾". Border, two clasped hands and "Home Mutual," raised. Medium weight. Second mark of this company. Issued 1848. Fairly common. From building on Ninth Street, St. Louis, Mo.

161. Zinc. Oblong. 6½" x 4¾". Border, two clasped hands and "Home Mutual," raised. Heavy weight, ⁵⁄₃₂" thick which is unusual for this type. Third mark of this company. Issued 1871. Very rare. From building on Tenth Street, St. Louis, Mo.

162. Zinc. Oblong. 6¾" x 4⅞". Border, two clasped hands and "Home Mutual," raised. Medium weight. Last mark of this company. Issued about 1878.

(163) MUTUAL INSURANCE COMPANY OF WASHINGTON COUNTY. HAGERSTOWN, MARYLAND. 1845-1935.

Cast iron. Rectangular. 9⁹⁄₁₆" x 7½". Raised, rounded border and two clasped hands in high relief. Raised "M. I. Co. O. W. C., A. D. 1846." Issued 1847.

164

165

166

167

168

169

170

171

172

173

174

175

176

177

178

179

180

181

68

182

183

184

(164-165) AMERICAN INSURANCE COMPANY. NEWARK, NEW JERSEY. 1846-

164. Tin. Rectangular. 7½" x 2⁵⁄₁₆". Border and "American" raised. From building in Rockford, Illinois. Very rare.

165. Tin. Diamond shape, slightly convexed. 5¾" x 5¾". "American" and Chinese characters in dark blue on speckled light blue enamel background. Mark used in China.

(166) ASSOCIATED FIREMEN'S INSURANCE COMPANY. BALTIMORE, MARYLAND. 1847-1899.

Cast iron. Oval. 9⅜" x 12". Raised border. Fireman with trumpet, holding burning brand, in high relief. Issued about 1848.

(167-176) OHIO FARMERS INSURANCE COMPANY. LE ROY, OHIO. 1848-

167. Lead. Rectangular. 4⅞" x 2". Incised "Ohio Farmers." First mark of this company. Issued 1861. From barn on farm on Bird Road between Charleston and National Pikes, east of Springfield, Ohio.

168. Tin. Rectangular. 6⅝" x 3¼". Painted "Ohio" arched over horizontal "Farmers." Issued about 1865. Rare. From building near Wellington, Ohio.

169. Tin. Rectangular. Border and lettering raised. "Ohio" slightly curved. "Farmers" strictly horizontal. (Courtesy of Ohio Farmers Insurance Company.)

170. Tin. Rectangular. Border and "Ohio—Farmers" raised. Black background. Size of lettering varies from mark No. 169. (Courtesy of Ohio Farmers Insurance Company.)

171. Heavy tin. Rectangular. 6¾" x 3¼". Border and "Ohio Farmers" raised. Issued about 1885. From farm dwelling at northwest corner of U. S. Highway 23 and U. S. Highway 6, Wood County, Ohio.

172. Heavy tin. Rectangular. 6¾" x 3¼". Border and "Ohio Farmers" raised. Issued about 1890.

173. Tin. Rectangular. 6¾" x 3¼". "Ohio Farmers," silver on black background. Issued about 1900.

174. Tin. Rectangular. 6⅝" x 3¼". "Ohio Farmers," gold on black background. Issued about 1920.

175. Tin. Rectangular. 6⅝" x 3½". "Ohio Farmers," in gold stenciling on black background. A variant of modern type plate issued about 1920 as an advertising medium.

176. Brass. Hexagonal. 2½" x 2½". Believed to have been issued for auto but also used as door plate. About 1920.

(177) PROTECTION MUTUAL FIRE INSURANCE COMPANY. THOMASTON, MAINE. 1848-

Tin. Oval. Lettering is hardly discernible due to effects of fire. (Courtesy of Insurance Company of North America.)

(178) SOUTHERN MUTUAL INSURANCE COMPANY. ATHENS, GEORGIA. 1848-

Brass. Oval. 7½" x 4¼". Border and "Southern Mutual" raised. Issued prior to the Civil War. Very rare.

(179-184) GLENS FALLS INSURANCE COMPANY. GLENS FALLS, NEW YORK. 1849-

179. Brass. Oval. 7" x 4¾". Border and "Glens Falls Insurance Co.," raised.

180. Brass. Oval. 7⁹⁄₁₆" x 4¾". Border and "Glens Falls Insurance Co.—N. Y.," raised. Very rare. From building in Connecticut.

181. Tin. Rectangular. 7" x 2¾". "Glens Falls, N. Y.," silver on black background.

182. Tin. Rectangular. 6¾" x 3¼". "Glens Falls," black on gold background.

183. Tin. Rectangular. 6¾" x 3¼". "Glens Falls—Old and Tried," gold on black background.

184. Tin. Diamond shape, slightly convexed. 5¾" x 5¾". "Glens Falls" and Chinese characters in dark blue on speckled light blue enamel. Mark used in China.

INSURED,
SPRINGFIELD
FIRE & MARINE,
MASS.

186

185

SPRINGFIELD

187

營業
SPRINGFIELD
保險

188

189

YORK
INSURANCE

190

192

191

CONNECTICUT
FIRE INS. CO.
HARTFORD, CT.

193

194

195

EQUITABLE
INS. CO.
INDIANAPOLIS.

196

197

198

70

199

200

201

(185) MISSOURI STATE MUTUAL FIRE AND MARINE INSURANCE COMPANY. SAINT LOUIS, MISSOURI. 1849-1907.

Zinc. Oval. 5⅞" x 3⅞". Border and "Missouri State Mutual," raised. Issued 1849. Very rare.

(186-188) SPRINGFIELD FIRE AND MARINE INSURANCE COMPANY. SPRINGFIELD, MASSACHUSETTS. 1849-

186. Tin. Rectangular. 6½" x 3¼". "Insured Springfield Fire & Marine, Mass.," gold on black background.

187. Tin. Rectangular. 6⅞" x 2⅜". Border and "Springfield," black on gold background. Very rare.

188. Tin. Diamond shape, slightly convexed. 5¾" x 5¾". "Springfield" and Chinese characters in dark blue on speckled light blue enamel background. Mark used in China.

(189) PROTECTION INSURANCE COMPANY. BOSTON, MASSACHUSETTS. 1849-1889.

Heavy tin. Rectangular. 8¼" x 3". Border and "Protection," raised.

(190) YORK COUNTY MUTUAL FIRE INSURANCE COMPANY. WEST BUXTON, MAINE. 1849-

Tin. Rectangular. 7⅞" x 3⅞". Border and "York Insurance," raised.

(191) ASSOCIATED FIREMEN'S INSURANCE COMPANY. PITTSBURGH, PENNSYLVANIA. 1850-1930.

Cast iron. Cut out fireman. 7⅞" x 8⅜". Figure of fireman with trumpet and fire hydrant. Circular panel below with lettering "Fire Company." Issued 1851.

(192-193) THE CONNECTICUT FIRE INSURANCE COMPANY. HARTFORD, CONNECTICUT. 1850-

192. Tin. Rectangular. 6⅝" x 3¼". Script lettering, "Connecticut Hartford," silver on black background.

193. Tin. Rectangular. 6¾" x 3½". Border and "Connecticut Fire Ins. Co. Hartford, Ct.," gold on black background.

(194-195) EAGLE INSURANCE COMPANY. CINCINNATI, OHIO. 1850-1894.

194. Tin. Oval. 9½" x 6½". Border, eagle, and "Insurance Co.," raised. First mark of this company. Issued about 1850. Very rare.

195. Cast iron. Oval. 11¾" x 8". Raised border. Eagle and ribbons in high relief. "Eagle Ins. Co. Cin. O.," in raised form on ribbons. Issued about 1855.

(196) EQUITABLE INSURANCE COMPANY OF INDIANA. INDIANAPOLIS, INDIANA. 1850-1903.

Tin. Rectangular with rounded top. 7⅞" x 3¾". Border and "Equitable Ins. Co., Indianapolis," raised.

(197) CITY FIRE INSURANCE COMPANY. NEW HAVEN, CONNECTICUT. 1850-1865.

Heavy tin. Rectangular. 8" x 3⅞". Border and "City Fire New Haven, Ct.," raised. (Courtesy of Earl B. Davison.)

(198-200) NIAGARA FIRE INSURANCE COMPANY. NEW YORK, NEW YORK. 1850-

198. Tin. Rectangular. 6⅞" x 3⅜". Border and "Niagara of New York," cream color on black background. First type mark of this company. From frame dwelling on south side of Main Street, West Salem, Ohio.

199. Tin. Rectangular. 6¾" x 3¼". Border and "Niagara—New York," silver on black background. Very rare.

200. Tin. Rectangular. 6½" x 3¼". Border and "Niagara Fire—New York," gold on black background.

(201) RICHLAND COUNTY MUTUAL INSURANCE COMPANY. MANSFIELD, OHIO. 1850-

Tin. Rectangular. 6⅞" x 2⅛". Border and "Richland," raised. Only type mark issued by this company, 1855. From residence on east side of Main Street, Thornport, Ohio.

THE DECADE OF SECURITY

1851-1860

From the standpoint of signeviery and the story which encircles the organization of those companies which emblazoned the trail of history with their marks, the next period, which produced a profusion of these signs, was the most interesting. Henry Carey, one of the founders of the Franklin Fire, had by 1851 become a man of unusual vision in the world of economics. In that year he published his *Harmony of Interests,* which stressed the theory that this country, with its unlimited natural resources and vast acreage, could attain the world's highest standard of living. Another idea propounded by Carey was that of the distribution of the population into the open land where each community could become largely self-sufficient and would thereby develop its own sciences, arts, economics, and education. Even though many leaders of his day disagreed with him, his forward-moving theories, aimed at reducing poverty to a minimum, were widely adopted in the decades to follow.

The people at large, those who forgot their selfish interests, were now becoming conscious of the obligations which their new civilization placed upon them. Free of the Old World oppressions, they had laid the foundations of the new Republic. By perseverance and courage they overcame the discouragement and despair born of devastations by conflagration and recurring financial crises. Agriculture assumed a new dignity, and industry thrived with the advancement of the newest inventions. Thoughts could now turn to the welfare of their fellowmen, and before the decade came to a close Abraham Lincoln, campaigning upon just such a platform, was elected to the presidency of the United States.

The welfare of the people was also the keynote in the fire insurance industry during this ten-year period. Although these years brought some very wild speculation among many underwriters, they also produced the first genuine safeguards for the insuring public. Insurance legislation of a substantial nature began in New York State in 1853, the year in which venture capital came out of hiding and more new fire insurance concerns had their beginnings than in any other year. It was a decade in which the first widely read insurance journals appeared, these being *Tuckett's Monthly Insurance Journal* in Philadelphia and the

Insurance Monitor in New York City. Insurance law became established, and most of our common law doctrines were taken from decisions made in this decade. The place of contract; what constitutes payment of premium; warranty and representation; and liability for theft were among the numerous subjects clearly settled by adjudication for the first time.

Massachusetts codified its insurance laws into a single act in 1856. Pennsylvania passed an act in the same year requiring full and complete tax returns and the publication of a company's financial conditions. Connecticut, too, passed reciprocity acts regarding fines and other fees in reference to representatives of foreign states, and Ohio passed a law in 1854 regulating agencies aimed at wildcat concerns. Vermont, Maryland, Rhode Island, Iowa, Virginia, Kentucky, Illinois, Michigan, and Missouri all enacted new laws pertaining to or regulating fire insurance companies. This was truly a decade of insurance expansion, for despite the fact that many of these beginners have dropped by the wayside, a substantial group of those who organized in the fifties remain among the leaders in our twentieth century. In this span of years another progressive move which gave a new security to investors and property owners was the start of the steam fire engine and the establishment of the first paid municipal fire departments.

Fire insurance underwriters were expanding their agencies to every state and territory of the Union, and new companies were formed as far to the west as the Mississippi River, outposts of these establishments being in Keokuk, Iowa, and Milwaukee, Wisconsin. Down in St. Louis, Missouri, eight associations of this decade left a profusion of zinc fire marks, for zinc ore was being extensively mined in that locale. The marks themselves portrayed an anchor denoting security, an American eagle with spread wings and, in the case of two of the companies, the traditional clasped hands. One company organized in Chicago, but there were three newcomers in Freeport and Rockford, these latter towns being heralded by some as the new insurance metropolis of the West, a designation which had long since applied to Cincinnati.

Neophytes marking property in Ohio numbered nine. The most unique plate there consisted of a round tin upon which was embossed a likeness of the Latta steam engine, the symbol of the Queen City Insurance Company. Moses Latta of Cincinnati invented the first successful steam fire engine in 1852, and it went into service in that city on January 1, 1853, as the first municipally paid organization in America. The contrivance was a ponderous affair weighing twenty-two thousand pounds, drawn partly by its own motive power, and augmented by four horses ridden in artillery fashion. Its adoption came only after fierce battles and debates by the old volunteer companies which did everything within their power to prevent its success. Partly because of the bitterness engendered by such opposition to progress and partly through the insistence of the insurance companies which decried the hit-or-miss style of volunteer fire-fighting methods, the transition from hand power to motive power, the change from the volunteer system to that of the municipally owned and paid fire department began here. The epoch of the old volunteers and their machines was a most colorful one, but it was no more colorful than the era of the steam engine, drawn by gorgeous spirited horses, racing to the scene of a fire. In Ohio, at Warren in the Western Reserve, an insurance agency devised its own fire mark to attach to insured properties, but this was a rare practice indulged in by only a few agencies.

Indianapolis was the locale of another beginner. And down on the Ohio River one company started at Louisville and another at Newport, Kentucky, not to be outdone by more venture capital at Wheeling, West Virginia. Pittsburgh, York, and Wilkes-Barre each produced a new sign of insurance in the fifties with progress very evident in Pittsburgh where commerce and insurance were materially affected by transportation. In 1851 the Pittsburgh and Ohio Railroad was completed to Beaver, and construction commenced on the Pittsburgh and Steubenville as well as the Pittsburgh and Cleveland Railroads. The first locomotive, the "Salem," arrived by boat. A year later the rail routes of the Pennsylvania Central and the Baltimore and Ohio opened to the East.

In Philadelphia a test was made in February, 1855 to determine the efficiency of the Miles Greenwood steam fire engine. This machine failed to produce the desired results so another steamer, the Young America manufactured by A. Shawk, was brought in from Cincinnati in May of the same year. This steamer was received so enthusiastically that a popular subscription was taken up and the machine purchased. Such new equipment was purchased by various volunteer companies in 1856 and in the following years until in 1859 twenty various steam fire engines were built for the companies in Philadelphia. The volunteer brigades in this city were probably better organized than in any other community. As a consequence the paid fire department was not organized until January 3, 1871; it began operations on March 15.

In the meantime the organization of the Fire Association was thriving. That group, however, did not include some twenty-eight other fire engine and hose companies. The latter concerns then initiated a movement to form another insurance company, the United Firemens Insurance Company of Philadelphia, which was incorporated April 2, 1860. As a notification to the members of these brigades they adopted a cast-iron oval fire mark containing the name of the organization, the policy number, and, in high relief, the image of a new steam engine, a type probably built by Reanie and Neafie of Philadelphia.

An unusually distinctive mark of assurance of this period was the unique iron casting portraying the symbol of Hope, an extremely rare mark which, according to Gillespie and Walsh in their 1915 recordings, represented the Hope Mutual Insurance Company of Philadelphia, incorporated February 27, 1854, a reference which the author believes to be most nearly authentic. On the other hand, Griswold, in 1891, shows this mark to be that of the Hope Fire and Marine Insurance Company of New York established in 1821. This concern became an exclusive marine writer in 1823 and closed its business in 1826. Consequently it is more likely that the mark belongs to the Philadelphia concern rather than to the New York institution. The era boasts of one other Philadelphia underwriter leaving its badge. This was the Girard Fire and Marine Insurance Company of which Joel Jones, its first president, was also the first president of Girard College. This establishment was strongly supported by M. C. and C. I. Du Pont.

In this decade staid New England provided the famous regulatory Massachusetts Insurance Department, under whose watchful eye two concerns of the state left behind their fire plates. Because Boston became one of the great construction centers for the expanding shipping industry it realized an ever-increasing need for insurance protection.

In Connecticut the Charter Oak Insurance Company used the emblem of that historic tree on its fire mark. The Phoenix and three other Hartford companies of this decade merely used the stamped name plates so prevalent in the coastal states. In Hartford there was strength and solidarity, but in New Haven The Home Insurance Company of that city, in leaving its ornate marks, also left a record of wild speculation which led to disaster. This company's fire mark left for our archives a badge which recorded the type of steam fire engine produced by the Silsby Manufacturing Company of Seneca Falls, New York; the engine

73

was then known as the Silsby Piston Engine. It also depicted the image of a burning building with a fireman, in position at the hydrant, connecting hose to pumper.

At the office of Moses R. King and Samuel Bond on August 3, 1855, the volunteer firemen of Newark, New Jersey, gathered to form the Newark Firemen's Insurance Company which changed its name to the Firemen's Insurance Company of Newark in 1874. This company was one of the few concerns in New Jersey to employ the fire plate.

The greatest advances of the decade, however, were made in the Empire State. At Evans Mills, ten miles from Watertown, the Agricultural Insurance Company was born. At Ogdensburg the Star Fire with its several types of star fire marks came into being. And to Brooklyn came the Williamsburgh City Fire and the Phenix Fire Insurance Company, the latter placing several types of horseshoe fire marks, emblematic of future good fortune, above the doors of their clients. In New York City there were eight newly formed companies whose marks have been left to posterity. One additional underwriter, the Hanover Fire Insurance Company, issued a tin house plate, according to historian Griswold, but so far as can be learned no specimen has been located.

In New York City, a number of volunteer firemen banded together to establish the Lorillard Fire Insurance Company whose first president was Cornelius V. Anderson, foreman of Engine Company No. 1 and later chief engineer of the New York Fire Department. The brass fire mark employed by this concern bore a pair of crossed torches. One other distinctive plate was used by a beginner in the secure fifties, the Continental Insurance Company, which adopted the clasped hands, an uncommon symbol for capital stock underwriters. The Continental, like most of the other newcomers in 1853, was undoubtedly influenced by the new general insurance laws of New York State passed in that year, by the news of the new steam fire engines fast becoming the vogue, and by the good feeling engendered by progress in this metropolis.

New York now had twenty daily newspapers. The principal population of the city extended for four miles northward along both rivers and eight important rail lines converged upon the city. In this year the Clearing House Association, which opened its offices at 14 Wall Street, was organized. Wall Street was fast becoming the backbone of American economy; the entire area surrounding it was a network of business concerns from whose doors flowed the wealth of trade throughout this country and the far ports of the world.

It was in 1853 that the merchants of Manhattan felt that the country was ready for a new fire insurance venture upon a scale not previously tried. A group of them converged upon the offices of Barney, Humphrey and Butler, at 29 Wall Street, on January 29 of that year to discuss the prospects for such a company. Before the meeting was concluded they had appointed Oliver E. Wood, a prominent dry goods and commission merchant, to act as chairman and Charles B. Hatch, a furnishing goods merchant at 97 William Street, as secretary. As a result resolutions were passed to organize The Home Insurance Company; that this company have forty-five directors and that S. L. Loomis of Hartford, Connecticut, be invited to serve as its first president. Legal notices were filed, necessary requirements were met, and the forty-five directors were selected. The latter list read like a *Who's Who* of the mercantile industry. There was, for instance, Levi P. Morton, a young Yankee merchant from Shoreham, Vermont, who began his career as a clerk in a small country store and later became congressman from New York City and Minister to France. While serving in the latter capacity, he was instrumental in securing the Statue of Liberty for the United States. After the Statue was secured, it was he who accepted that monument for this government and drove the first rivet at the unveiling ceremonies. In 1888 he became Vice President of the United States under President Benjamin Harrison. At the age of seventy, he was elected Governor of New York State. Morton was also chairman of the board of the Guaranty Trust Company and was one of this country's benevolent philanthropists.

Other original directors were Amos R. Eno, a cousin of Junius S. Morgan, who was soon to devote his entire energy to real estate development, including the erection of the original Fifth Avenue Hotel at a cost of over one million dollars; William H. Mellen of Claflin, Mellen & Co., the most prominent of dry goods establishments; and George Bliss, another successful dry goods merchant who was later associated with Levi P. Morton. There were also James Low, who became a director of the Phenix Bank; Alfred S. Barnes, the founder of the great publishing house bearing his name and one of the financial backers of the elevated railway in New York City; and John G. Nelson, a distinguished silk merchant in the city who was regarded by many to be superior in judgment to Stewart in his knowledge of silk. Nelson later headed the largest wire manufacturing concerns in America. Then, too, there was Theodore McNamee of the firm of Bowen and McNamee, famous for their Marble Palace Dry Goods Store located at 112 Broadway, the building occupied by The Home Insurance Company in May, 1858. The original list of directors included one each of the following: oil and candle merchant, hat merchant, tobacco merchant, real estate agent, insurance executive, lawyer, boot and shoe merchant, India rubber goods merchant, grocer, transportation agent; two each of bankers, clothing merchants, publishers and druggists, while the heavy artillery was headed by ten commission merchants and seventeen dry goods merchants. To these men it must have been a bright omen when the California Mail Steamer "Illinois" arrived at New York on April 11 with $2,095,000 in gold for that city; two mornings later, on April 13, 1853, they received the charter for The Home Insurance Company.

The original meeting on that day was held in a rear room of the Continental Bank at 12 Wall Street, but on May 1 The Home occupied its new quarters at 10 Wall Street. Simeon L. Loomis, the first president, and Charles J. Martin, the first secretary, together with all of the directors, had dedicated themselves to the projection of a new need in fire insurance underwriting. The plan was to expand and diversify the business throughout all of the states and provinces by the establishment of local agencies. Such a theory had previously been the subject of experimentation, but it had not been truly executed by other insurance companies. This progressive program was frowned upon by outside underwriters, but the company promptly launched its campaign. Before the year came to a close agencies had been established in New York, Pennsylvania, Massachusetts, Connecticut, Vermont, Montreal, Canada, Halifax, N. S., Ohio, St. Johns, N. B., Georgia, Illinois, Michigan, Kentucky, Quebec City, Indiana, West Virginia, Missouri, California, Wisconsin, Tennessee, South Carolina, Virginia, Mississippi, Alabama, North Carolina, Maine, Iowa, and Texas.

This was truly an innovation in the underwriting business. Although the agency organization naturally required some alterations in the early years, the company continued its forward stride until it became the greatest producer of fire insurance premiums in America. It had numerous types of fire marks which can still be found upon many properties throughout the states and thus bear witness to the extent of this company's expansion throughout the years. A mark in the German language attests to its entry into the agencies of Europe, and the one in Chinese recalls the time when The Home entered the Orient. Today the company has the distinction of being the first foreign concern to re-establish itself in Japan subsequent to World War II.

The success which has been The Home's can be attributed to two factors; first, the executive leadership which from its inception to the present day has been one of sound judgment, ambition, and keen understanding of the needs of the day; second, the constant increase of its original plan of agency expansion and development. The latter factor has produced and is still producing the highest type of local agent, a system which is definitely American and which will continue to be the bulwark of fire insurance underwriting. It seems most fitting that the leading fire insurance producer in America should also be the concern which has established in the H. V. Smith Museum a means of perpetuating for the ages the many physical and written mementos of such a romantic enterprise. It is this Museum which has made possible the recording of signeviery contained in this book.

The decade of the fifties was surely one of security with its new protective laws, the development of the steam fire engine (forerunner of our present motive power), and the growth of fire insurance companies which have persisted in business to secure commerce and the individual against loss. The period must go down in history as the one which produced the greatest number of survivors among the fire insurance centenarians when one keeps in mind such names as: the Insurance Company of North America, Milwaukee Mechanics, Providence-Washington, Hartford, Aetna, Hanover, Continental, Agricultural, Westchester, and The Home of New York.

202

203

204

205

206

207

208

209

210

211

212

213

214

215

216

217   218

(202) ASHLAND COUNTY MUTUAL FIRE INSURANCE
COMPANY. ASHLAND, OHIO. 1851-1887.

Heavy tin. Rectangular. 8⅜" x 3¼". "Ashland—1851" and
border raised. Only type of mark used by this company. Issued
1851. Rare. From frame cabin on South Washington Street, Circleville, Ohio.

(203-204) DAYTON INSURANCE COMPANY. DAYTON,
OHIO. 1851-1896.

203. Heavy tin. Rectangular. 6⅞" x 3⅛". "Dayton Ins. Co.
—Dayton, O." and border raised. First type mark of this company.
Issued 1851. Very rare. From brick dwelling on Simpson Street,
Dayton, O.

204. Heavy tin. Rectangular. 7¾" x 3¾". "Dayton Ins. Co."
and border raised.

(205) IRVING FIRE INSURANCE COMPANY. NEW YORK,
NEW YORK. 1851-1871.

Heavy tin. Rectangular. 7⅞" x 3⅞". "Irving—New York" and
border raised. (Courtesy of Earl B. Davison.)

(206) HAMILTON INSURANCE COMPANY. HAMILTON,
OHIO. 1851-1872.

Tin. Rectangular. 9¾" x 4½". "Insured, Hamilton" and border raised. Only type mark of this company. Issued 1851. Very rare.
From two-story brick residence on Washington Street, Hamilton, O.

(207) QUEEN CITY INSURANCE COMPANY. CINCINNATI,
OHIO. 1851-1870.

Tin. Round. 7¾" in diameter. Raised border, "Queen City
Ins. Co." and figure of famous Cincinnati "Latta" steam fire engine. Exceptionally rare.

(208) INDIANA FIRE INSURANCE COMPANY.
INDIANAPOLIS, INDIANA. 1851-1902.

Tin. Rectangular. 5¾" x 3". "Indiana—Indianapolis" and border raised. Very rare.

(209) QUINCY MUTUAL FIRE INSURANCE COMPANY.
QUINCY, MASSACHUSETTS. 1851-

Tin. Rectangular. 7" x 3¼". Border and "Insured in the
Quincy Mutual Fire Ins. Co. of Quincy, Mass." gold on black
background.

(210) ST. LOUIS MUTUAL FIRE AND MARINE INSURANCE COMPANY. SAINT LOUIS, MISSOURI. 1851-1901.

Zinc. Odd shape. 7" x 4". Raised border, end loops and "St.
Louis Mutual." Only mark used by this company. Issued 1851.
Fairly common.

(211-212) LORILLARD FIRE INSURANCE COMPANY.
NEW YORK, NEW YORK. 1852-1871.

211. Cast brass. Oval. 8⅜" x 6". Raised beaded border, two
crossed torches and "Lorillard—New York." Very rare.

212. Tin. Rectangular. 8⅝" x 3⅝". Raised border and gold
"Lorillard—New York" on black background.

(213-217) MILWAUKEE MECHANICS' MUTUAL INSURANCE COMPANY. MILWAUKEE, WISCONSIN. 1852-1887.

213. Tin. Rectangular. 7" x 3¼". "Milwaukee Mutual" gold
on black background. (Courtesy of Dwight Rutherford.)

214. Tin. Rectangular. 6¾" x 3⅛". Raised border and "Milwaukee Mutual" gold on black background. (Courtesy of Dwight
Rutherford.)

215. Cast iron. Oval. Raised roped border and "Milwaukee
Mechanics." (Courtesy of Insurance Company of North America.)

216. Tin. Rectangular. 6¾" x 3¼". Border and "Milwaukee
Mechanics'" black on silver background.

217. Heavy tin. Rectangular. 6⅞" x 3⅝". Border and gold
"Milwaukee Mechanics'" raised. Red background. Very rare.

(218) PENNSYLVANIA INSURANCE COMPANY. PITTSBURGH, PENNSYLVANIA. 1852-1891.

Tin. Rectangular. 8" x 4¾". Border and "Pennsylvania Ins.
Co." raised. Very rare.

220

219

221

222

223

224

225

226

227

228

229

230

232

231

233

78

235

234

236

(219) ROCK RIVER MUTUAL FIRE INSURANCE COMPANY. ROCKFORD, ILLINOIS. 1852-1869.

Tin. Rectangular. 7¾″ x 3¾″. Border and "Rock River Ins. Co." raised. From building near Freeport, Ill. Very rare.

(220-225) THE CONTINENTAL INSURANCE COMPANY. NEW YORK, NEW YORK. 1853-

220. Tin. Rectangular. 8⅜″ x 4½″. Border, two clasped hands and "Continental—New York" raised. Undoubtedly this company's first mark. Very rare.

221. Tin. Rectangular. 6⅞″ x 2¾″. Border and "Continental—New York" gold on black background. Probably second type mark of this company.

222. Tin. Rectangular. 6⅞″ x 3⅛″. Border and "Continental—New York" gold on black background.

223. Tin. Rectangular. 6⅛″ x 3¼″. Border and "Continental—New York." painted on black background. Very rare.

224. Tin. Rectangular. 7″ x 3¼″. Border and "Continental—New York" raised. Gold on black background. Last American issue. Common.

225. Iron. Diamond shape, slightly convexed. 5⅞″ x 5⅞″. "Continental" and Chinese characters in dark blue on speckled light blue enamel. Mark used in China. Now rare.

(226) GIRARD FIRE AND MARINE INSURANCE COMPANY. PHILADELPHIA, PENNSYLVANIA. 1853-

Tin. Rectangular. 6¾″ x 3⅜″. Border and "Girard Ins. Co. Philadelphia" black on gold background.

(227) THE WILLIAMSBURGH CITY FIRE INSURANCE COMPANY. BROOKLYN, NEW YORK. 1853-1916.

Tin. Rectangular. 6⅝″ x 3$\frac{3}{16}$″. Border and "Williamsburgh City—New York" gold on black background. Only type mark known to have been used by this company. Very rare.

(228) FARMERS FIRE INSURANCE COMPANY. YORK, PENNSYLVANIA. 1853-

Tin. Rectangular. 6¾″ x 3⅛″. Border and "Farmers—York, Pa." black on gold background. From a dwelling in St. Clairsville, Bedford County, Pa.

(229-239) THE HOME INSURANCE COMPANY. NEW YORK, NEW YORK. 1853-

229. Tin. Rectangular. 6⅜″ x 3⅛″. Border barely raised. Gold "Home—New York" slightly raised. First type mark of this company. Issued 1853.

230. Tin. Rectangular. 6⅛″ x 3⅛″. Border and "Home—New York" raised. Second type and rarest mark of this company. Issued about 1860.

231. Tin. Oval. 8$\frac{3}{16}$″ x 5$\frac{3}{16}$″. Heavy rolled border and raised "Home N. Y. Insurance" gold on black background. Third type mark of this company. Issued about 1861. Rare.

232. Tin. Rectangular. 6½″ x 3⅛″. Heavy raised border. Raised "Home—New-York." Similar to first mark used except for border. Issued between 1863 and 1867.

233. Tin. Oval. 8⅛″ x 5¼″. Slightly raised border and "Insured—Home—New-York" gold on black background. Fourth type mark of this company. Issued 1863 to 1868.

234. Tin. Oval. 8⅛″ x 5¼″. Heavy raised border and "Insured—Home—New York" gold on black background. Issued about 1870. Very rare.

235. Tin. Oval. 8⅛″ x 5¼″. Narrow rolled edge and heavily raised gold "Insured—Home—New York" on black background. A variant of the 1870 mark.

236. Tin. Rectangular. 6¾″ x 3⅜″. "The Home Insurance Company New York" silver on black background. Rare.

237

238

239

240

241

242

243

244

245

246

247

248

249

250

251

252

237. Tin. Diamond shape, slightly convexed. 5¾" x 5¾". "Home" and Chinese characters in dark blue on speckled light blue enamel. Mark used in China.

238. Tin. Rectangular. 6¹¹⁄₁₆" x 3⅜". "The Home Versicherungs-Aktiengesellschaft" white on black background. Mark used in Germany. Rare.

239. Heavy aluminum alloy. Rectangular with bowed top. 8" x 6½". "Home Insurance Co., New York" and monograms in lower corners stamped in red. Chinese characters, "Andersen, Meyer & Co., Ltd., General Agents" and design of eagle on shield stamped in black. Background aluminum color. Andersen, Meyer & Co., Ltd. were General Agents in Shanghai, China, established March 31, 1906, and representing a number of companies as late as 1931. It is believed that this mark was manufactured by and for this general agency probably during the 1920's.

(240) EAGLE FIRE INSURANCE COMPANY. BOSTON, MASSACHUSETTS. 1853-1862.

Copper. Oval. 8" x 5⅝". Raised ridged border and design of eagle surrounded by a rose, shamrocks and thistles. Believed to have been issued by the above company but source of mark is unverified.

(241) ARCTIC FIRE INSURANCE COMPANY. NEW YORK, NEW YORK. 1853-1897.

Tin. Rectangular. 6¹³⁄₁₆" x 3⅞". Border and "Arctic—New-York" raised. Found over door of old workshop at the rear of a furniture store on Central Avenue, Silver Creek, New York. Rare.

(242-246) PHENIX INSURANCE COMPANY. BROOKLYN, NEW YORK. 1853-1910.

242. Tin. Rectangular. 4⅜" x 4⅞". Raised black "Phenix" on raised gold horseshoe. Black background. Issued about 1855. Rare.

243. Brass. Horseshoe. 3⅝" x 3⅞". "Phenix" raised. Horseshoe inverted. Brass is very thin. Issued about 1865. Very rare.

244. Brass. Horseshoe. 3½" x 3⅞". "Phenix" raised. Issued about 1875. Rare.

245. Tin. Rectangular. 7" x 3¼". "Phenix—Brooklyn, N. Y." white on black background.

246. Tin. Rectangular. 7" x 3¼". Raised border and "Phenix —Brooklyn, N. Y."

(247-249) AGRICULTURAL INSURANCE COMPANY. WATERTOWN, NEW YORK. 1853-

247. Tin. Rectangular. 9⅜" x 2⅜". Border and "Agricultural" black on silver background.

248. Tin. Rectangular. 7" x 2½". Border and "Agricultural N. Y." black.

249. Tin. Diamond shape. 6¼" x 6¼". "Agricultural — U.S.A." and Chinese characters with monogram AAU raised gold. Border gold. Background blue. Modern plate used in China.

(250) STEPHENSON INSURANCE COMPANY. FREEPORT, ILLINOIS. 1853-1867.

Tin. Rectangular. 7⁵⁄₁₆" x 3⅜". Border and "Stephenson Ins. Co." raised. Very rare. From building in Freeport, Illinois, once home office building of this company.

(251) WESTCHESTER FIRE INSURANCE COMPANY. NEW YORK, NEW YORK. 1853-

Tin. Diamond shape, slightly convexed. 5¾" x 5¾". "Westchester" and Chinese characters in dark blue on speckled light blue enamel. Mark used in China.

(252) HOPE MUTUAL INSURANCE COMPANY OF PHILADELPHIA. PHILADELPHIA, PENNSYLVANIA. 1854-1860.

Cast iron. Oval. 6⅞" x 10⅞". Raised gold beaded border. Raised figure of "Hope" resting on anchor, red and gold on blue background. Exceedingly rare.

253

254

255

257

256

258

260

259

261

263

262

265

264

82

267

266

268

(253-255) STAR FIRE INSURANCE COMPANY. OGDENS-BURG, NEW YORK. 1854-1857.

253. Wood. Oval. 8¾″ x 11¼″. Lead star, eight wavy points, mounted on oval board. *(Courtesy of J. R. Middaugh.)*

254. Cast iron. Oval. 8½″ x 10⅞″. Star, eight wavy points, in high relief. Edge of casting is beveled.

255. Tin. Rectangular. 6⁹⁄₁₆″ x 3³⁄₁₆″. Border, star, and "Star Fire Ins. Co." raised. Issued about 1855. Very rare. From building in Ohio.

(256-262) THE PHOENIX INSURANCE COMPANY. HART-FORD, CONNECTICUT. 1854-

256. Tin. Rectangular. 7⅞″ x 4″. Raised border and "Phoenix Hartford" gold on black background. First type mark of this company. Issued about 1860. From old frame residence, New-town, Ohio.

257. Tin. Rectangular. 6⅞″ x 3¼″. Border and "Phoenix of Hartford" gold on black background. Second type. Issued about 1860. From building in Illinois.

258. Tin. Rectangular. 8⅜″ x 4⁵⁄₁₆″. Border and "Phoenix Hartford" raised. Third type. Issued about 1865. Rare.

259. Tin. Rectangular. 6½″ x 2⅝″. Border and "Phoenix" raised. Fourth type. Issued about 1865. Very rare. From building in Urbana, Ohio.

260. Heavy tin. Rectangular. 7¼″ x 3⅜″. Border and "Phoe-nix, Hartford" raised. Fifth type. Issued about 1868.

261. Tin. Rectangular. 6¾″ x 3¼″. Border and "Phoenix of Hartford" black on silver background. Last type mark of this company used in America. Issued about 1874.

262. Tin. Diamond shape. 6″ x 6″. "Phoenix" and Chinese

characters dark blue on speckled light blue enamel. Mark used in China.

(263-265) CITY FIRE INSURANCE COMPANY OF HART-FORD. HARTFORD, CONNECTICUT. 1854-1872.

263. Heavy tin. Rectangular. 7¼″ x 3⅜″. Border and "City Ins. Co. Hartford" raised. Rare. From building in Springfield, Ohio.

264. Tin. Rectangular. 7⅛″ x 3½″. Border and "City Fire Hartford" raised.

265. Tin. Rectangular. 7¼″ x 3½″. Border and "City Fire Hartford" raised.

(266) IOWA STATE INSURANCE COMPANY. KEOKUK, IOWA. 1855-1931.

Tin. Rectangular. 7⅞″ x 3⅞″. Border and "Iowa State Ins. Co. Keokuk" raised. Issued about 1860. Rare.

(267) FIREMEN'S INSURANCE COMPANY OF NEWARK, NEW JERSEY. NEWARK, NEW JERSEY. 1855-

Tin. Diamond shape, slightly convexed. 5¾″ x 5¾″. "Fire-men's" and Chinese characters dark blue on speckled light blue enamel. Mark used in China.

(268) FRANKLIN INSURANCE COMPANY. SAINT LOUIS, MISSOURI. 1855-1878.

Zinc. Odd shape. 7⅜″ x 5⅝″. Border and "Franklin Insurance Co. St. Louis" raised. Issued 1855. Rare. From building on Sixth Street, St. Louis, Mo.

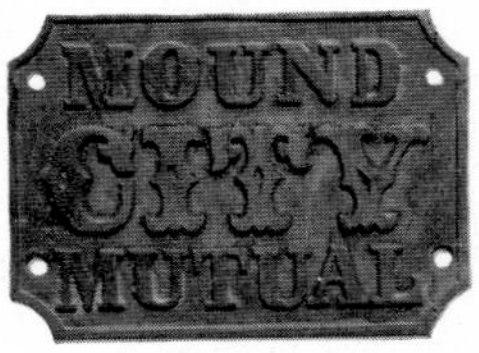

269

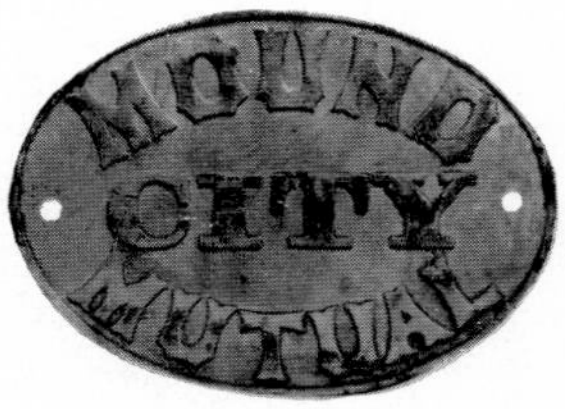

270

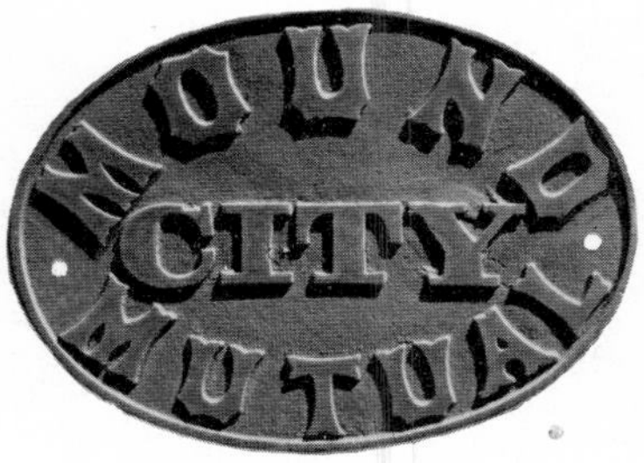

271

272

273

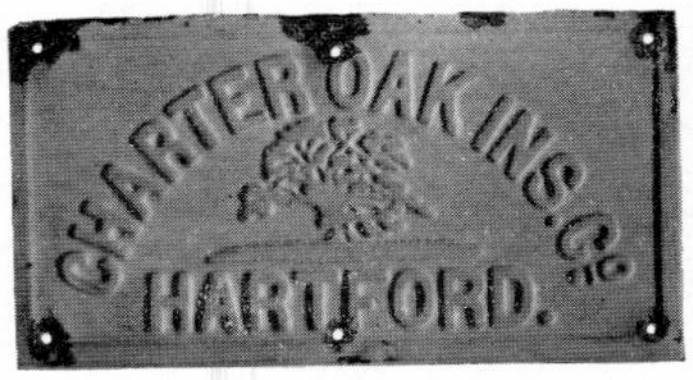

274

275

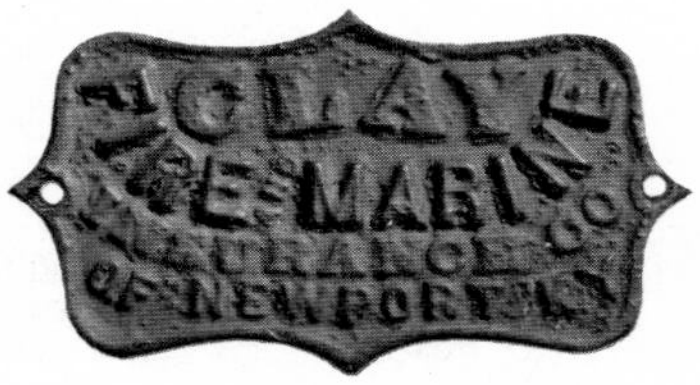

276

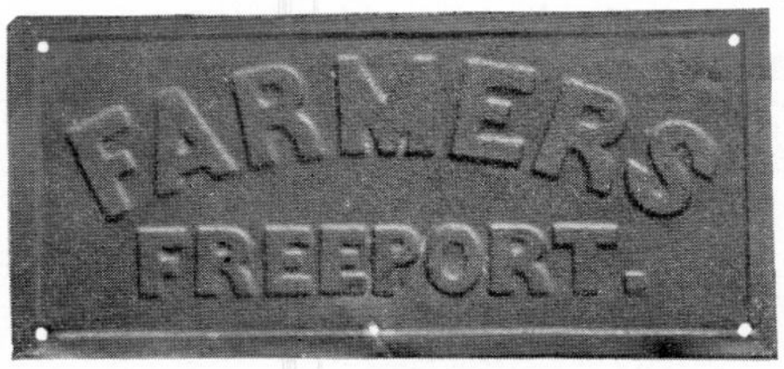

277

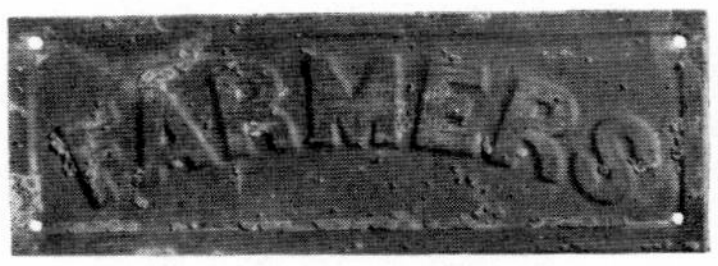

278

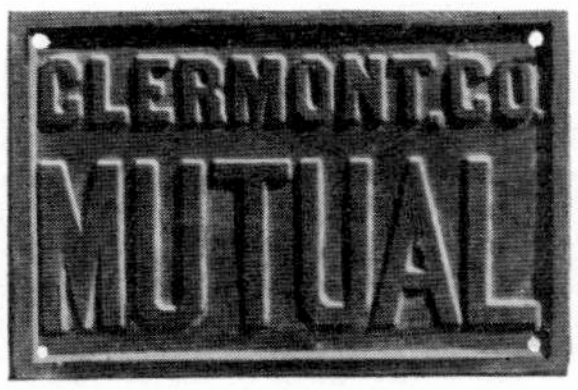

279

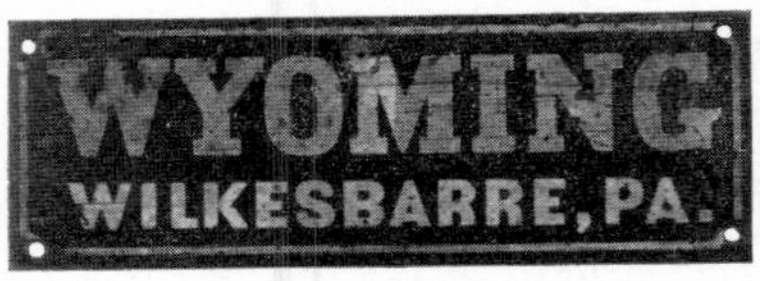

280

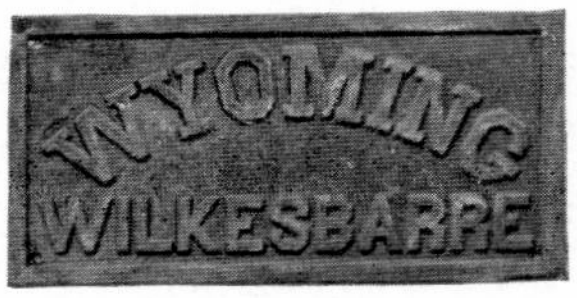

281

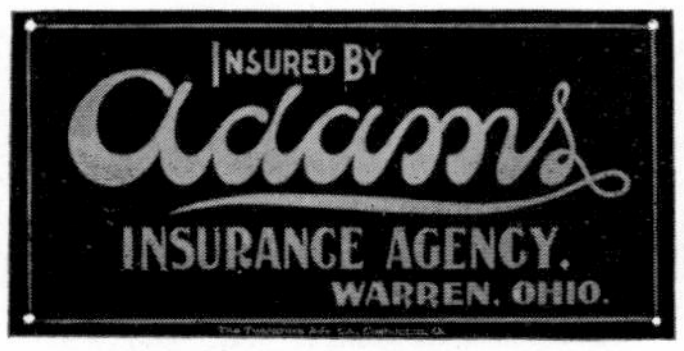

282

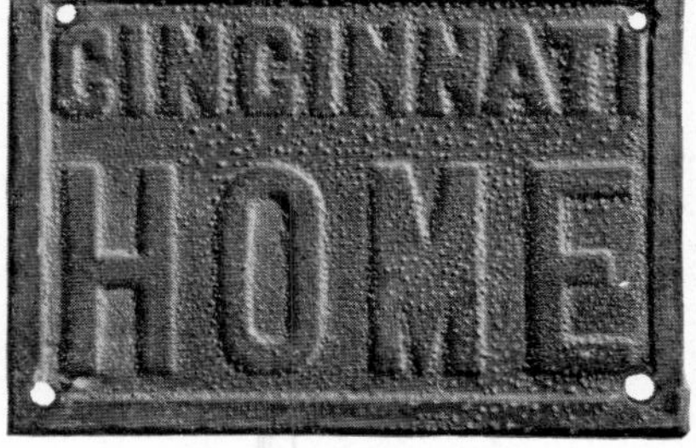

283

284

(269-271) MOUND CITY MUTUAL FIRE AND MARINE INSURANCE COMPANY. SAINT LOUIS, MISSOURI. 1855-1891.

269. Zinc. Oblong. 6⅝" x 4⅞". Border and "Mound City Mutual" raised. First type mark of this company. Very rare. Issued 1855. Note two styles of lettering. From building on Menard Avenue, St. Louis, Mo.

270. Zinc. Oval. 8" x 5¾". Border and "Mound City Mutual" raised. Second type mark of this company. Note two styles of lettering. Issued 1859. Very rare. From building on Geyer Street, St. Louis, Mo.

271. Zinc. Oval. 8" x 5¾". Border and "Mound City Mutual" raised. Note two styles of lettering, also spread of letters not found in other issues. Issued 1865. Exceedingly rare. From building in St. Louis, Mo.

(272-273) SECURITY INSURANCE COMPANY. NEW YORK, NEW YORK. 1856-1870.

272. Tin. Rectangular. 6⅞" x 3⅛". Border and "Security—New York" raised. Issued about 1858. Very rare. From one-story cabin on Fair Street, Xenia, Ohio.

273. Tin. Rectangular. 7⅞" x 3⅞". Border and "Security New York" raised. Issued about 1865. Very rare.

(274) CHARTER OAK INSURANCE COMPANY. HARTFORD, CONNECTICUT. 1856-1871.

Tin. Rectangular. 8½" x 4½". Border, design of charter oak tree and "Charter Oak Ins. Co. Hartford" raised.

(275) CITIZENS' FIRE, MARINE AND LIFE INSURANCE COMPANY. WHEELING, WEST VIRGINIA. 1856-1877.

Cast iron. Odd shape. 12⅞" x 5½". Border, design and "Citizens Inse. Co." raised. Exceedingly rare.

(276) CLAY FIRE AND MARINE INSURANCE COMPANY. NEWPORT, KENTUCKY. 1856-1879.

Cast iron. Odd shape. 8¼" x 4⅛". Border and "Clay Fire and Marine Insurance Co. of Newport, Ky." raised.

(277-278) FARMERS FIRE INSURANCE COMPANY. FREEPORT, ILLINOIS. 1857-1876.

277. Tin. Rectangular. 7⅞" x 3¾". Border and "Farmers Freeport" raised. Issued about 1860. Rare. From building in Freeport, Ill.

278. Tin. Rectangular. 7⅞" x 2⅞". Border and "Farmers" raised. Issued 1865. Rare.

(279) CLERMONT COUNTY MUTUAL INSURANCE COMPANY. NEW RICHMOND, OHIO. 1857-1876.

Heavy tin. Rectangular. 6¾" x 4¾". Border and "Clermont, Co. Mutual" raised. Issued 1858. Very rare. From barn on south side of Bethel-Cincinnati Highway, on east city limit line of Mount Holly, Ohio.

(280-281) WYOMING INSURANCE COMPANY. WILKESBARRE, PENNSYLVANIA. 1857-1875.

280. Tin. Rectangular. 6⅞" x 2½". Border and "Wyoming —Wilkesbarre, Pa." gold on black background.

281. Tin. Rectangular. 7⅞" x 3⅞". Border and "Wyoming Wilkesbarre" raised.

(282) ADAMS INSURANCE AGENCY. WARREN, OHIO. 1857-

Tin. Rectangular. 7" x 3½". Border and "Insured by Adams Insurance Agency, Warren, Ohio" silver on black background. Only a few American agencies ever issued their own marks.

(283-284) HOME INSURANCE COMPANY. CINCINNATI, OHIO. 1857-1883.

283. Tin. Rectangular. 6¾" x 4¾". Border and "Cincinnati Home" raised.

284. Heavy tin. Rectangular. 6⅞" x 3¼". Border and "Cincinnati Home" raised.

285

286

287

288

290

291

289

293

294

292

296

295

297

298

299

300

301

302

(285-286) HOPE MUTUAL INSURANCE COMPANY. SAINT LOUIS, MISSOURI. 1857-1901.

285. Zinc. Shield shape. 6" x 6¾". Border, anchor and "Hope Mutual" raised. First type mark of this company. Very rare. Very few issued.

286. Zinc. Shield shape. 6" x 6¾". Border, anchor and "Hope Mutual—St. Louis" raised. Second type mark of this company. Issued 1858. Fairly common.

(287) MERCHANTS' INSURANCE COMPANY. HARTFORD, CONNECTICUT. 1857-1871.

Heavy tin. Rectangular. 7⅞" x 3⅞". Border and "Merchants' Hartford." raised.

(288) WESTERN MUTUAL FIRE AND MARINE INSURANCE COMPANY. SAINT LOUIS, MISSOURI. 1857-1874.

Zinc. Oval. Border, two clasped hands and "Western Mutual" raised. (Courtesy of Insurance Company of North America.)

(289) BUTLER INSURANCE COMPANY. HAMILTON, OHIO. 1858-1872.

Heavy tin. Rectangular. 9¾" x 4½". Border and "Butler Insurance, Co." raised. Issued 1860. Very rare. From building in Hamilton, Ohio.

(290) NEW ENGLAND FIRE AND MARINE INSURANCE COMPANY. HARTFORD, CONNECTICUT. 1858-(?).

Tin. Rectangular. 9" x 4¼". Border and "New England Hartford." raised.

(291) PEOPLE'S INSURANCE COMPANY. SAINT LOUIS, MISSOURI. 1859-Prior to 1870.

Zinc. Oval. 8" x 5¾". Border, design of eagle and "People's Ins. Co." raised. Issued 1859. Very rare.

(292-293) FIREMENS INSURANCE COMPANY. DAYTON, OHIO. 1859-1891.

292. Tin. Rectangular. 6⅞" x 3⅜". Border and "Firemens—Dayton, O." raised. First type mark of this company. Issued 1859. From frame mercantile building on Wayne Street, Dayton, O.

293. Tin. Rectangular. 7¾" x 3¾". Border and "Firemens Ins. Co. Dayton, Ohio" raised. Second type mark of this company. Issued 1861. From brick building on Howard Street, Dayton, O.

(294) WASHINGTON MUTUAL FIRE INSURANCE ASSOCIATION. LOUISVILLE, KENTUCKY. 1859-

Tin. Oval. 5⅞" x 3⅞". Border, bust of Washington and "D.W.G.—F.V.G." raised. (Deutsche Washington Gesellschaft Feuer Versicherungs Gesellschaft). Issued 1860. Rare. From dwelling on Clay Street, Louisville, Ky.

(295-297) AMERICAN INSURANCE COMPANY. CHICAGO, ILLINOIS. 1859-1883.

295. Heavy tin. Rectangular. 6⅝" x 3". Border and "American Chicago" gold on black background. First type mark of this company. Rare. From farm building in Bourbon Township, Marshall County, Indiana.

296. Heavy tin. Rectangular. 6¾" x 3¼". Border and "American Chicago" raised. Second type mark of this company. Issued 1865. Rare. From frame dwelling on First Street, Newark, O.

297. Heavy tin. Rectangular. 6⅞" x 3¼". Border and "American Chicago." gold on black background. Size of mark and lettering varies from No. 295.

(298-299) GERMANIA FIRE INSURANCE COMPANY OF NEW YORK. NEW YORK, NEW YORK. 1859-1918.

298. Tin. Rectangular. 7" x 3⅜". Border and "Insured Germania—A. D. 1859—New York" black on silver background. Very rare.

299. Tin. Rectangular. 7⅞" x 4". Border and "Germania Co. New York" raised.

(300-302) HOME INSURANCE COMPANY. NEW HAVEN, CONNECTICUT. 1859-1871.

300. Copper. Oval. 8¼" x 5⅞". Roped border, scene of fireman, hydrant, buildings with one aflame and Silsby steam fire engine, and "Home Insurance Co. New Haven." raised. From old building situated on a side street in Osceola, Tioga County, Pa.

301. Cast iron. Oval. 8¼" x 5⅞". Roped border, scene of fireman, hydrant, buildings with one aflame and Silsby steam fire engine, and "Home Insurance Co. New Haven." raised.

302. Tin. Rectangular. 6¾" x 3⅛". Border and "Home New Haven" raised.

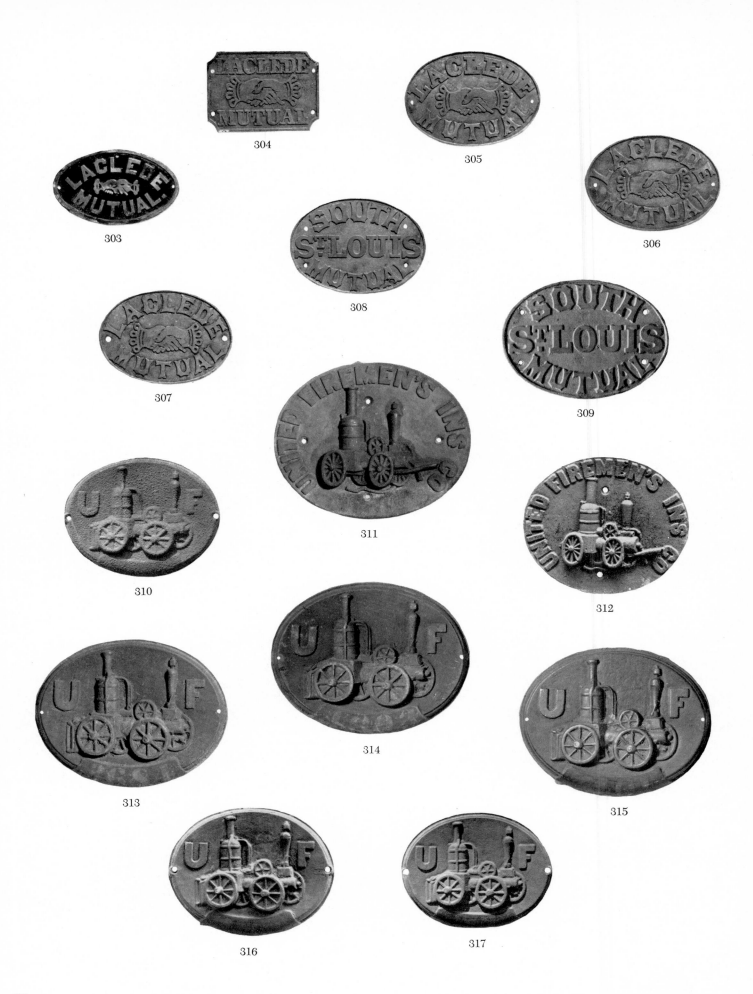

304

305

303

308

306

307

309

311

310

312

314

313

315

316

317

88

318

319

320

(303-307) LACLEDE MUTUAL FIRE AND MARINE INSURANCE COMPANY. SAINT LOUIS, MISSOURI. 1859-1903.

303. Tin. Oval. 7 3/8" x 4 5/8". Very thin. Raised border, pair of clasped hands and "Laclede Mutual" gold on black background. First type mark of this company. Very rare. From building on Soulard Street, St. Louis, Mo.

304. Zinc. Oblong. 6 1/2" x 4 3/4". Border, pair of clasped hands and "Laclede Mutual" raised. Second type mark of this company. Exceedingly rare. From dwelling on Twelfth Boulevard, St. Louis, Mo.

305. Zinc. Oval. 8" x 5 3/4". Border, pair of clasped hands and "Laclede Mutual" raised. Note two styles of lettering. Third type mark of this company.

306. Thin zinc. Oval. 7 7/8" x 5 11/16". Border, pair of clasped hands and "Laclede Mutual" raised. Fourth type mark of this company. Rare.

307. Heavy zinc. Oval. 7 3/4" x 5 5/8". Border, pair of clasped hands and "Laclede Mutual" raised. Fifth and last type mark of this company. Fairly common.

(308-309) SOUTH ST. LOUIS MUTUAL FIRE AND MARINE INSURANCE COMPANY. SAINT LOUIS, MISSOURI. 1859-1878.

308. Zinc. Oval. 8" x 5 3/4". Border and "South St. Louis Mutual" raised. Note two styles of lettering. First type mark of this company. Rare. From building on Lafayette Street, St. Louis, Mo.

309. Zinc. Oval. 7 3/4" x 5 5/8". Border and "South St. Louis Mutual" raised. Note two styles of lettering. Second type mark of this company. Smaller than first type. Very rare.

(310-320) UNITED FIREMEN'S INSURANCE COMPANY. PHILADELPHIA, PENNSYLVANIA. 1860-

310. Cast iron. Oval. 11 3/4" x 9". Raised "U F." Old model steam fire engine in high relief. Wheels have eight spokes. Bevel edge. Issue of 1862.

311. Cast iron. Oval. 11 1/2" x 9 1/2". Raised "United Firemen's Ins Co" and old model steam fire engine in high relief. Four nail holes. Wheels have twelve spokes. Largest mark of this type used by this company.

312. Cast iron. Oval. 11 1/4" x 9 3/8". Raised "United Firemen's Ins Co" and old model steam fire engine in high relief. Wheels have twelve spokes.

313. Cast iron. Oval. 11 7/8" x 9 3/16". Raised "U F." Old model steam fire engine in high relief. Wheels have eight spokes. Bevel edge. Policy number 3684 on panel below represents contract issued to Joseph Helferson on August 22, 1872, and covered $1,600 on brick dwelling situated northwest corner George and Orchard Streets, Philadelphia, Pa.

314. Cast iron. Oval. 12" x 9 1/4". Raised "U F." Old model steam fire engine in high relief. Wheels have eight spokes. Bevel edge. Policy number 4002 was issued on December 7, 1872, and covered brick store and dwelling located at 610 South 7th Street, Philadelphia, Pa. Larger than mark No. 313.

315. Cast iron. Oval. 11 1/2" x 9". Raised "U F." Old model steam fire engine in high relief. Bevel edge. Wheels have eight spokes. Policy number 7401 was issued on July 8, 1875.

316. Cast iron. Oval. 11 1/2" x 9 1/2". Raised "U F." Old model steam fire engine in high relief. Bevel edge. Wheels have eight spokes. Policy number 7776, barely legible, represents contract issued September 18, 1875, which covered a brick dwelling situated on north side of Sycamore Street, 226 feet east from 39th Street, Philadelphia, Pa.

317. Cast iron. Oval. 11 3/8" x 8 13/16". Raised "U F." Old model steam fire engine in high relief. Bevel edge. Wheels have eight spokes. Policy number 8880 was issued on August 4, 1876, and covered brick dwelling at 1315 South 4th Street, Philadelphia, Pa.

318. Cast iron. Oval. 11 1/2" x 9 1/2". Raised "United Firemen's Ins. Co." Old model steam fire engine in high relief. Wheels have twelve spokes. Policy number 9071.

319. Cast iron. Oval. 10 7/8" x 8 3/8". Raised "U F." Old model steam fire engine in high relief. Bevel edge. Wheels have eight spokes. Smallest type mark of this company. Policy number 10203 was issued on October 13, 1877, and covered on brick dwelling located on west side of "H" Street, 135 feet south of McKean Street, Philadelphia, Pa.

320. Cast iron. Oval. 11" x 9". Raised "United Firemen's Ins Co." Old model steam fire engine in high relief. Wheels have twelve spokes. Policy number 10440 was issued on December 10, 1877, and covered brick building occupied as a coal office, stable and dwelling at 1815-17 North 10th Street, Philadelphia, Pa.

CIVIL STRIFE AND RECONSTRUCTION

1861-1870

The sixties started out with a bang! At the close of 1860 South Carolina, which early in the country's history had declared itself for independence, seceded from the Union. Its action was followed early the next year by Florida, Georgia, Alabama, Mississippi, Louisiana, and Texas. Heading the Confederate States of America, which was formed in February, was the Mississippi planter, Jefferson Davis. Hostilities between the states started in 1861 at Fort Sumter near Charleston and continued until the spring of 1865. Often this war is referred to as a war between the North and the South. In actual fact, however, the division was not so pronounced as to fix a definite boundary line. The sympathies were varied and widespread throughout the land even though when sectionalized, they became predominant.

One might imagine that the establishment of new fire insurance companies would cease during the years of war. The signevierist records, however, that an equal number of companies of this decade had their inception both during the war and subsequent to the cessation of hostilities. Some of this expansion can be attributed to the wartime economy, but of greater import was the continued movement of the population and industry in a westward direction. The Homestead Act, passed by Congress in 1862 to encourage loyalty to the Union, provided one hundred and sixty acres of land for each homesteader in certain sections of the West. This act stimulated a movement in that direction which exceeded the migration to California when gold was discovered.

New insurance ventures on the eastern seaboard before the fall of Richmond were limited to two in New York State, one in Connecticut, and another in Maine. Philadelphia, on the other hand, became a sort of port of egress for and return from the battlefields southward and much of Pennsylvania was the scene of conflict so it is understandable that only two companies saw their beginnings there during these years. The border state of Kentucky produced one company, but across the river in Ohio the same half decade gave birth to some twelve new underwriters. Ohio, whose native son Ulysses S. Grant was made Commander in Chief of the United States Armies in 1864, was the focal point from which the migration

to the West and North radiated. Insurance-wise each important city in the state sprouted a new company.

Further north the city of Detroit became the gateway to the state of Michigan, the southern part of which was rich in agriculture. In the gateway city itself the paid fire department, which was activated in 1860, had rough going over the cobblestone streets which were short, narrow passageways forming the old palisaded town first laid out by Cadillac. During the war period, however, they began to use cedar paving blocks which in turn stimulated employment in the upstate wooded sections. To encourage further agrarian activity in this outpost of the North, transportation facilities were needed badly. The settlers took heart when in 1862 the first railroad was built from Owosso to Lansing. The railroad brought in new agricultural implements and supplies and returned with the fruits of the land itself. The Pere Marquette system, which began in 1864 with a road from Flint to Saginaw, added to the rapid expansion of the area so that when the line was later extended to Detroit that city's factories expanded in the industries of smelted copper products, woodworking, machinery and steam engine manufacturing, leather, flour and meal, boots, furs, soaps and candles. Such new economy demanded further fire insurance indemnity which was provided by four additional carriers domiciled in the important centers extending from Detroit as far west as Kalamazoo.

To the south Indiana brought forth four companies, two of which were located at Lafayette; the Indiana Central Insurance Company with a capital of five hundred thousand dollars and The Home Insurance Company of Lafayette, which had a much smaller capital but boasted of an impressive directorate headed by Governor O. P. Morton, the Honorable R. C. Gregory, and an additional galaxy of military and political officialdom. The company ceased business four years after its origin. Chicago, Quincy, and Freeport in Illinois gave birth to seven exponents of the fire marks. In Missouri at St. Louis and nearby Hannibal we find zinc badges of four concerns which bear witness to their courage during the wartime economy. Expansion continued, for in 1863 in the rugged but wealthy frontier city of San Francisco, two companies had their beginnings; one, the Fireman's Fund Insurance Company, remains to give evidence of the character and longevity of the pioneers of the Golden State.

The period in history known as the "War Between the States" came to an end in the spring of 1865, and a most marked change came over the fire insurance business. There was a tremendous expansion of capital during the remainder of the decade and many new companies were formed, those organized at this time being mostly of the agency type. It was in this half decade, too, that rail service between the two coasts was begun; Cyrus Field completed the laying of the Atlantic Cable; Alaska was purchased from Russia for $7,200,000; and a new form of locomotion was introduced to America when Pierre Lallement of Paris constructed his "boneshaker" wooden bicycle, contributing to the opening of the first Velocipede Riding School by Pearsall Brothers at 932 Broadway in New York City.

This period witnessed a great stir in national politics beginning with the death of President Lincoln. Then came the trial of President Johnson "for high crimes and misdemeanors in office" and his subsequent acquittal. The election of General U. S. Grant to the presidency followed. In the New York Legislature there was much agitation for regulatory laws covering the construction of certain types of buildings as a fire safety measure. The old volunteer fire departments of New York City and Brooklyn ceased to exist in the latter part of 1865, and the Metropolitan Fire District organization was completed soon afterward. The attitude of a new independence and sovereignty of states was so pronounced that state after state passed laws placing restrictions, taxes, and deposit laws upon companies, making it almost impossible to operate. In November, 1865, the companies, in an effort to supersede the multiplicity of state burdens, appointed a committee to draft a suitable federal law placing insurance under federal supervision and asked that committee to work with Congress for its passage. While the effort did not meet with approval, the companies in 1865 and 1866 had such tremendous fire losses and increased expenses brought on in this post-war era that some general remedy was needed. In consequence, in the latter year, the National Board of Fire Underwriters was established, and some uniformity in rates, policy contracts, and forms was adopted by the subscribing companies. Arson was on the increase, overinsurance became prevalent, and the Board acted to meet these emergencies. Non-Board companies, however, advertised insurance at low rates, and there was an abundance of wildcat fire insurance companies, particularly in the midwestern states.

The State Auditor of Ohio, in his report for 1867, called the special attention of the legislature to the insufficient laws when he commented on such organization; "Five residents of Ohio, who can control $20,000, organize an insurance company, subscribe the $100,000 capital stock (required by law), pay in the $20,000, elect themselves directors, indorse each other's notes, and commence the business of insurance. They are dealing in fancy stocks, and invest the $20,000 in such stock, and change them from day to day as their gambling emergencies may require. They issue policies, and the money received for premiums enables them to continue their fancy stock operations." The next year the legislature, obviously impressed, passed laws fixing a sounder basis of organization and giving new powers to the State Auditor. Iowa brought her wildcats under subjection in 1868 as did California. Missouri and Illinois came next in 1869; Kentucky and Wisconsin followed in 1870.

Of the companies who planted their footprints firmly into the sands of time and posted fire marks upon houses, the most unusual specimens of marks of this reconstruction era came from the southland and its border states. Alabama, Tennessee, and Kentucky each recorded one new underwriter. Louisiana had two, West Virginia three, and Missouri produced four. All three of the West Virginia concerns were located in Wheeling which had become a hub of industrial activity after this new state had separated from the Old Dominion of Virginia. During the war the iron mills continued to make armor plate for ships; subsequently the industry expanded, establishing the city permanently as a steel city of considerable magnitude. They, too, formed their first paid fire department in 1868, contributing in this manner to the new order of security for the citizenry, while simultaneously providing a safety standard for the new insurance companies venturing the funds of their stockholders in the program of indemnity for loss by fire.

In 1865 the Indians were still fomenting trouble in the vicinity of St. Paul, Minnesota. Despite them, however, courageous pioneers of the Northwest in that year formed the St. Paul Fire and Marine Insurance Company, which continues to operate at the old stand today. Their mark of assurance was a true sign of security to the settlers in this "land o'lakes" country; it contributed to the building of empire as well as did such people as the Hill's of railroad fame and the Weyerhaeuser's who built another empire in lumber. Wisconsin's citizens gave names to two new insurance ventures—one name, "Hekla," representing an Icelandic volcano, must have been given by a citizenry predominantly Scandinavian. House plates of two additional Illinois insurers of this decade have been located in Lansing and Detroit, Michigan, where the need for an additional underwriter in each city was felt. The opening of the St. Mary's Canal had lowered the cost of shipments from the mines to the lower Great Lakes. As a result the economy of Detroit was vastly affected, for even in that early period this city became an important port. Cincinnati by this time had reached a population of over two hundred thousand and remained as a center of insurance, retaining a majority of the additional companies founded in the Buckeye State at the close of our decade.

The economy of the East had resolved itself on a conservative plane. There is no better evidence of this than the fact that in signeviery for this last half of the 1860's marks are portrayed for only two new companies in Pennsylvania, one in New Hampshire, and four in upstate New York. Though the organizational pace had slowed, the results for a collector of fire marks have been most satisfying, for in this decade newly established companies extending over eighteen states numbered some seventy-four—the greatest figure on record for any ten-year period. Here, too, were the real beginnings of a renewed union in national government—a people seeking new opportunity on a widespread scale and a sincere desire on the part of the insurance industry as well as public officials to secure properly the welfare of the buyer. All of this portended a better understanding and a greater security and peace of mind for the peoples of America.

321

322

323

324

325

326

327

328

329

330

331

332

333

(321-323) CITY MUTUAL INSURANCE COMPANY. SAINT LOUIS, MISSOURI. 1861-1878.

321. Zinc. Oval. 8″ x 5¾″. Border and "City Mutual" raised. Note two styles of lettering. First type mark of this company. Larger than other types. Issued 1861 in limited quantity. Very rare. From building on Seventh Boulevard, St. Louis, Mo.

322. Zinc. Oval. 8″ x 5¾″. Border and "City Mutual" raised. Note two styles of lettering. A heavy variant of mark No. 321.

323. Zinc. Oval. 7¾″ x 5⅝″. Border and "City Mutual" raised. Note two styles of lettering. Second type mark of this company. Slightly smaller than first. From building on Eleventh Street, St. Louis, Mo. Rare.

(324) FARMERS AND MERCHANTS INSURANCE COMPANY. QUINCY, ILLINOIS. 1861-1883.

Tin. Rectangular. 6¾″ x 3¾″. Border and "F & M. Ins. Co—Quincy" raised.

(325) MERCHANTS' INSURANCE COMPANY. CHICAGO, ILLINOIS. 1861-1871.

Tin. Rectangular. 7¾″ x 3⅞″. Border and "Merchants—Chicago" raised. (Courtesy of Earl B. Davison.)

(326-327) WINNESHEIK INSURANCE COMPANY. FREEPORT, ILLINOIS. 1861-1871.

326. Tin. Square. 5¹⁵⁄₁₆″ x 5¹⁵⁄₁₆″. Border and "Winnesheik Ins. Co. Freeport—Ills." raised. Very rare. From building in Freeport, Ill.

327. Tin. Rectangular. 5⅝″ x 3¹⁄₁₆″. Border and "Winnesheik Ins. Co." raised. Very rare. From building in Illinois.

(328) THE OAKLAND COUNTY FARMERS' MUTUAL INSURANCE COMPANY. OXFORD, OAKLAND COUNTY, MICHIGAN. 1862-About 1869.

Heavy tin. Rectangular. 7⅞″ x 3⅞″. Border and "Oakland Ins." raised. (Courtesy of Earl B. Davison.)

(329) THE RELIANCE INSURANCE COMPANY OF PHILADELPHIA. PHILADELPHIA, PENNSYLVANIA. 1862-1949.

Tin. Rectangular. 6⅞″ x 3¼″. Border and "Reliance of Philadelphia." black on green-gold background.

(330) UNION FIRE INSURANCE COMPANY. BANGOR, MAINE. 1862-1864.

Tin. Rectangular. 7″ x 3¼″. Changed name to Union Insurance Company 1864. Border and "Insured Union Bangor" had been gold. From dwelling in South Bedington, Maine.

(331) NEW YORK CENTRAL INSURANCE COMPANY. UNION SPRINGS, NEW YORK. 1863-1880.

Tin. Rectangular. 9⅞″ x 3¾″. Border and "New York Central Ins. Co." raised.

(332-333) MIAMI VALLEY INSURANCE COMPANY. DAYTON, OHIO. 1863-1896.

332. Tin. Rectangular. 7⅞″ x 3⅜″. Border and "Miami Valley—Dayton, O." gold on black background. First type mark of this company. From brick dwelling on Garfield Street, Dayton, O.

333. Tin. Rectangular. 7¾″ x 3¾″. Border and "Miami Valley Ins. Co.—Dayton, Ohio." raised. Second type mark of this company. From frame dwelling on South Fifth Street, Dayton, O.

334

335

337

336

339

338

340

342

341

343

344

345

346

348

347

349

350

(334) PACIFIC INSURANCE COMPANY. SAN FRANCISCO, CALIFORNIA. 1863-1871.

Cast iron. Rectangular. Border and "Pacific Insurance Co.—San Francisco" raised. *(Courtesy of Jack Piver.)*

(335-336) FARMERS MUTUAL FIRE OF MONROE AND WAYNE COUNTIES. DETROIT, MICHIGAN. 1863-

335. Tin. Rectangular. 6½" x 3". Border and "Farmers Mutual Ins." had been gold. Rare. From building at Detroit, Michigan.

336. Heavy tin. Rectangular. 10" x 2¾". Border and "Farmers" gold on black background. *(Courtesy of Earl B. Davison.)*

(337) FIRE AND TORNADO INSURANCE COMPANY. FREEPORT, ILLINOIS. 1863-(?).

Brass. Oval. Border and "Fire and Tornado, Freeport." raised. *(Courtesy of Howard Bradshaw.)*

(338-339) FIREMAN'S FUND INSURANCE COMPANY. SAN FRANCISCO, CALIFORNIA. 1863-

338. Tin. Oval. 7¼" x 4⅝". Reproduction. Border design of hose attached to hydrant and "Fireman's Fund Insurance Co. S. F." raised.

339. Iron. Diamond shape. 5⅞" x 5⅞". Monograms, "FFICO," date 1863, and AAU and Chinese characters dark blue on speckled light blue enamel. Mark used in China. Rare. Issued about 1920.

(340) INDIANA CENTRAL INSURANCE COMPANY. LAFAYETTE, INDIANA. 1863-Believed prior to 1868.

Tin. Rectangular. 7¾" x 3¾". Border and "Ind. Central Ins. Co." raised. Issued 1865. Unique. From old frame farm residence on south side of U. S. Highway 50, about five miles east of Montgomery, Ind.

(341) PROTECTION INSURANCE COMPANY. GOSHEN, INDIANA. 1863-1866.

Tin. Rectangular. Border and "Protection Ins. Co. Goshen." raised. *(Courtesy of Howard Bradshaw.)*

(342) YONKERS AND NEW YORK FIRE INSURANCE COMPANY. NEW YORK, NEW YORK. 1863-1871.

Heavy tin. Rectangular. 6½" x 3⅛". Border and gold "Yonkers & New York" raised. Black background.

(343) FARMERS AND MERCHANTS INSURANCE COMPANY. DAYTON, OHIO. 1864-1872.

Tin. Rectangular. 8½" x 4½". Border and "Farmers & Merchants Ins. Co.—Dayton, Ohio." raised. Issued about 1865. Very rare. From brick building on First Street, Dayton, O.

(344-346) HOME INSURANCE COMPANY. COLUMBUS, OHIO. 1864-1883.

344. Tin. Rectangular. 6¾" x 3⅜". Border and "Home—Col's.—Ohio." raised. First type mark of this company. Issued 1865. Rare. From old frame dwelling in Groveport, O.

345. Tin. Rectangular. 6¾" x 3⅜". Border and "Home—Columbus" raised. Second type mark of this company. Issued 1867. From flour mill located 3½ miles west of Somerset, O.

346. Heavy tin. Rectangular. 6½" x 3¼". Border and gold "Home—Columbus, O." raised. Background had been black.

(347-349) NORTH ST. LOUIS MUTUAL FIRE INSURANCE COMPANY. SAINT LOUIS, MISSOURI. 1864-1888(?).

347. Heavy zinc. Oval. 7½" x 5⅜". Border and "North St. Louis Mutual" raised. Note two styles of lettering. Four nail holes. First type mark of this company. Issued 1865. Very rare. From St. Louis, Mo.

348. Very thick zinc. Oval. 7½" x 5½". Border and "North St. Louis Mutual" raised. Note two styles of lettering. Four nail holes. Mark is ¼" thick. Very rare variant of first type of this company. Issued 1865.

349. Thin zinc. Oval. 7¼" x 5¼". Border and "North St. Louis Mutual" raised. Note two styles of lettering. Four nail holes. Second type mark of this company. Smaller than first issue. Rare.

(350) FRANKLIN INSURANCE COMPANY. COLUMBUS, OHIO. 1864-1899.

Tin. Rectangular. 6⅝" x 3¼". Border and "Franklin of Columbus, O." black on silver background.

352

351

353

355

354

356

357

358

359

360

361

362

363

364

96

365

366

367

(351-352) PUTNAM FIRE INSURANCE COMPANY. HART-FORD, CONNECTICUT. 1864-1871.

351. Tin. Rectangular. 6½" x 3¼". Border and "Putnam of Hartford" gold on black background. Scarce.

352. Heavy tin. Rectangular. 6½" x 3¼". Border and gold "Putnam—Hartford" raised. Background black.

(353) SPRINGFIELD FIRE INSURANCE COMPANY. SPRINGFIELD, OHIO. 1864-1870.

Tin. Rectangular. 7¾" x 3¾". Border and "Springfield Fire Insurance Co." raised. Issued about 1864. Very rare. From residence on Gallagher Street, Springfield, O.

(354) FARMERS AND MERCHANTS INSURANCE COM-PANY. INDIANAPOLIS, INDIANA. 1864-1870.

Tin. Rectangular. Border and "Farmers & Merchants. Indianapolis." raised. (Courtesy of Howard Bradshaw.)

(355) HOME INSURANCE COMPANY. LAFAYETTE, INDIANA. 1864-1868.

Tin. Rectangular. Border and "Home—Lafayette, Ind." raised. (Courtesy of Howard Bradshaw.)

(356) MICHIGAN CENTRAL MUTUAL INSURANCE COM-PANY. KALAMAZOO, MICHIGAN. 1864-(?).

Tin. Rectangular, rounded top. Border and "Mich. Central Ins. Co. Kalamazoo." raised. (Courtesy of Insurance Company of North America.)

(357-359) MICHIGAN STATE INSURANCE COMPANY. ADRIAN, MICHIGAN. 1864-1879.

357. Heavy tin. Rectangular. 6⅞" x 3¼". "Mich. State Adrian" had been gold on black background. (Courtesy of Earl B. Davison.)

358. Tin. Rectangular. 7½" x 3". Border and "Mich. State Adrian." raised.

359. Tin. Rectangular. 7¾" x 3½". "Mich. State Adrian" varies from lettering of mark No. 357. Border raised. (Courtesy of Earl B. Davison.)

(360) GERMANIA FIRE AND MARINE INSURANCE COM-PANY. CINCINNATI, OHIO. 1865-1890.

Tin. Rectangular. 7" x 3½". Painted border and "Germania—Cincinnati." Issued about 1870. Very rare. From building at Sabina, O.

(361) SUN FIRE INSURANCE COMPANY. CLEVELAND, OHIO. 1865-1876.

Tin. Rectangular. 6½" x 3⁵⁄₁₆". Border and "Sun Fire Ins. Co." raised. Issued 1865. Very rare.

(362) TEUTONIA FIRE INSURANCE COMPANY. CLEVE-LAND, OHIO. 1865-1871.

Tin. Rectangular. 7¾" x 3⅛". Border and "Teutonia—Cleveland, O." raised. Issued 1865. Unique. From one-story frame residence on East Main Street, Crestline, O.

(363) UNION INSURANCE COMPANY. DAYTON, OHIO. 1865-1870.

Tin. Rectangular. 7⅜" x 3¾". Border and "Union Ins. Co.—Dayton, Ohio." raised. Issued about 1865.

(364-367) GERMAN INSURANCE COMPANY. FREEPORT, ILLINOIS. 1865-1906.

364. Tin. Rectangular. 6¹⁵⁄₁₆" x 2½". Border and "German—Freeport, Ill." black on silver background. First type mark of this company. Issued about 1865.

365. Tin. Rectangular. 6¾" x 3¼". Border and "German—Freeport." silver on black background.

366. Tin. Rectangular, rounded top. 7⅞" x 4". Border and "German Insurance Co." raised. Issued 1865.

367. Tin. Rectangular. 6¼" x 2⅜". Border and "German" raised.

368

369

370

371

372

373

374

375

376

377

378

379

380

381

382

383

384

385

98

(368-369) MANUFACTURERS' AND MERCHANTS INSUR-
ANCE COMPANY. PITTSBURGH, PENNSYLVANIA.
1865-1900.

368. Tin. Rectangular. 6¾" x 3¼". Border and "M. & M.
Pittsburgh." silver on black background. Issued 1865.

369. Tin. Rectangular. 7⅞" x 3⅞". Border and "M & M Ins.
Co." raised. Issued 1866. From small brick dwelling on General
Robinson Street, Pittsburgh, Pa.

(370-371) OHIO INSURANCE COMPANY. DAYTON, OHIO.
1865-1895.

370. Tin. Rectangular. 7⅝" x 3½". Border and gold "Ohio
Ins. Co. Dayton." raised. First type mark of this company. Issued
1865.

371. Heavy tin. Rectangular. 7⅜" x 3¾". Border and "Ohio
Ins. Co. Dayton." raised. Issued 1870. Very rare. From two-story
brick building on West Center Street, Germantown, O.

(372) TRADERS INSURANCE COMPANY. CHICAGO,
ILLINOIS. 1865-1906.

Tin. Rectangular. 6¾" x 3⅛". Border and "Traders—Chicago"
raised. Issued about 1870. Only known type mark used.

(373) THE ADAMS FIRE AND MARINE INSURANCE
COMPANY. CINCINNATI, OHIO. 1865-1868.

Tin. Rectangular. 7⅜" x 2½". Border and "The Adams."
raised.

(374) GLOBE INSURANCE COMPANY. CINCINNATI,
OHIO. 1865-1893.

Heavy tin. Rectangular. 6⅞" x 3¼". Border and "Globe—
Cin'ti, O." raised. (Courtesy of Earl B. Davison.)

(375-376) SAINT PAUL FIRE AND MARINE INSURANCE
COMPANY. SAINT PAUL, MINNESOTA. 1865-

375. Heavy tin. Rectangular. 6⅞" x 4". Border and "Insure
in the Saint Paul Fire & Marine Insurance Co." cream color on
dark blue background. Semi-modern type mark issued about 1900.

376. Tin. Diamond shape, slightly convexed. 5¾" x 5¾".
"Saint-Paul" and Chinese characters dark blue on speckled light
blue enamel. Mark used in China.

(377) JEFFERSON FIRE INSURANCE COMPANY.
STEUBENVILLE, OHIO. 1865-1881.

Tin. Rectangular. 9" x 3⅜". Border and "Jefferson. Steubenville." raised. Issued about 1866.

(378) ENTERPRISE FIRE AND MARINE INSURANCE
COMPANY. CINCINNATI, OHIO. 1865-1891.

Tin. Rectangular. 6⅞" x 3¼". Border and "Enterprise Cincinnati" raised. Issued about 1865. Very rare. From residence on
north side of U. S. Highway 73, Trenton, O.

(379) JEFFERSON MUTUAL INSURANCE COMPANY.
SAINT LOUIS, MISSOURI. 1865-1879.

Heavy zinc. Oval. 8⅛" x 5¾". Border and "Jefferson Mutual
Ins. Co." raised. Note two styles of lettering. Very rare.

(380) REPUBLIC INSURANCE COMPANY. CHICAGO,
ILLINOIS. 1865-1871.

Tin. Rectangular. 7⅜" x 3". Border and "Insured Republic"
raised.

(381-382) STATE MUTUAL FIRE AND MARINE INSUR-
ANCE COMPANY. HANNIBAL, MISSOURI. 1865-1873.

381. Zinc. Oval. 7⅞" x 5¾". Border, Missouri State Seal and
"State Mutual" raised. Note two styles of lettering. First type mark
of this company. Issued 1865. Rare. From building on Clark
Street, St. Louis, Mo.

382. Zinc. Oval. 7¾" x 5¹¹⁄₁₆". Border, Missouri State Seal
and "State Mutual" raised. Note two styles of lettering. Mark is
thick and is a slightly smaller variant of first type of this company.
Issued 1865.

(383-385) TEUTONIA INSURANCE COMPANY. DAYTON,
OHIO. 1865-1918.

383. Heavy tin. Rectangular. 6⅝" x 3¼". Border and "Teutonia—Dayton, O." raised. Believed to be first type mark of this
company. Issued about 1868. From old frame dwelling on Canal
Street near Putnam, Zanesville, O.

384. Heavy tin. Rectangular. 6⅞" x 3¾". Border and "Teutonia Dayton." raised. Believed to be second type mark of this company. Issued about 1870.

385. Heavy tin. Rectangular. 7⅞" x 3¾". Border and "Teutonia Ins. Co.—Dayton, Ohio." raised. Third type mark of this company. Issued 1873. Very rare. From one-story brick residence on
Richards Street, Dayton, O.

386

387

388

390

389

391

393

392

394

395

396

397

398

399

400

401

402

403

404

405

(386) UNITED LIFE, FIRE AND MARINE INSURANCE COMPANY. COVINGTON, KENTUCKY. 1865-1871.

Tin. Rectangular. 6¾″ x 4¾″. Border and "United Ky. Ins. Co." raised. Very rare.

(387) AETNA FIRE AND MARINE INSURANCE COMPANY. WHEELING, WEST VIRGINIA. 1866-1888.

Tin. Rectangular. 6⅞″ x 3¼″. Border and "Aetna—Wheeling, W. Va." raised. Issued 1869. Very rare. From two-story brick building on Eoff Street, Wheeling, W. Va.

(388-391) DETROIT FIRE AND MARINE INSURANCE COMPANY. DETROIT, MICHIGAN. 1866-

388. Brass. Oval. 7⅝″ x 4¾″. Border and "Detroit F & M Ins. Co." raised.

389. Heavy tin. Rectangular. 6¾″ x 3¼″. Border and "Detroit Fire & Marine" had been gold on black background. (Courtesy of Earl B. Davison.)

390. Tin. Rectangular. 6¾″ x 3⅜″. Border and "Detroit Fire & Marine" raised.

391. Tin. Rectangular. 6¾″ x 6¼″. Border and "Detroit Fire & Marine" raised. Style of letters slightly different from that of mark No. 390.

(392) OHIO INSURANCE COMPANY. CHILLICOTHE, OHIO. 1866-1879.

Heavy tin. Rectangular. 7½″ x 3⅝″. Border and "Ohio Ins. Co. Chillicothe." raised. Only type mark of this company. Issued 1866. From brick residence on Sycamore Street, Chillicothe, O.

(393) THE HEKLA INSURANCE COMPANY. MADISON, WISCONSIN. 1866-1890.

Tin. Rectangular. 6″ x 3″. Border and gold "Hekla" raised. Black background.

(394) KANSAS CITY FIRE AND MARINE INSURANCE COMPANY. KANSAS CITY, MISSOURI. 1866-1872.

Tin. Rectangular. 7¼″ x 4″. Border and "Kansas City F. and M. Insurance Co." raised.

(395) MOBILE FIRE DEPARTMENT INSURANCE COMPANY. MOBILE, ALABAMA. 1866-1879.

Cast iron. Oval. 11⅝″ x 7⅞″. Design of fireman's helmet in high relief. "M F D I Co" raised. Very rare.

(396) THE PIONEER MUTUAL INSURANCE COMPANY. SAINT LOUIS, MISSOURI. 1866-1869(?).

Lead. Oblong. 5½″ x 2¾″. Border and "Pioneer St. Louis" raised. Note two styles of lettering.

(397) GERMAN INSURANCE COMPANY. DAYTON, OHIO. 1867-1872.

Tin. Rectangular. 8⅜″ x 4⅜″. Border and "German Ins. Co.—Dayton—Ohio." raised. Only type mark of this company. Very rare. Issued 1867. From building in Urbana, O.

(398-400) COOPER FIRE INSURANCE COMPANY. DAYTON, OHIO. 1867-1911.

398. Tin. Rectangular. 6¾″ x 3⅛″. Border and gold "Cooper—Dayton, O." raised. Note two styles of lettering. Background black. First type mark of this company. Issued 1867.

399. Tin. Rectangular. 5¼″ x 2⅛″. Border and "Cooper—Dayton, O." raised. Note two styles of lettering. Second type mark of this company. Rare. From brick residence on Richard Street, Dayton, O.

400. Tin. Rectangular. 6¾″ x 3¼″. Border and "Cooper—Dayton, O." raised. Issued 1870. Very rare. From a residence in Dayton, O.

(401-402) BUFFALO GERMAN INSURANCE COMPANY. BUFFALO, NEW YORK. 1867-1917.

401. Heavy tin. Rectangular. 6¾″ x 3¼″. "Buffalo German" black on gold. "Ins. Co." gold on black. Border gold.

402. Tin. Rectangular. 6⅞″ x 3¼″. "Buffalo German" gold on black background.

(403-405) ROCKFORD INSURANCE COMPANY. ROCKFORD, ILLINOIS. 1867-1899.

403. Tin. Rectangular. 6¹⁵⁄₁₆″ x 2⁷⁄₁₆″. Painted border and "Rockford." Very rare. From building in Rockford, Ill.

404. Tin. Rectangular. 7½″ x 2⅜″. Border and "Rockford" raised. Very rare. Issued about 1870. From building in Rockford, Ill.

405. Tin. Rectangular. 6¾″ x 2⅜″. Border and "Rockford" silver on black background. Rare.

406

407

408

409

411

410

409

413

414

412

416

417

419

420

415

418

421

422

423

(406) FARMERS, MERCHANTS AND MANUFACTURERS INSURANCE COMPANY OF THE MIAMI VALLEY. HAMILTON, OHIO. 1867-1876.

Tin. Rectangular. 6⅞" x 4⅞". Company name hardly discernible at this time.

(407) HOLLAND PURCHASE INSURANCE COMPANY. BATAVIA, NEW YORK. 1867-1887.

Tin. Rectangular. 6⅞" x 2½". "Holland Purchase—Batavia, N. Y." barely discernible.

(408) BLOOMINGTON FIRE INSURANCE COMPANY. BLOOMINGTON, ILLINOIS. 1867-1871.

Tin. Rectangular. 8" x 3". Border and "Insured Bloomington" raised.

(409) GERMAN FIRE INSURANCE COMPANY. WHEELING, WEST VIRGINIA. 1867-1932.

Heavy tin. Rectangular. 8⅝" x 4". Border and "Insured German Fire Ins. Co. Wheeling, W. Va." raised.

(410) GUARDIAN FIRE AND MARINE INSURANCE COMPANY. PHILADELPHIA, PENNSYLVANIA. 1867-1871.

Heavy cast iron. Oval. 11⅝" x 8¾". Quite heavily convexed with figure of a guardian angel in high relief and "Guardian" raised.

(411) KENTON INSURANCE COMPANY. COVINGTON, KENTUCKY. 1867-1891.

Tin. Rectangular. 6⅝" x 4⅝". Border and "Kenton Kentucky" raised. Very rare.

(412-413) STATE FIRE INSURANCE COMPANY. LANSING, MICHIGAN. 1867-1876.

412. Heavy tin. Rectangular. 6½" x 3⅜". Border and "State Fire Ins. Co." raised. *(Courtesy of Earl B. Davison.)*

413. Tin. Rectangular. 6¾" x 3¼". Border and "State—Lansing." raised. *(Courtesy of Earl B. Davison.)*

(414) WATERTOWN FIRE INSURANCE COMPANY. WATERTOWN, NEW YORK. 1867-1882.

Tin. Rectangular. 7" x 2⅜". Border and "Watertown Ins. Co." black. Background had been white.

(415) ST. JOSEPH FIRE AND MARINE INSURANCE COMPANY. SAINT JOSEPH, MISSOURI. 1868-1879.

Tin. Rectangular. 7¾" x 3¾". Border and "St. Joe' F. & M. Ins. Co. St. Joe, Mo." raised.

(416-417) THE ALLEMANNIA FIRE INSURANCE COMPANY OF PITTSBURGH. PITTSBURGH, PENNSYLVANIA. 1868-

416. Tin. Rectangular. 7" x 3¼". Border and "Allemannia—Pittsburgh" black on silver background. Probably the first type mark issued by this company.

417. Tin. Rectangular. 6⅞" x 3⅜". Border and gold "Allemannia Pittsburgh." raised. Background black. Very rare.

(418-419) NORTHWESTERN NATIONAL INSURANCE COMPANY. MILWAUKEE, WISCONSIN. 1869-

418. Tin. Rectangular. 7" x 3¼". Border and "Northwestern National Ins. Co. Milwaukee" black on green-gold background.

419. Brass. Round. 3" in diameter. Borders and "Insured in the Northwestern National—Service—Strength—Safety" raised brass. Background black enamel. Door plate, possibly auto plate. Modern type.

(420) HICKSVILLE FIRE DEPARTMENT. HICKSVILLE, LONG ISLAND, NEW YORK. 1869-

Heavy aluminum. Maltese cross. 6½" x 6½". Border, lettering and designs raised. Center circle red.

(421-422) NEW HAMPSHIRE FIRE INSURANCE COMPANY. MANCHESTER, NEW HAMPSHIRE. 1869-

421. Brass. Rectangular. 12" x 2½". "New Hampshire" cut into brass and blackened.

422. Tin. Diamond shape, slightly convexed. 5¾" x 5¾". "New Hampshire" and Chinese characters dark blue on speckled light blue enamel. Mark used in China.

(423) NEW ORLEANS MUTUAL INSURANCE ASSOCIATION. NEW ORLEANS, LOUISIANA. 1869-1902

Brass. Round. 11¼" in diameter. Border and "New Orleans Mutual Insurance Association" raised.

424

425

426

428

427

429

(424-425) PEABODY FIRE AND MARINE INSURANCE COMPANY. WHEELING, WEST VIRGINIA. 1869-1899.

424. Cast iron. Odd shape. "Insured Peabody Wheeling" and design at sides raised. *(Courtesy of Insurance Company of North America.)*

425. Tin. Rectangular. 6¾" x 3⅛". Border and "Peabody—Wheeling, W. Va." raised. Issued 1871. Very rare. From residence on Main Street, St. Marys, West Va.

(426) ANDES INSURANCE COMPANY. CINCINNATI, OHIO. 1870-1872.

Tin. Rectangular. 6½" x 3¼". Border, "Andes" and star black on gold background.

(427) PEOPLE'S INSURANCE COMPANY. NEW ORLEANS, LOUISIANA. 1870-1887.

Brass. Shield shape. 9" x 11¼". Border, design of fireman with trumpet, and "The People's Insurance" raised.

(428) AMERICAN CENTRAL INSURANCE COMPANY. SAINT LOUIS, MISSOURI. 1870-

Tin. Rectangular. 7⅜" x 3⁵⁄₁₆". Border and "American Central." raised. Very rare.

(429) UNION FIRE INSURANCE COMPANY. NASHVILLE, TENNESSEE. 1870-Prior to 1873.

Cast iron. Odd shape. 6¾" x 10¼". Center is concave with hydrant and "U F I Co" raised.

SURVIVAL OF THE FITTEST
1871-1880

Our last chapter closed on a note of stabilization in industry and in the fire insurance business, a most natural process in a maturing social order. Sometimes nature or the acts of the gods help the process along and that is exactly what happened in the early part of the 1870's. Some of the weak were strengthened, but many fell by the wayside; it was for fire insurance a period in which only the fit survived.

House plates of fire insurance companies give evidence that at least twenty concerns had their inception in the 1870's. Of these eight were located in Ohio. Cleveland started the decade with the establishment of the Hibernia Fire, and in 1871 Cincinnati contributed the Aurora and the Amazon. That year the city was visited by a series of large fires, the greatest resulting in the destruction of the whisky establishment of Mills, Johnson and Company. In that year, too, the Memphis City Fire began to operate in Tennessee, and the National Fire Insurance Company came forth in Connecticut. On March 15, 1871, the organization of Philadelphia's first paid fire department was completed. Fire was now fought with modern steam engines, and insurance concerns were so optimistic that competition grew and rates were cut.

By this time the great London and New York conflagrations had been forgotten by the majority of citizens; the absence of any serious fires resulted in general complacency and unconcern. Nature, however, has a way of conspiring to teach mankind object lessons whenever he settles down in such tranquility, and this was the year for such a jolt. Upon the western prairies the summer sun had shone for four long months from cloudless skies and in Chicago, as elsewhere in the West, the buildings were dry as tinder. In October the city was annoyed by a series of small fires which kept the firemen busy around the clock but were quenched by the local fire fighters with a minimum of loss. Then, at eleven o'clock on Saturday night, October 7, 1871, a fire caught in a planing mill, starting a conflagration which was augmented by yet another. The second started in the stable of one O'Leary where, according to legend, the lady's sick cow kicked over a lantern (some say that is where the fire originally started). At any rate, a high wind, supplemented by the heat drafts created by the fires themselves, fanned the flames until a major part of the city was devastated and over one hundred and sixty million dollars worth of property destroyed.

During the three previous years fire insurance had been conducted in Chicago on a very thin margin of profit. Now some two hundred insurance companies were confronted with a loss of ninety million dollars, sixty-four of them coming to grief. The loss to insurance capital was tremendous. Loans had to be called, stocks had to be sold on a forced basis, stockholders had to meet extraordinary assessments, and the entire economy of the country was affected. New companies were formed to fill the breach left by the failures following the Chicago fire, and new standards of finance and safeguards of physical protection were set up. Local and national insurance organizations which had become inactive in the lush years were revitalized and insurance generally was placed upon a much sounder basis than ever before. Most of the well-financed and well-managed companies which survived still remain to guarantee the wealth of the nation against a repetition of such a catastrophe.

Three months after the great Chicago fire, in January, 1872, the Manhattan Fire Insurance Company was founded in New York City. In March of the same year the German American, whose name was subsequently altered to the Great American Fire Insurance Company, was organized.

Up in Boston, the community, by nature sound and conservative, had prepared well for any fire emergency by maintaining a department of twenty-one horse-drawn engine companies. In the fall of 1872 the city was visited by an epidemic of distemper prevalent among the horses, and transportation services had to be completely suspended. Some trucking was done by ox teams, but the fire service decided that the heavy steamers were to be drawn by hand, for which work the help of volunteers was enlisted. The amount of apparatus to respond to each first alarm was greatly reduced and a curtailed schedule was put into effect. By early November many of the horses had recovered and the epidemic had abated to such an extent that horse-drawn street railways could again resume service. Apparently the Board of Engineers of the Fire Department had not considered resuming the use of horses to draw their engines so that when a fire broke out on November 9 they were still on their limited schedule and the firemen labored with great difficulty to draw their cumbersome engines to the scene of fire. By the time of their arrival the fire was completely out of control and all the city's apparatus had to be called out, though contemporary records indicate that the engines were from five to fifty-five minutes late in responding to the respective calls. The conflagration spread rapidly and even though the help of outside cities was enlisted, the fire destroyed the best buildings and stocks in the city. The loss covered sixty-five acres, destroyed seven hundred and seventy-six buildings having an assessed value of thirteen million, five hundred thousand dollars, and consumed merchandise and other personal property valued at over sixty million dollars. This second devastating shock to insurance companies in a little more than one year affected not only those concerns but, once again, the entire economy of the nation.

Now it was truly a matter of survival of the fittest. Before the year closed the *Insurance Law Journal* was established for the purpose of supplying the industry with the full text of insurance decisions in the courts of last resort all over the United States. Because of the failure of even some of the large companies during these dark days, additional corrective legislation was being prepared. It was too late, however, to avert the financial panic of 1873, which was contributed to in no small measure by these two severe devastations.

Brilliant and inventive minds are always with us and in times of stress stand out more distinctly because of the diffused background. So it was that in 1873 Andrew Carnegie headed a group of capitalists who started a huge steel mill near Pittsburgh, forming the nucleus of the huge Carnegie Steel Corporation. This was also the year in which Christopher Latham Sholes invented an apparatus which was to revolutionize the writing practices of all the peoples of the world—the first practical typewriter which was manufactured by the firm of E. Remington & Sons whose plant was located at Ilion, New York. The citizens of Boston, shaking off the aftereffects of the great conflagration, had begun a revival of commerce and were so confident of their future that they subscribed to the new Dwelling House Fire Insurance Company. A similar venture of 1873, the Residence Fire Insurance Company, had its origin in Cleveland, Ohio, while out in Galveston, Texas, the Merchants Fire Insurance Company had its start. Before the year ended the Lumbermen's Insurance Company was established in Philadelphia by men in the lumber business; that concern was the last of the underwriters of that city to provide a fire mark made of cast iron. Authorities claim that it was used for advertising purposes only, although there is much evidence to show that long afterwards marks made of varying materials were utilized as signs of assurance elsewhere.

There was every evidence in 1874 that the economy of the world would be enhanced by the discovery of a new type of motive power discovered by John Ernest Keely, whose invention was generated by musical vibrations. Demonstrations given by Keely produced many unexplained and extraordinary effects resulting in enthusiastic financial support for the formation of a stock company in New York to develop this machine of "perpetual motion." The venture did not meet with the success anticipated and when the inventor-genius passed on to the great beyond, undoubtedly accompanied by the strains of his musical vibrations, it was found that the device was operated by a well-concealed compressed air apparatus, the entire project being a fraud. Longer-lived and of far greater integrity were the Forest City Fire Insurance Company formed the same year in Rockford, Illinois, and the Firemen's Insurance Company of New Orleans, Louisiana, the latter company utilizing a large brass fire mark as their house sign.

Railroads had linked together the states and the territories, but the safety requirements held speed down to what we in the twentieth century would consider a snail's pace. In 1875 this tempo was radically changed, however, when George Westinghouse invented the first successful air brake.

The year 1875 was notable for the organization of the Farmers Mutual of Kewanee, Illinois, the Brady Township Mutual at West Unity, Ohio, and the Phoenix Mutual in Cincinnati, while in 1876 (the year in which Alexander G. Bell transmitted the first words by electric telephone at Boston to his assistant Thomas A. Watson), the Ohio Mutual placed its first fire mark upon an insured property in its home town of Salem.

Origin of the Farmers Mutual in Dayton, Ohio, was almost simultaneous with the announcement in 1877 that Thomas A. Edison had received his first patent for a phonograph which played sound impressions made upon tinfoil. One more year and the Bell Telephone Company of New York was organized, issuing on October 23 its first directory, which consisted of a small card listing the subscribers who were called by name and not by a number as they are today. Also in 1878 Thomas Edison secured the help of J. P. Morgan and other financiers to establish the Edison Electric Light Company. In the next year he perfected the first incandescent lamp.

Our decade closes with the founding of the Des

Moines Fire Insurance Company in 1880, a year made memorable by the election of James A. Garfield to the presidency of the United States. It was a period of devastating disaster, of courage, and of reconstruc-tion, and in the economic and fire insurance fields attention was focused upon those companies which survived the rigors of fate, with good management reaping ample reward for its circumspection.

431

430

432

434

435

433

436

(430) HIBERNIA FIRE INSURANCE COMPANY. CLEVELAND, OHIO. 1871-1878.

Tin. Rectangular. 6⅞" x 3¼". Border and "Hibernia Ins. Co." raised. Unique. Removed from two-story frame dwelling on South Street, Galion, O.

(431-432) AURORA FIRE AND MARINE INSURANCE COMPANY. CINCINNATI, OHIO. 1871-1891.

431. Tin. Rectangular. 7" x 3¼". Border and "Aurora Cincinnati." had been gold on black background. First type mark of this company. Very rare. From two-story brick building on West Main Street, Columbus, O.

432. Heavy tin. Rectangular. 6¾" x 3¼". Border and gold "Aurora" raised. Second type mark of this company. Mark common in Columbus, Ohio, only. (Specimen has finish restored.) From small brick residence on East Donaldson Street, Columbus, O.

(433-435) NATIONAL FIRE INSURANCE COMPANY. HARTFORD, CONNECTICUT. 1871-

433. Tin. Rectangular. 6⅞" x 3½". Border and "National—Hartford." raised. Issued about 1875. Rare. From brick mercantile building on Richard Street, Dayton, O.

434. Heavy tin. Rectangular. 6⅞" x 3¼". Border and "National of Hartford" gold on black background. Second type mark of this company. Issued about 1890.

435. Aluminum. Rectangular. 7" x 3¾". Border and "Compania de Seguros Contra Incendios National de Hartford Connecticut—E. U. A." raised. Background black. Modern type mark used in South American countries.

(436) AMAZON INSURANCE COMPANY. CINCINNATI, OHIO. 1871-1891.

Heavy tin. Rectangular. 4⅞" x 5⅞". Design of shield in center with buildings and "Amazon Insurance Co. of Cincinnati."

437

438

439

441

442

440

443

445

444

446

448

447

449

452

450

451

453

108

(437) MEMPHIS CITY FIRE AND GENERAL INSURANCE COMPANY. MEMPHIS, TENNESSEE. 1871-1886.

Thin cast iron. Rectangular. 10⅝" x 7³⁄₁₆". Model of early steam fire-engine and "M.F." raised. Rounded corners. Positive identification of mark unconfirmed.

(438) MANHATTAN FIRE INSURANCE COMPANY. NEW YORK, NEW YORK. 1872-1882.

Tin. Rectangular. 7⅞" x 3⅞". Border and "Manhattan—New York" raised. Issued about 1874. Rare. From frame cottage on Lafayette Street, Greenfield, O.

(439) GERMAN AMERICAN INSURANCE COMPANY. NEW YORK, NEW YORK. 1872-1917.

Tin. Rectangular. 6¾" x 2¾". Border and "German American New York." gold on black background.

(440) GREAT AMERICAN INSURANCE COMPANY. NEW YORK, NEW YORK. 1872-

Tin. Diamond shape. 5⅞" x 5⅞". "Great American," monogram "AAU," date "1872" and Chinese characters white on green enamel. Mark used in China.

(441) DWELLING HOUSE INSURANCE COMPANY. BOSTON, MASSACHUSETTS. 1873-1894.

Tin. Rectangular. 7" x 2½". Border and "Dwelling House—Boston" black on silver background.

(442) LUMBERMEN'S INSURANCE COMPANY. PHILADELPHIA, PENNSYLVANIA. 1873-

Cast iron. Diamond shape. 9" x 9". Border represents four logs overlapping at ends. Monogram, "L. I. Co.," in center. Issued about 1873.

(443) MERCHANTS INSURANCE COMPANY. GALVESTON, TEXAS. 1873-1875.

Tin. Rectangular. 8⅜" x 3½". Border and "Insured in Merchants Ins. Co. Galveston, Texas." painted. (Courtesy of Dwight Rutherford.)

(444) RESIDENCE FIRE INSURANCE COMPANY. CLEVELAND, OHIO. 1873-1877.

Tin. Rectangular. 7" x 2½". "Residence Ins. Co." gold on black background.

(445) FOREST CITY INSURANCE COMPANY OF ROCKFORD. ROCKFORD, ILLINOIS. 1874-1914.

Tin. Rectangular. 6⅞" x 2⁷⁄₁₆". Border and "Forest City." silver on black background.

(446) FIREMEN'S INSURANCE COMPANY OF NEW ORLEANS, LOUISIANA. NEW ORLEANS, LOUISIANA. 1874-1898.

Cast iron. Oval. 7⅞" x 11½". Fire hydrant with hose and "F I Co" raised. Issued about 1875.

(447) BRADY TOWNSHIP FIRE INSURANCE COMPANY. WEST UNITY, OHIO. 1875-

Tin. Rectangular. 7¹⁄₁₆" x 3¼". "Brady Ins. Co." barely discernible.

(448) FARMERS MUTUAL INSURANCE COMPANY. KEWANEE, ILLINOIS. 1875-

Tin. Rectangular. 7" x 2½". Border and "Farmers." Very rare. Removed from building in Illinois.

(449) PHOENIX MUTUAL FIRE INSURANCE COMPANY. CINCINNATI, OHIO. 1875-1892.

Tin. Rectangular. 7" x 3½". Border and "Phoenix Mutual of Cincinnati" black on gold background.

(450) THE OHIO MUTUAL INSURANCE COMPANY. SALEM, OHIO. 1876-

Wood. Odd shape. 13⅞" x 13". Ornamentation and "1809" raised. Label from the Ohio Mutual Insurance Company, Salem, Ohio, states, "from first brick house built near Salem, Ohio, old Coy House on Franklin Road. . . . Thos. Lepper." Is an antiquity unverified as a fire mark.

(451) FARMERS MUTUAL FIRE INSURANCE COMPANY. DAYTON, OHIO. 1877-1900.

Tin. Rectangular. 6¾" x 3¼". Border and "Farmers Mutual" raised. Only type mark of this company. From two-story brick dwelling on estate situated east side of State Highway 4, about six miles south of Marion, O.

(452-453) DES MOINES FIRE INSURANCE COMPANY. DES MOINES, IOWA. 1881-1910.

452. Tin. Rectangular. 6⅞" x 2⅜". Border and "Des Moines" silver on black background. Issued about 1885. Very rare.

453. Tin. Rectangular. 7⅝" x 1⅞". "Des Moines" silver on black background.

A PERIOD OF INVENTION AND PROGRESS
1881-1890

The new Republic had passed its century mark and a review of the past ten decades gives evidence of the many growing pains experienced by this nation. Only the strong and stout of heart could rise to the challenge presented by the events of the century. After each disappointment, disaster, or setback, the people emerged stronger than ever before, imbued with a renewed vigor and effort not only to retain but also to extend the rewards which could be secured in the free-enterprise system. In the profession of insurance there had been a successive forward march in the establishment of companies, and though many dropped by the wayside, others survived to become even more stable and successful.

It has been shown that the first American companies were formed in the original colonies and that later in the Union they extended to the North, the South, and the West; in the latter section they organized at a rapid pace particularly during the past three decades. In the 1880's only ten new insurance ventures—those who left their marks—started in six states, and the slower tempo thus inaugurated remains during the balance of this narrative. The slow-down was not an indication of retrogression, stagnation, or lack of interest on the part of investors; it was rather the result of a stabilization in the business created by corrective legislation and court decisions in the various states, which by this decade have made fire insurance a sound and conservative investment for the stockholder and a guarantee of fair treatment for the policyholder. It was the culmination of the combined effort which could be attained only under such a system of free endeavor as has been the backbone of the American form of constitutional government.

This writing is limited to those concerns who left their imprint behind in the form of a fire mark. One of these, the last to be founded in Cincinnati, Ohio, was the Security Fire which was established in 1881, the same year that saw the organization of the Columbia Fire of Dayton. A year later another new company was formed at Abilene, Kansas.

In both 1883 and 1884 one new fire underwriter was originated in Des Moines and Omaha. In the latter year another kind of group formed a combination or trust to control production of cotton seed oil.

In this year Grover Cleveland was elected President of the United States, Mergenthaler invented the linotype process, and the world's first long-distance telephone line was strung between New York and Boston. All of these events had a direct influence upon the economics of the country and consequently upon insurance. The many new inventions kept insurance underwriters alert to new hazards, and their requirements in turn caused the inventors to supply proper safeguards. A German named Carl Benz built the first successful gasoline-driven motor car in 1885, while a fellow German named Gottlieb Daimler produced the first motorcycle. Another new combine was formed to control production and distribution of linseed oil; almost simultaneously Portsmouth, New Hampshire, gave birth to the Granite State Fire Insurance Company.

Reference has been made to business combines and trusts, and, as would be natural in a free nation, there developed opposing forces. There was a combination of trade unions, both of a local and national nature, which met at Columbus, Ohio, in 1886 to form the American Federation of Labor. In the face of this new move on the part of labor, the following year saw the establishment of a new trust covering sugar, lead, whiskey, plate glass, and wire nails. Yet nothing stood in the way of mechanical advances, for the same period was the one in which R. E. Olds built a buggy driven by a steam engine for which gasoline was the fuel. Transportation went forward in great strides and on September 23, 1887, in New York City, an electric car, powered by storage batteries located under the seats of the passengers, was proven a success on the Fourth Avenue line from Twenty-third Street to One Hundred-seventeenth Street. Electricity provided the stimulus for many new inventions, and so it was that on November 26, 1888, the Daft Electric Motor was tried out with great success on the Ninth Avenue Elevated Railroad in New York City. It drew three loaded cars and was such a tremendous success that it was at once adopted for permanent use.

In an effort to control the large combines formed throughout the country the Sherman Anti-Trust Act, prohibiting and regulating all acts "in restraint of trade," was passed in 1890. As the years passed on this law was supplemented by other acts, all pointing toward a tighter control upon industry, while those engaged in commerce have repeatedly relied upon their constitutional rights of free enterprise.

Interspersed among the marks of assurance, (the last two of this decade being provided by the Granite State Fire of Portsmouth, New Hampshire, and the Patrons Mutual of Glastonbury, Connecticut), the record of inventions, the advance of industry, and its related labor ranks all leave a trail of progress such as the world had never witnessed before. This decade was the forerunner of a half century of the greatest evolution and attainment man has ever achieved.

454

455

456

457

458

459

KANSAS FARMERS

460

(454) SECURITY INSURANCE COMPANY. CINCINNATI, OHIO. 1881-1922.

Tin. Rectangular. 8⅛" x 3⅛". Border and "Security" raised.

(455-458) COLUMBIA FIRE INSURANCE COMPANY. DAYTON, OHIO. 1881-

455. Tin. Rectangular. 6⅞" x 3¼". Border and "Insured—Columbia—Dayton" raised. Very rare. From a Dayton, O. residence.

456. Tin. Rectangular. 6⅞" x 3³⁄₁₆". Border and "Columbia—Dayton, O." raised. From a Dayton, O. residence.

457. Tin. Rectangular. 6⅞" x 3¼". Border and "Columbia—Dayton, O." raised. Border and spacing of lettering different from mark No. 456.

458. Tin. Rectangular. 7" x 3¼". Raised border and "Columbia—Dayton, O." black on silver background. Last type mark of this company.

(459) COUNCIL BLUFFS INSURANCE COMPANY. COUNCIL BLUFFS, IOWA. 1881-1895.

Tin. Rectangular. 7" x 3¼". Border and "Ins. Co." gold on black background. "Council Bluffs" black on gold.

(460) KANSAS FARMERS MUTUAL FIRE INSURANCE COMPANY. ABILENE, KANSAS. 1882-1886.

Tin. Rectangular. 6¾" x 3¼". Border and "Kansas Farmers" gold on black background.

462

461

463

465

464

466

(461) ACME INSURANCE COMPANY. DES MOINES, IOWA. 1883-1885.

Tin. Rectangular. 6¾" x 2⅜". Border and "Acme" black on silver background.

(462) NEBRASKA AND IOWA INSURANCE COMPANY. OMAHA, NEBRASKA. 1883-1891.

Tin. Rectangular. 6¾" x 2½". Border and "N. & I." silver on black background.

(463) CAPITAL FIRE INSURANCE COMPANY OF DES MOINES. DES MOINES, IOWA. 1884-1909.

Tin. Rectangular. 6⅞" x 3⁵⁄₁₆". Border and "Capital — Des Moines." black on gold background.

(464) THE HOME FIRE INSURANCE COMPANY OF OMAHA. OMAHA, NEBRASKA. 1884-1934.

Tin. Rectangular. 6¾" x 3¼". Border and "Home Fire of Omaha." black on green-gold background.

(465) GRANITE STATE FIRE INSURANCE COMPANY. PORTSMOUTH, NEW HAMPSHIRE. 1885-

Tin. Rectangular. 7" x 3¼". Border and "Granite State Fire Insurance Co." silver on black background.

(466) PATRONS MUTUAL FIRE INSURANCE COMPANY. GLASTONBURY, CONNECTICUT. 1887-

Tin. Rectangular. 8⅞" x 3⅜". Border and "Patrons Mutual" black on silver background.

A group of colorful and important fire marks issued by American Insurance companies and now exhibited in the H. V. Smith Museum of The Home Insurance Company. Black and white reproductions and descriptions may be found in these pages.

BEGINNING AN ERA OF COMPETITION
1891-1900

This ten-year period brought an era during which all sorts of competition were encountered in many lines of endeavor. In the insurance business some of the companies resorted to questionable advertising until that malpractice was eliminated by regulation. Unscrupulous publications aided the process, but at the turn of the century the business was so well policed that order prevailed. Royalty was recognized when the Queen Insurance Company of America started on its career in New York in 1891, simultaneous with Thomas A. Edison's application for a patent for a "kinetographic camera," the first invented for taking moving pictures. Edison's discovery initiated the development of an industry which was destined to become a leader in America; its magnitude has often concerned fire insurance underwriters just as much as the hazards of its earlier years tested the ingenuity of safety engineers.

While the moving picture industry developed rapidly and on a grand scale there was still another mechanism which brought on an age such as the world had never known before. In 1892 Duryea really became the father of the American automobile when he completed his first gasoline car. He was followed promptly by Henry Ford who produced "a vehicle scarcely larger than a tricycle, with a very crude steering apparatus, and driven by a small one-cylinder engine with a pulley clutch." Fire insurance companies, including those formed that year in West Virginia and Kansas, did not yet realize that in less than a decade these inventions would pose a vast problem for their underwriters. In our period of time automobile insurance is a tremendous premium producer,

but it also poses problems in safety which tax the ability of the best engineers in the business.

The new gasoline-driven vehicles and the first electric auto designed and built by William Morrison of Des Moines, Iowa, were the topic of the day at the World's Fair in Chicago when it opened on October 21, 1892. Fire insurance coverage is always a problem upon such exhibition properties and that Fair was no exception. The spotlight was still focused upon Edison, for before the year came to an end he and some other interests brought about the formation of the General Electric Company. Another consolidation followed immediately when George Westinghouse and his friends formed the Westinghouse Electric and Manufacturing Company. The stocks of both these concerns have proven to be excellent sources of investment for fire insurance companies. Though their products could prove to be hazards to users and breeders of fires, their splendid record of safety standardization has been an outstanding contribution to fire prevention.

Organization of new fire companies practically ceased when the great panic of 1893 engulfed the country. The stock market broke and factories closed. With no employment to be found, Jacob Coxey of Ohio conducted his famous march on Washington to demand relief from the government. The strike at the Pullman Company in Chicago served to accentuate poverty and need. In the midst of this unrest, the creation of the Hawaiian Republic on July 4, 1894, and the election of its first President, Sanford B. Dole, gave some measure of confidence to existing fire underwriters in America who promptly extended their facilities to these "Islands of Happiness" where the mark of assurance soon became a sign of distinction.

Though America was still in the throes of economic setbacks, an indication of reviving confidence came with the establishment of the Alliance Co-operative Insurance Company in Topeka, Kansas, and the Eagle Mutual at Boston, Massachusetts. Even then the release of new funds for insurance establishments was thinly spread during the remainder of the decade, for in 1896, when mail could be delivered in country areas through inauguration of the "Rural Free Delivery" service and stock sold through that medium, only the Planters Mutual of Pine Bluff, Arkansas, and the Citizens Fire of Columbia, South Carolina, came into being.

All our present-day insurance selling by means of the air waves can be attributed to a small beginning in 1896 when Guglielmo Marconi took out his first patent papers for wireless telegraphy in England. He secured his first American patents in July of the following year, and it is entirely possible that the State Insurance Company of Des Moines, Iowa, starting that year, may have purchased some of the Marconi stock. The author well remembers the inventor's tour through the midwestern states a few years later when he demonstrated his wireless equipment and solicited stock subscriptions to sponsor a discovery which would in later years make it extremely easy for underwriters to transmit insurance proposals between England and America.

The Fraternal Order of Eagles formed in Kansas City, Missouri, in 1898, or some of its adherents, used a mark above the doors of their homes, but so far as can be ascertained this was not used in connection with fire insurance. On the premise that at a later date some such connection may be established, the mark and record are being preserved. The failure of signevierists to list any other marks in this year was probably due to the uncertainty created by the declaration of war with Spain. President McKinley proclaimed a suspension of hostilities on August 12, 1898, and together with that announcement and the news of the discovery of gold in the Klondike, business at once began its recovery. As the century came to a close the Globe and Rutgers Fire Insurance Company was organized in New York City and the Indianapolis Fire Insurance Company began operations in that midwestern city. In that year, too, the citizens of Pitman, New Jersey, formed the Pitman Fire Patrol and issued a fire mark to be posted on the houses of its members as a sign of protection.

This decade was truly the begining of an era of competition. The insurance companies had knuckled down to sound underwriting practices and honest advertising techniques. They had inaugurated a program of service to their policyholders. In this manner they have progressed throughout the intervening years so that even today, when competition thrives, the beneficiary of this effort to serve is the policyholder. Insurance is so definitely involved with the automotive industry that before leaving this decade we should recall that while Henry Ford organized the Detroit Automobile Company to finance his experiments in 1898, the first man on record to buy a car in America was Robert Allison of Port Carbon, Pennsylvania. On March 24, 1898, he purchased a one-cylinder Winton car from Alexander Winton. It was this transaction which inaugurated a sales competition comparable only to that of the insurance industry, both endeavors resulting in benefits to the buyers.

467

468

469

470

114

472

473

474

475

476

471

(467)   QUEEN INSURANCE COMPANY OF AMERICA. NEW YORK, NEW YORK.   1891-

Tin. Rectangular. 6⅝" x 2⅜". "Queen" silver on black background.

(468)   PROTECTION FIRE INSURANCE COMPANY. CHARLESTON, WEST VIRGINIA.   1892-1894.

Cast iron. Rectangular. 9" x 6¾". Phoenix and "Protection Insurance Co." in high relief. Very rare.

(469)   THE SHAWNEE FIRE INSURANCE COMPANY. TOPEKA, KANSAS.   1892-1910.

Tin. Rectangular. 9¾" x 2½". "Shawnee Fire—Topeka, Kansas." white on black background. "Shawnee Fire" lettering is slightly raised.

(470)   THE ALLIANCE COOPERATIVE INSURANCE COMPANY. TOPEKA, KANSAS.   1895-

Tin. Rectangular. 6" x 3¼". Border and "Alliance Co-operative of Topeka" silver on black background. Lettering is slightly raised.

(471)   EAGLE MUTUAL FIRE INSURANCE COMPANY. BOSTON, MASSACHUSETTS.   1895-1897.

Cast iron. Odd shape. 7¾" x 7⅞". Raised design of eagle with olive branch in each claw and "Fire" beneath. Flaming torch

forms top of mark. Although unverified, this is believed to be the mark of the above concern.

(472)   THE PLANTERS MUTUAL INSURANCE ASSOCIATION. PINE BLUFF, ARKANSAS.   1896-1905.

Tin. Rectangular. 8" x 2½". Border and "Insured in Planters" silver on black background.

(473)   CITIZENS FIRE INSURANCE COMPANY. COLUMBIA, SOUTH CAROLINA.   1896-1896.

Cast iron. Circular. 8½" in diameter. Design is raised. Exceedingly rare.

(474-475)   STATE INSURANCE COMPANY OF DES MOINES. DES MOINES, IOWA.   1897-1913.

474. Tin. Rectangular. 6¾" x 3¼". "State of Des Moines" black on silver background. Border had been black. Issued about 1900.

475. Tin. Rectangular. 6¾" x 3¼". Border and "State of Des Moines" black on gold background. Issued about 1900. Rare.

(476)   FRATERNAL ORDER OF EAGLES. KANSAS CITY, MISSOURI.   1898-

Heavy bronze. Horseshoe shape. 4¼" x 6¼". Spread eagle at top, two clasped hands and "Good Luck" across center. From dwelling in Massachusetts. House plate used by members of this fraternal insurance organization but use as a fire mark unverified.

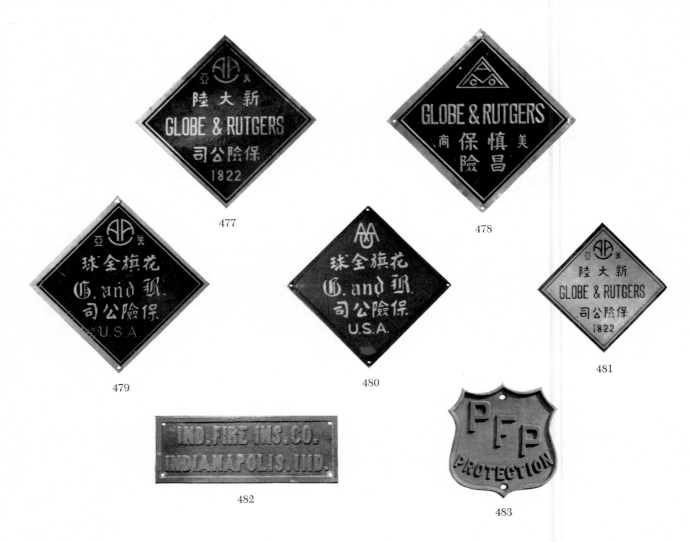

477

478

479

480

481

482

483

(477-481) GLOBE AND RUTGERS FIRE INSURANCE COMPANY. NEW YORK, NEW YORK. 1899-

477. Tin. Diamond shape. 6⅝″ x 6⅝″. Border "Globe & Rutgers," monogram AAU, date "1822" and Chinese characters gold on light green background. Mark used in China.

478. Tin. Diamond shape. 6½″ x 6½″. Border, "Globe & Rutgers," monogram A M Co, and Chinese characters gold on dark blue background. Mark used in China.

479. Tin. Diamond shape. 6¼″ x 6¼″. Border, monogram AAU, "G. and R.," "U.S.A." and Chinese characters white on dark blue background. Mark used in China.

480. Tin. Diamond shape, slightly convexed. 5⅞″ x 5⅞″. Monogram AAU, "G. and R.," "U.S.A." and Chinese characters white on blue enamel background. Mark used in China.

481. Tin. Diamond shape. 6½″ x 6½″. Border, monogram AAU, "Globe & Rutgers," date "1822" and Chinese characters gold on light green background. Mark used in China.

(482) INDIANAPOLIS FIRE INSURANCE COMPANY. INDIANAPOLIS, INDIANA. 1899-1908.

Tin. Rectangular. 8⁹⁄₁₆″ x 3³⁄₁₆″. Border and "Ind. Fire Ins. Co. Indianapolis, Ind." raised. Rare.

(483) PITMAN FIRE PATROL, INCORPORATED. PITMAN, NEW JERSEY. 1899-

Alloy casting. Shield shape. 6¾″ x 6⅜″. Border and "P F P— Protection" raised. Plates in hands of members only.

AN EPOCH OF SPEED

1901-1940

The four decades ending in 1940 can well be described as an era of speed with the automobile racing through rapid stages of development until, at the close of this period it was superseded by modern aircraft, an even speedier conveyance. Volunteer fire engine companies became motorized and operated for the benefit of their entire communities. They no longer looked to fire insurance companies for rewards, and consequently there was no longer any need for a mark of assurance.

The two companies which were organized in 1904 and used marks were the Farmers Mutual of Barry County, Missouri, and the Guardian Mutual of Pittsburgh, Pennsylvania. Both of them utilized the plates in outlying sections. Another year of trial for fire insurance underwriters came in 1904 when the Baltimore conflagration wiped out twenty-five hundred buildings in an area of one hundred and forty acres, including seventy-five blocks, and caused a loss of seventy million dollars.

One other insurance company was started at the beginning of 1906. It was the Middlewest Fire of Valley City, North Dakota, the last American company founded which issued and used a building mark for domestic purposes. Had its organizers anticipated the San Francisco earthquake and fire of April 18 of that year they might have hesitated in this venture. That fire burned for many days and participants described the terror which came without warning when the earth seemed to drift without a foundation in the universe, when the human mind became confused by the planetary instability. Human faculties were paralyzed, and suddenly the city was engulfed in a mass of flames. Sources of water supply were wrecked and man stood almost helpless in the midst of a great conflagration. In San Francisco four thousand acres, including one thousand city blocks containing over fifteen thousand buildings, were razed. The total loss exceeded three hundred million dollars. Over 1000 citizens perished and 98,860 people were homeless. In reference to this disaster Sydney Tyler, noted correspondent and author, writes: "San Francisco, by dint of fire and earthquake, has heretofore learned the value of insurance . . . San Francisco was cheered, while the great fire was still sweeping

through the city by the announcement that technicalities would be waived. The great companies which made this announcement are to be accounted among the notable factors in the rehabilitation. When San Francisco stands again, with the awful events of April 1906 only memories, a tremendous share of the credit will belong to these great business concerns, which put no quibble in the way of payment of losses, despite the fact that jointly tens of millions could have been saved to their treasuries. . . . Fortunately the insurance on the Pacific Coast is carried only in the large concerns. This fact proved to be important."

The strength and stability of a great majority of the insurance companies were proven by their ability to meet the conflagrations of Baltimore and San Francisco head-on. Following precedence, laws and practices were again strengthened until today the ability of an insurance company to fulfill its contracts is as sound as that of any type of financial institution. The acid test came in the 1930's during the depression in America when it was conclusively proven that supervision by the various states gave efficiency and soundness to the system which regulated the companies. As a result of the Baltimore and San Francisco fires new standards for building construction, city planning, fire prevention, and protection received the joint attention of the insurance companies and the public.

The story of signeviery in America is drawing to a rapid close. The Fidelity Phenix Fire Insurance Company (1910), a merger of two old and solid concerns; the Merchants Fire Insurance Company (1910); the Hudson Insurance Company (1918); the American Foreign Insurance Association (1919); and the American International Underwriters (1926), all of New York City, issued a modern type mark of assurance for use in connection with their foreign business. The Round Lake, Illinois, Volunteer Fire Department issued a mark solely for its members in 1929, and the new Charter Oak Fire Insurance Company of Hartford, Connecticut, distributed a replica of an old fire mark as an advertisement when it began to operate in 1935.

The story of the progress of fire insurance in America as recorded by the signs which once played such an important part in identifying insured properties is now completed. It is the narration of a business which covers a span of one hundred and fifty years in this country. While only forty-four of those companies represented by fire marks and organized during the eighteenth and nineteenth centuries remain in business today, that number is supplemented by forty-nine who did not issue marks and a large number of newcomers. The over-all number is now greater than at any time in the nation's history. Today the fire insurance business still flourishes under a system of free competition safeguarded by state supervision which gives protection to policyholders and stockholders alike. The kaleidoscopic portrayal of events throughout the decades has been fast and progressive. To the footprints of assurance should go the credit for recording a romantic business establishment which has become one of America's greatest enterprises, one which provides a cornerstone for the nation's credit.

484

485

486

487

488

489

490

491

492

493

494

495

496

497

(484) FARMERS MUTUAL INSURANCE COMPANY. BARRY COUNTY, MISSOURI. 1904-

Tin. Rectangular. 7″ x 3½″. Border and "Farmers Mutual Ins. —Barry Co., Mo." white on light blue background.

(485) GUARDIAN MUTUAL FIRE INSURANCE COMPANY. PITTSBURGH, PENNSYLVANIA. 1904-1906.

Heavy cast iron. Round. 8⅞″ in diameter. Figure of guardian angel and "M F" raised.

(486) MIDDLEWEST FIRE INSURANCE COMPANY. VALLEY CITY, NORTH DAKOTA. 1906-1913.

Tin. Rectangular. Border and "Insured in Middlewest Fire Insurance Co.—Valley City, N. D." painted black on light background. *(Courtesy of C. R. Tobin.)*

(487-489) FIDELITY-PHENIX FIRE INSURANCE COMPANY OF NEW YORK. NEW YORK, NEW YORK. 1910-

487. Tin. Diamond shape, slightly convexed. 5¾″ x 5¾″. "Fidelity Phoenix" and Chinese characters dark blue on speckled light blue enamel background. Mark used in China.

488. Aluminum. Rectangular. 8″ x 5¾″. Phenix seal in black and red. Company name stamped black letters. Modern type plate used in Britain and its colonies.

489. Aluminum. Rectangular. 6″ x 4¼″. Phenix seal in black and red. Company name stamped black letters. Modern type plate used in Britain and its colonies. Smaller than mark No. 488.

(490) MERCHANTS FIRE ASSURANCE CORPORATION OF NEW YORK. NEW YORK, NEW YORK. 1910-

Tin. Diamond shape. 6½″ x 6½″. Slightly raised border, design of phoenix rising from flames of burning building, "Merchants —U. S. A." and Chinese characters red and black on gold background. Mark used in China.

(491) HUDSON INSURANCE COMPANY. NEW YORK, NEW YORK. 1918-

Tin. Diamond shape. 6½″ x 6½″. Border, monogram AAU, "Hudson," "U.S.A." and Chinese characters gold on dark blue background. Mark used in China.

(492-494) AMERICAN FOREIGN INSURANCE ASSOCIATION. NEW YORK, NEW YORK. 1918-

492. Iron. Round. 3¾″ x 3¾″. "AFIA" and Chinese characters white on blue enamel background.

493. Iron. Square. 5⁵⁄₁₆″ x 5⁵⁄₁₆″. "AFIA" and Chinese characters blue on red enamel background. Mark used in China.

494. Tin. Rectangular. 8″ x 5″. "AFIA" seal and Chinese characters black on light green background. Issued about 1918. Mark used in China.

(495) AMERICAN INTERNATIONAL UNDERWRITERS CORPORATION. NEW YORK, NEW YORK. 1926-

Tin. Diamond shape. 6⅜″ x 6⅜″. Monogram I.I.O., "International Insurance Office," "U.S.A." and Chinese characters white on dark blue background. Mark used in China.

(496) ROUND LAKE VOLUNTEER FIRE DEPARTMENT. ROUND LAKE, ILLINOIS. 1929-

Aluminum. Rectangular. 4″ x 2″. "Fire Protection — Round Lake Volunteer Fire Dept.—Expires June 30, 1932" and border natural aluminum with black background. From a building in Round Lake, Illinois. Issued 1932.

(497) THE CHARTER OAK FIRE INSURANCE COMPANY. HARTFORD, CONNECTICUT. 1935-

Metal alloy. Oval. 9⅛″ x 6⅞″. Border, design of the charter oak tree and "The Charter Oak Fire Insurance Company—Hartford, Connecticut" raised. Modern mark.

119

There are a few footprints of assurance whose trails have caused the signevierist considerable anxiety in attempting to chart their course. There is mark No. 498, which came from the Stroud Collection of Philadelphia, and is said by some to represent the Duval Insurance Company of Duval County, Jacksonville, Florida; another collector believes it to be a symbol of a New York concern. No records can be found to substantiate either contention, yet the sign appears to be old and genuine, and the design and motif are typical of a fire mark.

Item No. 499 is an unusual brass mark of a mutual aid association and was removed from a building in Missouri, where in 1832 no insurance supervision existed. It has, therefore, been impossible to list the location of the association's headquarters or to give its history.

Another attempt to follow the wandering course of illusion was made in connection with marks No. 500 and No. 501 which also appear to be genuine and emblematic of fire insurance. With no authenticated record of these signs, there was added confusion when a similar fire mark was displayed in a prominent Washington museum, together with a card stating that it represented the Tiptonville Mutual Fire Insurance Company of Tiptonville, Tennessee, and that the concern ceased business about 1850. These footprints seemed to have faded into oblivion in 1949 when the Deputy Insurance Commissioner of the state of Tennessee found a record in their State Library which stated that the first house ever constructed in Tiptonville was in 1857. Intrigued by this discovery, the author arranged a visit to that city near the shores of the famous Reelfoot Lake and upon further inquiry

of the natives concluded that the identification of the mark must have been erroneous. Possibly some day someone will come forth with a proper identification.

Another collector has found a mark—No. 502—bearing the name Tuscarora, alleged to have been removed from a building in Cincinnati, Ohio, though to this day no record has been found of a fire insurance company bearing that name in any community. Item No. 503 is also a perfect example of a true fire mark, although no one has yet been able to identify it. Of marks No. 504 and No. 505, one collector insists that these were issued by the Virginia Fire and Marine Insurance Company. The company itself and other Virginia authorities do not believe that this concern used such a plate. Therefore, the trail left by these two marks joins the others *ad infinitum*.

A plate which has had a general distribution is similar to No. 506, said by some to represent the Fame Insurance Company of Philadelphia. It is agreed quite generally among collectors, however, that this was cast as a stove plate. The spurious fire marks which trick the neophyte are far more clever in their composition since they usually represent some recognized specimen. Examples of these can be seen in illustrations Nos. 507 through 511. Their imperfections are enlarged upon in the captions. In almost all of these fakes the castings are extremely rough and irregular and in most cases are much heavier than those found in genuine marks. Such footprints, of course, lead nowhere. The student of signeviery is therefore once more cautioned to follow the definite imprints of record. There are still many true signs to be found, and only those genuine marks left by the industry itself constitute the real essence of history.

498

499

500   501   502

503   504   505   506

(498)   DUVAL INSURANCE COMPANY. NEW YORK, NEW YORK. ? - ?

Cast iron. Rectangular. 9¾″ x 7¾″. Border, pair of clasped hands and "Duval" raised. While it is presumed that this mark was issued by the above company, official insurance records throughout the United States do not disclose the identity of the concern. From the Stroud collection, Philadelphia. Another collector, who secured the mark in Florida, believes that it represents a company from that state.

(499)   SAINT FERDINAND FIRE AND MUTUAL AID ASSOCIATION. ?. ? - ?.

Brass. Rectangular. 9¹⁵⁄₁₆″ x 3⅞″. Punched imprint, "St. Ferdinand Fire & Mutual Aid Association—1832-1837—Dues Paid." No record of location or history of this association has been found. (Courtesy of Norris G. Abbott, Jr.)

(500-501)   TIPTONVILLE MUTUAL FIRE INSURANCE COMPANY. TIPTONVILLE, TENNESSEE.   ? -1850.

500.   Cast iron. Oval. 11⅝″ x 6⅝″. Beaded border. Model of old double-decker hand pump and "Insured" raised. One collector believes this to be mark of company indicated but Tiptonville, Tennessee, was unsettled in 1850.

501.   Cast iron. Oval. 11⅝″ x 6⅝″. Model of old double-decker hand pump and "Insured" raised. One collector believes this to be a variant of mark No. 500, an unverified concern.

(502)   TUSCARORA FIRE INSURANCE COMPANY. CINCINNATI, OHIO.   ? - ?.

Tin. Rectangular. 7″ x 2½″. "Tuscarora" barely discernible. The finder of this mark states it was removed from a building in Cincinnati, Ohio, and that the property owner believed it to be of an early local company. No record can be found of such a concern in the Ohio State library or other similar sources throughout the United States.

(503)   UNKNOWN.

Thin cast iron. Oval. 5¼″ x 8″. Scalloped border and model of old style hand pump raised.

(504)   UNKNOWN.

Cast iron. Rectangular with rounded top. 5¾″ x 8⅝″. Border and scene of burning building raised.

(505)   UNKNOWN.

Cast iron. Rectangular with rounded top. 5¾″ x 8⅝″. Border and scene of burning building raised. Border is thinner than in mark No. 504.

(506)   FAME INSURANCE COMPANY. PHILADELPHIA, PENNSYLVANIA.   1856-1878.

Cast iron. Oval. 8³⁄₁₆″ x 12½″. Beaded edge and raised figure of seated scribe. This is mark No. 39 of the Stroud collection. Its source is unverified although one dealer in Philadelphia believes that it was issued by the above company. However, there is considerable doubt regarding this mark. It is more likely that it was a stove ornament.

507

508

509

510

511

(507) CHAMBERSBURG FIRE INSURANCE COMPANY. CHAMBERSBURG, PENNSYLVANIA. 1833-1872.

Cast iron. Oval. 9⅛″ x 9¾″. An example of the faker's efforts. The raised letters, engine and border are very rough and uneven as compared to a genuine mark.

(508) FIREMEN'S INSURANCE COMPANY. PITTSBURGH, PENNSYLVANIA. 1834-

Cast iron. Rectangular. 11⅝″ x 8″. The faker did a very poor job of imitating, since the iron is filled with imperfections and the border and engine are far more irregular than found upon a genuine mark.

(509) MUTUAL FIRE INSURANCE COMPANY OF GERMANTOWN AND VICINITY. PHILADELPHIA, PENNSYLVANIA. 1843-

Cast iron. Rectangular. 11½″ x 8½″. A poorly executed fake since it merely depicts the clasped hands and omits the company name. The casting is also too rough to be a genuine mark.

(510) INSURANCE COMPANY OF NORTH AMERICA. PHILADELPHIA, PENNSYLVANIA. 1792-

Wood. Shield shape. A fake made from a cut out copper eagle mounted on an unorthodox shield.

(511) LEXINGTON FIRE, LIFE AND MARINE INSURANCE COMPANY. LEXINGTON, KENTUCKY. 1836-Prior to 1872.

Cast iron. Oval. 11¾″ x 8¾″. The oval is irregular and the eagle and letters poorly imitated while the nail holes are newly drilled. The "aging" has been done recently—a poor fake.

FOOTPRINTS OF ASSURANCE

PART THREE

British Fire Marks

Including Ireland and Scotland

BRITISH FIRE MARKS

The narrative of the foregoing American section lent itself easily to a description of the military, political, and other influences upon the establishment of fire insurance concerns. Because of the fact that from the very beginning of American history there was a semblance of freedom and free enterprise which was accentuated subsequent to the war with Britain, the attendant influences could quite readily be divided into periods forming exact decades. In approaching the story of British fire insurance companies and in referring to the fire marks which they issued, however, it is not possible to follow the same outline because the conditions and influences in the British Isles have varied considerably in form. Thus, in discussing the influences upon our subject at the beginning of British history, it has been necessary to refer to specific eras rather than decades. When fire insurance came into being in Great Britain there did not exist that type of freedom of action which the British people have finally attained. The story here related of the eras surrounding the founding and development of underwriting concerns must deal, through necessity, solely with the high points in the history of Britain itself. The gradual surrender of the monarchal and almost despotic restraint of the masses has to a very great extent released the energies of free enterprise which made further commercial expansion possible. From that standpoint we believe that the development of our story will be of interest to the general reader as well as to the signevierist.

THE PURITAN PERIOD

1649-1714

The story of the fire mark in America began in a setting formed by the migration to this country of a band of individuals known as Puritans, a sect which had once been so powerful as to have committed the almost sacrilegious act of beheading their King, Charles I. Their rise to power in England, the violence and bloodshed which attended their reformation, and the cold, grey years of their austere command over the nation have all been thoroughly documented by many historians. And, of course, most readers are acquainted with England's reaction to the Puritans and her subsequent hostility to the new world. All of this need not concern us here, for it is our expressed intention to relate only those incidents and events which influenced the establishment of fire insurance concerns in England, Ireland, and Scotland and the identifying devices adopted by each. It might, however, be advantageous to furnish a general sketch of the events leading up to the time when some form of constitutional government was established—the only atmosphere, incidentally, in which fire insurance has been able to thrive and serve property owners to the fullest extent.

Following the execution of Charles I on January 30, 1649, the government was conducted by a Rump Parliament which was dissolved by Oliver Cromwell on April 20, 1653. In December of that year the nation's first written constitution, known as the "Instrument of Government," was drafted, rendering all the acts of Cromwell, who had been endowed with supreme powers and the title of Lord Protector, subject to the review of the courts. Administration of the government then became a joint parliamentary and executive endeavor. This "Little Parliament," as it was known, was eventually referred to as the "Barebones Parliament," an appellation suggested by the name of one of its members. This man was a religious eccentric named Praise-God Barebones who, in a moment of glory, burdened his son with the name Unless-Christ-had-died-for-thee-thou-hadst-been-damned Barebones. Fortunately for the fire insurance industry, the son survived both the name and his father's zeal. We know him today as a pioneer insurance underwriter and the founder of England's first fire insurance office.

Cromwell, whose popularity had waned during those trying years, died on September 3, 1658. With his passing the Puritans, leaderless and divided, gradually lost their once mighty influence and gave way to the restoration of the monarchy. Charles II was recalled, and in 1660 the "French King," as he became known, ascended the throne. But Charles and all his successors would never again be a law unto themselves, for thanks to Cromwell and the Puritans, ensuing monarchies have always been tempered with constitutional government.

The "Restoration" ushered in an era of intrigue and cynicism which resulted in a general deterioration of moral standards. It was an era of vulgarity and brutality during which the King engaged in costly wars, accepted bribes from foreign powers, and lavishly entertained a parasitic court. It was, however, an age distinguished by reason and inquiry. Many of its men—Newton, Hobbes, Locke, and Dryden to name a few—made significant and lasting contributions to human affairs. Released from a feverish interest in politics and theology, a new spirit of free inquiry, coupled with an intense interest in scientific thought, prevailed. In London, the outstanding minds of the day reflected upon a study of the physical world, the observation of phenomena and the laws which govern them. The pursuit of science became a passion with many and was the order of the day.

London has always been a city of sharp contrasts. In this period particularly the contrasts were exaggerated, for in comparison with the luxury of the court, the city of London proper—a medieval slum area of wooden houses and narrow, winding streets built on marshy land—was fair game for plague or fire, both of which soon struck with a fury unmatched in history.

The Plague visited the city first in 1665, taking a total of 100,000 lives. Just when it seemed that the residents of the city were recovering from the shock, another great disaster struck on September 2, 1666. A fire, which began in the heart of London, swept unchecked through the entire city, reducing it to ashes from "the Tower to the Temple." Though the need had always existed for some form of protection against loss by fire, it was not seriously considered until dramatically demonstrated by this devastating conflagration which destroyed 13,200 homes and 373 acres of property at a loss of an estimated £10,730,-500. Measured in present-day calculations of exchange this probably represented some forty million American dollars.

At the time of this fire only leather hand buckets and syringes were used to combat the flames. When one considers that these devices held only a few quarts of water, one must realize their total inadequacy. Soon, however, a new enterprise was to develop which would start a chain of improvements in fire-fighting methods.

The son of Praise-God Barebones, previously mentioned as having been so verbosely named, now became Dr. Nicholas Barbon. Though bred a physician, he had failed in that profession and subsequently engaged in building, motivated by a desire for profit. It is said that "He was one of the first and most considerable builders of the City of London, after the Great Fire." For thirty years he engaged in a number of building and rebuilding programs. He also had the welfare of the owners and citizenry at heart, for in 1667 he set up an office as an individual underwriter for insuring houses and buildings. Apparently the business continued in this manner until 1680, at which time he was joined by Mr. Samuel Vincent, Mr. John Parsons, Mr. Felix Calvert, and others. The business then assumed the name of The Fire Office.

Of this group Strype, in 1720, wrote: "There is yet another practice of great benefit and convenience used in London and that is the Insuring of houses against Fire, which any man may do for a little money for the term of seven years, and so renew again if he pleases. For which there is a certain Office kept in the City called the Fire Office in Cornhill and in Fleet Street. All houses thus insured are known by a plate fixed upon them, being the resemblance of a Phenix in a flame. This Office maintains in pay a competent number of strong expert men with their accoutrements, who are always ready at hand when any of these Insured houses chance to be on fire to quench the same."

This is one of several records which indicate that The Fire Office was undoubtedly the first fire insurance concern to organize and one of the first to use a fire mark, although no mark has ever been located. It was also the earliest concern to employ its own fire brigade. Recognized as the first joint-stock or proprietary company for fire insurance in London and probably in the world, The Fire Office was a pioneer of the free-enterprise system under which Britain finally became such a great power. James II, successor to his brother Charles II, who died in 1685, granted the patent or incorporation papers to The Fire Office in 1688. Because of the popular symbol of its fire mark, this company assumed the name of Phoenix Office in 1705.

Even today fire marks which were previously unheard of are found. Since the written record so prominently refers to the use and design of this first Phoenix, it is the hope of signevierists and insurance historians everywhere that one day a specimen of this first mark of an important industry will be uncovered.

In 1681 the proposals for another fire insurance venture, petitioned for by a persistent deputy named Newbold, were reviewed by the council in London. After due consideration they recommended that, instead of granting the powers to the Corporation, the City of London "might undertake ye said design." This suggestion was favorably received and the Corporation, as it was known, began insuring houses at lower rates than those of The Fire Office. Since there is no evidence that the city Corporation issued fire marks, nor did it have a staff of firemen, it is only natural to assume that their operating costs were lower than those of the private enterprise. From its inception a running war of words was exchanged between this Corporation and The Fire Office, until the former was declared illegal and beyond the corporate powers of the city. A rebuff to public ownership, the demise of this early socialistic venture left The Fire Office as the only insurance company in London.

Even three centuries ago monopolies were short-lived, for the record shows that following the failure of the Corporation scheme, another company was started in 1683 and heralded by the following notice which appeared in the London press: "The Friendly Society, or A proposal of a New Way or Method for Securing Houses from any considerable loss by Fire, by way of Subscription and Mutual Contribution." Since the plan existed for over a century and formed the basis for other similar concerns, it is interesting to quote from their proposals of October, 1684: "1. Every person entering into this Society is to subscribe an instrument whereby he shall be obliged to submit to a rate or tax, the same not exceeding 30s. for every 100 £. he shall secure on any house or houses, when any fire shall happen; which money is nevertheless to remain in his own hands but to be subject to this condition; That in case any house belonging to any one of the Society shall be burnt or damnified by, or by reason of fire, then every person of the Society is to pay such a proportion of money as will suffice to discharge and satisfie the money secured on any house so burnt or damnified." Regulations of the Society agreed upon by the "Trustees Inrolled in Chancery" included: "XVII—To prevent any Fraud in getting any Policy by indirect means after a House is Burnt, no House is to be esteemed a Secured House till the Mark hath been actually affixed thereon."

William Hale of King's Walden, Hertfordshire, was one of the two founders of the Society, and the design of the fire mark was a sheaf of arrows taken from the Hale crest. That this office also maintained its own fire brigade is evidenced by regulation XVIII which read: "Watermen and other labourers to be imploy'd at the charge of the Undertakers to assist at the quenching of Fires." It is the record of the Privy Council of London which refers to the organizers as "the Undertakers," a term which later was changed to "underwriter," or one who assumes a risk of insurance.

During the first century following the Great Fire we find faint traces of other insurance plans, but none of any great importance. However, in 1696 a mutual organization was formed when the Amicable Contributors established themselves at Tom's Coffee House in St. Martin's Lane. Its fire mark is described as consisting of two clasped hands with a crown over them, a symbol of friendship and good faith and possibly an indication of the mutual principle. It was upon their basic principles that so many mutuals in America and other countries established themselves. Because of the popularity of their symbol they, too, deemed it desirable to change their name to the Hand-in-Hand in 1698 (some historians say 1714) and for over two centuries these marks distinguished themselves as signs of security. In 1905, the organization passed to the Commercial Union, one of the stalwart British insurance corporations.

While the latter part of the seventeenth century witnessed new and greater measures of security from loss by fire, Europe itself was undergoing a revolution, both bloody and bloodless. Religion and politics were in a constant turmoil. The era saw the passing of King James and the Reign of William and Mary who were also embroiled in the same dissensions. Oppressed peoples from the continent flocked to England, increasing its population, stimulating the expansion of industry, and developing new ones. The influx of French Huguenots created an extension of silk maufacturing, while Flemish immigrants introduced the art of calico printing. Commerce began to thrive with a great colonization. With expanding trade and the addition of many new personal property items on the part of the citizens, there was a need for insurance on goods as well as houses and that demand was soon to be satisfied.

Following William's death, Anne succeeded to the throne on March 8, 1702. Inexperience, a strong head, and prejudiced counsel were responsible for another succession of wars on the continent. In this gloomy picture one stroke of statesmanship succeeded when a union was ratified between England and Scotland in 1707, although it took the Scottish people a half century to realize that they would benefit by this act. In this period of continued unrest there came into being a fire insurance development which still thrives. In 1706 Charles Povey founded the Exchange House Fire Office as a one-man enterprise similar in concept to that employed by Barbon. Other underwriters joined him in 1708, and they formed a board of management which included ten directors and a similar number of governors. That same year he proposed a salvage corps and saw to it that each insured received a fire mark containing the image of a sun. The historical references also indicate that this was evidently the first concern to insure movable goods as well as houses, thereby filling a dire need for security. In 1709 the Exchange House Fire Office transferred its business to the newly formed Company of London Insurers. On April 7, 1710, a deed of co-partnership was signed, stating that the Company of London Insurers had set up an insurance office named the Sun Fire Office. It had arranged to extend insurance to all parts of Great Britain and Ireland, thus beginning a system of expansion and diversification of underwriting which became the basis of sound protection in America a century and a half later.

From the start it was stipulated that a mark representing the sun be nailed to the insured houses, its number to correspond with the subscriber's policy.

"The mark so affixed was to be the guide to the Salvage Corps men as to the houses at which they were to render assistance in the event of fire." The company originally used marks of lead, and later, of copper, until 1807 when it was directed that they be made of tin. The mark of assurance used by the Sun has probably been the most prolific of all such signs and speaks well for the success of the company throughout its almost two and one half centuries of existence. Born in an era when the restoration of monarchy had evolved into a series of schisms, of monarchial intrigues and conspiracies, this company, like so many of England's citizens, has displayed a strength of character and endurance which has become symbolic of the nation itself.

Shortly after the establishment of the Sun Fire Office, in August, 1714, Queen Anne died, ending the rule of the House of Stuart and with it the precepts and prejudices of Puritanism which had survived the revolution of 1688. With her death these influences became fragmentary and ineffectual.

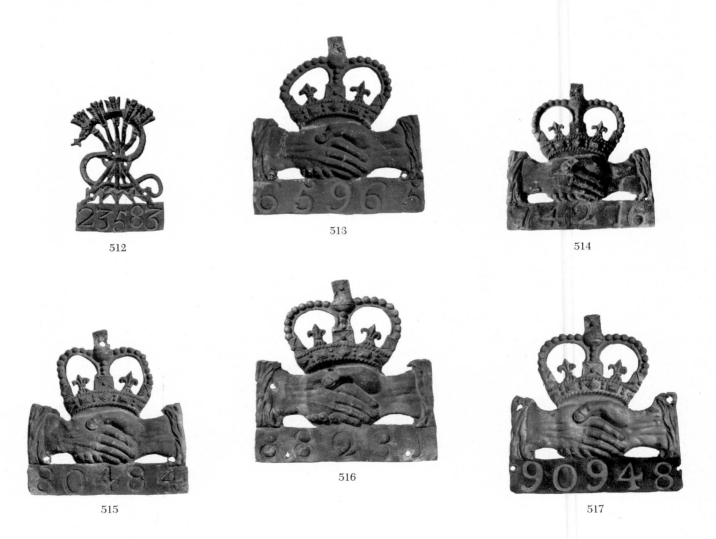

512

513

514

515

516

517

The brigades of the Phoenix Fire Office, County Fire Office and the Westminster Fire Office shown racing to the scene of a fire in London. The print is dated September 1, 1808.

518

519

520

521

522

523

(512) THE FRIENDLY SOCIETY. LONDON, ENGLAND. 1683-About 1790.

Lead. Odd shape. 6″ x 8″. The device is from the crest of the arms of Wm. Hale of Kings Walden, Herts, one of the two promoters of the Company. A snake entwined round five golden arrows with black heads and silver feathers—one upright (in pale) and four in saltire (crossed). *(Courtesy of Licenses and General Insurance Company.)*

(513-529) HAND-IN-HAND FIRE AND LIFE INSURANCE SOCIETY. LONDON, ENGLAND. 1696-1905.

513. Lead. 8″ x 8½″. Pair of clasped hands, open crown and panel bearing policy No. 65965.

514. Lead. 8″ x 8½″. Pair of clasped hands, open crown and panel bearing policy No. 74216.

515. Lead. 8″ x 8½″. Pair of clasped hands, open crown and panel bearing policy No. 80484.

516. Lead. 8⅛″ x 8⅛″. Pair of clasped hands, open crown and panel bearing policy No. 88231.

517. Lead. 8½″ x 8″. Pair of clasped hands, open crown and panel bearing policy No. 90948.

518. Lead. 8⅛″ x 8⅛″. Pair of clasped hands, open crown and panel bearing policy No. 94517. Large cuffs.

519. Lead. 7⅞″ x 8″. Pair of clasped hands, closed crown and panel bearing policy No. 101437. Large cuffs. Issued about 1725.

520. Lead. 7⅞″ x 8⅜″. Pair of clasped hands, closed crown and panel bearing policy No. 102723. Large cuffs. Issued about 1725.

521. Lead. 7⅞″ x 8″. Pair of clasped hands, closed crown and panel bearing policy No. 102849. Large cuffs. Issued about 1725.

522. Lead. 7⅞″ x 8⅜″. Pair of clasped hands, closed crown and panel bearing policy No. 102993. Large cuffs. Issued about 1725.

523. Lead. 8″ x 8½″. Pair of clasped hands, closed crown and panel bearing policy No. 103031. Large cuffs.

524

525

526

527

528

529

530

531

532

533

534

535

536

537

538

539

540

541

524. Lead. 7¾″ x 8½″. Pair of clasped hands, closed crown and panel bearing policy No. 103136. Large cuffs.

525. Lead. 7¾″ x 8½″. Pair of clasped hands, closed crown, open back and panel bearing policy No. 103603. Large cuffs.

526. Lead. 7¼″ x 8½″. Pair of clasped hands, closed crown, open back and panel bearing policy No. 104215. Large cuffs. Issued about 1725.

527. Lead. 7¾″ x 8½″. Pair of clasped hands, closed crown, open back and panel bearing policy No. 104763. Large cuffs.

528. Lead. 8″ x 8⅛″. Pair of clasped hands, closed crown and panel bearing raised "Hand in Hand."

529. Lead. Pair of clasped hands, closed crown, open back, large cuffs. Differs from other marks in that it has no panel for policy number or name. (Courtesy of Bertram Williams.)

(530-560) SUN INSURANCE OFFICE, LIMITED. LONDON, ENGLAND. 1710-

530. Lead. 5¾″ x 6⅞″. Sun with sixteen rays, alternating straight and wavy indicative of light and heat. Panel below bears policy No. 6490. Issued about 1714-1715.

531. Lead. 5¾″ x 7″. Sun with sixteen rays, alternating straight and wavy. Panel below bears policy No. 37458.

532. Lead. 6¾″ x 7″. Sun with sixteen rays, alternating straight and wavy. Panel below bears policy No. 164186.

533. Heavy lead. 6⅞″ x 7⅛″. Sun with sixteen rays, alternating straight and wavy. Panel below bears policy No. 196815.

534. Lead. 7″ x 7″. Sun with sixteen rays, alternating straight and wavy. Panel below bears policy No. 289153.

535. Heavy lead. 6⅞″ x 7⅛″. Sun with sixteen rays, alternating straight and wavy. Panel below bears policy No. 432512.

536. Lead. 6⅞″ x 7″. Sun with sixteen rays, alternating straight and wavy. Panel below bears policy No. 435273.

537. Lead. 7″ x 6⅞″. Sun with sixteen rays, alternating straight and wavy. Panel below bears policy No. 446929.

538. Lead. 7″ x 7⅛″. Sun with sixteen rays, alternating straight and wavy. Panel below bears policy No. 464806.

539. Lead. 6¾″ x 6¾″. Sun with sixteen rays, alternating straight and wavy. Panel below bears policy No. 478904.

540. Lead. 6¾″ x 6¾″. Sun with sixteen rays, alternating straight and wavy. Panel below bears policy No. 496208.

541. Lead. 6¾″ x 6¾″. Sun with sixteen rays, alternating straight and wavy. Panel below bears policy No. 503842.

543

544

542

545

546

547

548

549

550

551

552

553

554

132

555

556

557

558

559

560

542. Lead. 6¾″ x 6¾″. Sun with sixteen rays, alternating straight and wavy. Panel below bears policy No. 517589.

543. Lead. 6¾″ x 6¾″. Sun with sixteen rays, alternating straight and wavy. Panel below bears policy No. 538656.

544. Lead. 6¹¹⁄₁₆″ x 6⅜″. Sun with sixteen rays, alternating straight and wavy. Panel below bears policy No. 602926.

545. Lead. 6¾″ x 6¾″. Sun with sixteen rays, alternating straight and wavy. Panel below bears policy No. 676560.

546. Lead. 6⅝″ x 6½″. Sun with sixteen rays, alternating straight and wavy. Panel below bears policy No. 745632.

547. Lead. 6¾″ x 6¾″. Sun with sixteen rays, alternating straight and wavy. Panel below bears policy No. 786726.

548. Tin. 6⅛″ x 6⅝″. Raised sun with sixteen rays, alternating straight and wavy. Panel below bears policy No. 905869. Exceedingly rare.

549. Copper. Circular. 7¼″ x 5¾″. Raised sun with twenty rays, wavy. Gold on black background. Has loops at sides for fastening to building.

550. Copper. Circular. 7⅛″ x 5¾″. Raised sun with twenty rays, wavy. Gold on dark green background. Has loops at sides for fastening to building.

551. Copper. Circular. 7⅜″ in diameter. Raised sun with sixteen rays, alternating straight and wavy. "Sun Fire Office—1710" raised around border. Design and lettering gold on black background.

552. Zinc. Circular. 6¼″ in diameter. Raised sun with sixteen rays, alternating straight and wavy. Gold on green background.

553. Tin. Rectangular. 3¾″ x 4⅞″. Border, sun and "Sun of London" gold on black background. First type mark used by this company upon admission to America. Very rare.

554. Tin. Rectangular. 3¾″ x 4⅞″. Sun and "Sun of London" silver on black background. Issued in America about 1890. Rare unused specimen.

555. Tin. Circular. 7″ in diameter. Raised sun with sixteen rays, alternating straight and wavy, gold on red background. "Sun—London—1710" raised gold on maroon band. Outer border raised gold.

556. Tin. Circular. 7″ in diameter. Raised sun with sixteen rays, alternating straight and wavy, gold on red background. "Sun—Londres—1710" raised gold on maroon band. Outer border raised gold. Modern.

557. Tin. Circular. 7″ in diameter. Raised sun with sixteen rays, alternating straight and wavy, gold on red background. "Sun—Londres—1710" raised gold on black band. Outer border raised gold. Issued for use in the Colonies.

558. Tin. Circular. 7¼″ in diameter. Raised sun with sixteen rays, alternating straight and wavy, gold on red background. "Sun Fire Office—1710" and Chinese characters gold on black band. Outer border raised gold. Modern mark used in Dutch East Indies.

559. Tin. Rectangular. 9⅜″ x 9″. Design and lettering yellow and white on blue background. Modern mark used in Palestine.

560. Bronze. Circular. 7″ in diameter. Raised sun with twenty-four rays, alternating straight and wavy. Ring attached for hanging. There seems to be no record of this being a fire mark nor does the plate provide a means for mounting. This may have been used on some equipment or device of the company.

ERA OF THE FIRST AND SECOND HANOVERIANS
1714-1760

At the time of Anne's death the two-party political system had become fairly well established. It was through the swift action of one of them, the enterprising Whig party then in control, that on the afternoon of the Queen's death, the heralds went about London and Westminster proclaiming George as King of Great Britain. The new King had been Elector of Hanover. A German by birth who spoke no English, he surrounded himself with an entourage of German attendants. He also brought to the English Court a dullness and tarnish which isolated it. Yet its isolation was a blessing in disguise, for George's complete indifference to political affairs encouraged more active participation in representative government. Before the death of this first Hanoverian king (1727) the accepted custom was for the cabinet to deliberate over matters of import to the nation, *en masse,* and then announce to the crown their opinions and decisions. In reality this was the first step in the direct development of a democratic form of government, brought about by a diffident monarch.

During the first six years of George's reign a like number of fire insurance concerns were established and several of them are still very active and outstanding, while the remainder were taken under the protective wings of other British fire insurance companies surviving today. In that respect this was a most unusual decade (1711-1720), influenced by an extraordinary series of circumstances. A group of outstanding traders and merchants in London banded themselves together in 1714 for the purpose of providing indemnification from loss by fire to goods, wares, and merchandise. At first the group was named The Union or Double Hand-in-Hand Fire Office, adopting as its emblem two pairs of joined hands to denote union. It had a sort of working arrangement with the Hand-in-Hand, agreeing not to accept proposals upon buildings. But when this latter concern also commenced to insure goods in 1805, the Union began to insure buildings.

The second firm to begin operations in this decade was the Westminster Fire Office, established upon the same general plan as the Hand-in-Hand. Organized in 1717, an order was placed for fire marks on September 5th of that year, and at another meeting it was determined "That Ye marke of the office to be Ye Portcullis and Plum and Feathers." The portcullis was taken from the crest of Westminster, while the feathers represented the arms of the Prince of Wales who was later to become George II. The Prince, incidentally, had personally assisted in combatting a fire at the French Chapel and Library in Spring Gardens near Westminster. The Westminster Fire Office has the distinction of having a set of twenty-one single chairs and three arm chairs made for their directors in the year 1792, the back of the chair representing the same design which is employed on their fire mark.

Rural Bristol, in the year 1718, witnessed the organization of a somewhat limited co-partnership plan of fire insurance later known as the Bristol Crown Fire Office which was finally taken over by the Sun in 1837. Almost simultaneously, the country was confronted with an economic phenomenon which rendered it unsavory for any group to initiate a new fire insurance venture for almost fifty years. In the year 1720, there were three exceptions to which we will refer later, but otherwise no new fire insurance concern was organized until the year 1767.

This financial dilemma began when the British government found itself burdened by a national debt of over fifty million pounds sterling upon which it was paying from 7 to 8 per cent interest. A scheme was devised in which the South Sea Company was formed to take over this debt on a long-term basis at from 4 to 5 per cent interest, thus placing the government into the hands of only one creditor instead of many. In return the company was to be granted a monopoly of trade in the South Seas. Later the agreement was expanded to include traffic in Negro slaves with the Spanish plantations under what was known as the Assiento Treaty. The South Sea Company sold stock upon several plans and by August, 1720, the shares, which had sold for one hundred and thirty pounds sterling only a few months before, had advanced to one thousand pounds sterling.

This was an era of peace and recovery, and the populace was eager to invest its newly made money in almost any scheme for quick profit. Funds had been invested in sound mercantile and manufacturing

Contemporary view of the London scene during the time of the South Sea Bubble when much of the populace pawned their belongings to purchase stock in the various speculations.

projects as well as in the earlier organized insurance concerns. Now, however, stimulated by the wild frenzy created by the rise of what became known as "The South Sea Bubble," every conceivable sort of an investment scheme was floated by the unscrupulous. Stock was sold for improving a fishery, various salt schemes, and a company for melting down carpenters' chips and sawdust and running them into planks and boards. Most audacious of all was a scheme "for carrying on an undertaking of great advantage, but nobody to know what it is." A capital of half a million pounds sterling was asked for this project. After receiving deposits of two guineas each from one thousand subscribers in a single morning, the promoter decamped. It is estimated that some five hundred million pounds sterling were so invested. When the South Sea Company decided to make an example of some of these fraudulent concerns by taking court action, the entire bubble burst, and the people were suddenly confronted with the realization that thousands of them were ruined. *History of Banking* gives a list of one hundred and eighty-five of these wildcat projects, including thirty relating to some phase of insurance. In regard to insurance there was a section in the Bubble Act to the effect that after June 24, 1720, all such defined undertakings would be subject to penalties, and the King issued a proclamation which would cause the act to be put in execution.

The Friendly Insurance Society of Edinburgh, Scotland, was founded as a mutual by the signing of a Deed of Settlement on January 13, 1720, before the Bubble Act was passed. It probably escaped annihilation because it was a mutual and so was not affected by the restrictive laws placed upon corporate organizations. Also Edinburgh had been visited by a series of fires and there was a genuine need for some form of fire insurance. This was the first recorded instance of a group subscribing to perpetual policies, a plan later adopted by some American concerns. The company was a success, and forty years after its origin it extended its insurances throughout Scotland.

The Bubble Act had been passed in June, but on July 12, 1720, the Lords Justices in Council granted charters to the Royal Exchange Assurance and the London Assurance, both of which have now survived all of the economic storms of the past. Probably one reason that the Royal Exchange was given recognition was that it was the culmination of a proposed consolidation of several chartered concerns, the oldest being the Mines Royal Company (not insurance) which was granted Letters Patent back in 1564. Another reason for the granting of the charter in this extraordinary period was that the petitioner and chairman of the company was Thomas Lord Onslow, former speaker of the House of Commons and a most prominent political figure. The earliest proposals for fire

135

insurance indicate one of the reasons for this company's success: "For the timely assistance of such as are assured by this Corporation, they have provided several engines and a sufficient number of firemen to work the engines, and watermen all cloathed in yellow, with proper instruments to extinguish fires, and a sufficient number of porters with bags, etc., for removing goods, having every one a badge, with the same figure as on the top of these proposals, to distinguish them from servants belonging to other offices; and for the fidelity of the said firemen and porters, the Corporation has taken sufficient security, so that the assured, in case of danger, may safely intrust any watermen wearing such badges into their houses, and the porters with their goods. And the same figure as on the badges will be affixed on buildings, etc., assured by this Corporation." The many types of fire marks issued by this company—a familiar mark of trade in many countries—all depicted the image of the Royal Exchange.

Lord Chetwynd, a member of an old Shropshire family, had been refused a charter for an insurance scheme of his own, and subsequently he gave his support to the application for a charter by the London Assurance Corporation. Nominally, that application was in opposition to Lord Onslow of the Royal Exchange, but it was stated that the two worked together *sub rosa*. Relton says: "Lord Chetwynd was one of the Lords of His Majesty's Household, and is supposed to have been nominated in the Charter as Governor of the London Assurance for the same reason as Lord Onslow was for the Royal Exchange." Both did secure charters and both were successful financially. The London Assurance gave the same sort of protection to their policyholders as did the Royal Exchange, although the attire of the London personnel was green while their fire mark and attendants' badges contained a Britannia holding a harp and supported by the London Arms. One writer thinks it a miracle that these bubble companies did not drown in the flood of disaster which ruined so many of London's citizens, since some of their directors were financially involved in the débacle personally and lost all or most of their private estates in the government's effort to relieve the situation. The promotion of any other new company was not possible under such economic conditions, because the public had lost confidence in the business world. No businessman would wish to be associated, as director or official of a newly formed company, where he might be subject to prosecution and possibly the loss of any personal capital or assets. Thus venture capital was held in restraint for over four decades.

In the meantime the Parliament carried on to the best of its ability until the death of George I in 1727. He was succeeded by George II, who, being of somewhat the same character as his predecessor, met with great opposition. Sir Robert Walpole of South Sea Bubble fame was probably the strongest character in the land and was able to control Parliament. Having made himself supreme in the Cabinet, he thus became England's first "Prime Minister." War with Spain was declared in 1739, followed by the War of the Austrian Succession, and another uprising occurred in Scotland. Wars followed in Europe, in India, Africa, and in the Americas. Just at the time when English arms seemed to triumph, George II died. The period which ended with his passing on October 25, 1760, this era of the first and second Hanoverians, was one of chaos, organization, and reorganization. It nevertheless contained elements most influential in the progress of a more democratic society. The South Sea Bubble episode made the citizenry conscious of the value of solidarity and conservatism in their investment policies, factors which have prevailed, to place British fire insurance in the upper ranks of that great industry.

561

562

563

564

565

566

567

568

569

570

571

572

573

(561-575) UNION ASSURANCE SOCIETY. LONDON, ENGLAND. 1714-1907.

561. Heavy lead. 7⅞″ x 10¼″. Four clasped hands, cut out. "Union" raised on panel above; policy No. 24256 on panel below. Issued about 1770.

562. Lead. 7⅝″ x 10¼″. Four clasped hands, cut out. "Union" raised on panel above; policy No. 26123 on panel below.

563. Heavy lead. 7⅞″ x 10¼″. Four clasped hands, cut out. "Union" raised on panel above; policy No. 26329 on panel below.

564. Copper. 6¾″ x 9¼″. Four clasped hands, "A. D. 1714" and "Union" raised.

565. Copper. 7″ x 9½″. Border, four clasped hands, "A. D. 1714" and "Union" raised gold on red and black background.

566. Copper. 7″ x 9⅝″. Border, four clasped hands, "Union" and "Established 1714" raised.

567. Heavy copper. 6⅞″ x 9⁹⁄₁₆″. Border, four clasped hands, "Fire" and "Union" raised gold on red and black background.

568. Tin. 7⅛″ x 9⅝″. Border, four clasped hands, "Fire" and "Union" raised.

569. Tin. 7¾″ x 10″. Border, four clasped hands, "Fire" and "Union" raised. From building in the south of Europe.

570. Tin. 7″ x 9½″. Border, four clasped hands, "A. D. 1714" and "Union" raised, gold on red and black background.

571. Tin. 9⅝″ x 7″. Border, "Union of London—1714" and four clasped hands surrounded by garter, raised. From building in Greece.

572. Heavy tin. Oval. 10⅝″ x 7⅝″. Characters, "Union of London" and "1714" barely discernible. Had been gold. From building in the south of Europe.

573. Copper. Oval. 7⅛″ x 8⅛″. Heavy raised border. Scene of burning building, four clasped hands and "Union No. 1" raised. This is a replica of the first waterman's badge of this company.

574

575

576

577

578

579

580

581

582

583

584

585

586

587

588

590

589

591

574. Iron. Rectangular. 10" x 7⁵⁄₁₆". Border, "A. D. 1714-Union Assurance Society," and Chinese characters red on white enamel background. Four clasped hands surrounded by garter black on red.

575. Tin. Rectangular. 9⅜" x 7⅞". Border, gold "Union" and Chinese characters and red, white and blue Union Jack raised on red background.

(576-584) WESTMINSTER FIRE OFFICE. LONDON, ENGLAND. 1717-1906.

576. Lead. 6¾" x 9⅝". Panel bearing policy No. 22474 below portcullis. This portcullis was originally the badge used by the House of Tudor (Henry VII) and a representation of it is to be seen in Henry VII Chapel at Westminster Abbey. It is said to be a pun on the name Tudor (two-door) but this is surmise. The portcullis was used in the arms of the old Liberty of Westminster (now the City of Westminster), where the Company had, and still has, its headquarters. The ostrich feathers as a crest were probably added out of compliment to the then Prince of Wales (later George II) who had given evidence of his interest in keeping down the ravages of fire in the Liberty. Edward III's banner was crowned by ostrich feathers. He introduced them to English Royal Heraldry probably deriving them from his wife, Philippa, of Hainault. This destroys the legend of their being adopted by his son the Black Prince from King John of Bohemia, who was killed at Crecy. It was the Black Prince however, who made them famous. This plume is encircled (enfiled) with a circlet from the Prince of Wales' coronet, the use of which requires Royal permission. The plume is now the badge of the heir apparent.

577. Lead. 6¾" x 9¾". Panel bearing policy No. 30174 below fenestrated portcullis and Prince of Wales' feathers.

578. Lead. 6¾" x 9⅝". Panel bearing policy No. 32354 below fenestrated portcullis and Prince of Wales' feathers.

579. Lead. 6⅞" x 9⅝". Panel bearing policy No. 35322 below fenestrated portcullis and Prince of Wales' feathers.

580. Lead. 6¾" x 9⅛". Panel bearing policy No. 38676 below fenestrated portcullis and Prince of Wales' feathers.

581. Lead. 5½" x 9½". Panel bearing policy No. 51370 below portcullis, unpierced, and Prince of Wales' feathers.

582. Lead. 5⅝" x 9¾". Panel bearing policy No. 52845 below portcullis, unpierced, and Prince of Wales' feathers.

583. Lead. 5¾" x 9¾". Panel bearing policy No. 52916 below portcullis, unpierced, and Prince of Wales' feathers.

584. Copper. 9¾" x 6". Raised "Westminster—A. D. 1717" and portcullis with Prince of Wales' feathers. Had been gold.

(585-587) THE BRISTOL CROWN FIRE OFFICE. BRISTOL, ENGLAND. 1718-1837.

585. Heavy lead. 6³⁄₁₆" x 7⅝". Crown in high relief had been gold and red. Policy No. 9811 on gold panel below.

586. Lead. 6½" x 8". Raised crown and "Bristol" in panel below.

587. Lead. 6½" x 8". Raised crown and "Bristol" in panel below. Crown is heavier and stamping deeper than other types of Bristol marks. Exceedingly rare.

(588-596) FRIENDLY INSURANCE SOCIETY OF EDINBURGH. EDINBURGH, SCOTLAND. 1720-1847.

588. Lead. Pair of clasped hands in relief with raised "Deo Juvante" meaning "with God's help," above. Policy No. 1274 in panel below. Rare. (Courtesy of Licenses and General Insurance Company, Ltd.)

589. Lead. 5¾" x 4¾". Pair of clasped hands, raised. Policy No. 1760 in panel below. Issued about 1772.

590. Lead. 5¾" x 4¾". Pair of clasped hands, raised. Policy No. 5620 in panel below.

591. Lead. 5½" x 4¾". Pair of clasped hands, raised. Policy No. 5718 in panel below.

592

593

594

595

596

597

598

599

600

601

602

603

604

605

606

607

608

592. Lead. 5¾″ x 4¾″. Pair of clasped hands, raised. Policy No. 7683 in panel below.

593. Lead. 5¾″ x 4¾″. Pair of clasped hands, raised. Policy No. 8343 in panel below.

594. Lead. 5¾″ x 4¾″. Pair of clasped hands, raised. Policy No. 12459 in panel below.

595. Cast iron. 7″ x 4¼″. Pair of clasped hands, raised. "Friendly" raised in panel below.

596. Cast iron. 7″ x 4¾″. Pair of clasped hands, raised. "Friendly" raised in panel below.

(597-608) THE LONDON ASSURANCE. LONDON, ENGLAND. 1720-

597. Lead. Policy No. 613 in panel below with "G" on tab beneath it denoting "goods" insured. Made by Henry Ball in 1721. The figure is a representation of Britannia, one of the oldest characters in English history. When Hadrian built his wall in A. D. 120 between Carlisle and Wallsend (Segedunum) to keep out the Scots he issued coins to celebrate the event showing a draped figure of a woman seated on a rock wearing a helmet and armed with a spear and oval shield. It represented the Roman "Watch on the Wall" and was symbolic of the Roman State and power. Charles II used the figure showing her watch on the sea frontier. The engraver to the Mint at that time, John Roettiers, took for his model the famous beauty, Duchess of Richmond. "A pretty thing it is" wrote Samuel Pepys, "that he should choose *her* face to represent Britannia." The design has continued in use to this day. It is still displayed on the "tail" side of pennies. In the marks Britannia is seated upon the world with a shield showing City of London arms and a harp. The latter is presumed to refer to Ireland. It is known the Company had an agent in Dublin after the grant of the Fire Charter in 1721, but even if fire marks were issued prior to opening business in Ireland, it is obvious that it was the Governor's intention to open there at an early date. The harp used in the mark is heraldic (English) type and not an original Irish one—the O'Neill, an original of which is in Trinity College, Dublin. *(Courtesy of Licenses and General Insurance Company, Ltd.)*

598. Lead. Seated figure of Britannia with shield, spear and pierced harp. Policy No. 614 in panel below with "H" on tab beneath it denoting "house" insured. Made by Henry Ball in 1721. *(Courtesy of Licenses and General Insurance Company, Ltd.)*

599. Lead. Seated figure of Britannia with shield, spear and pierced harp. Policy No. 3017 in narrow panel below. Made and originally painted by Richard Waller, 1722-1723. *(Courtesy of Bertram Williams.)*

600. Lead. 6⅞″ x 8¾″. Seated figure of Britannia with shield, spear and harp. Policy No. 34295 in panel below. Issued in 1766. Manufactured by Lukyn Betts, plumber, and painted by Robert Ross.

601. Lead. 6⅞″ x 8¾″. Seated figure of Britannia with shield, spear and harp. Policy No. 35615 in panel below. Issued in 1769. Manufactured by Lukyn Betts, plumber, and painted by Robert Ross.

602. Lead. 6⅜″ x 8⅜″. Seated figure of Britannia with shield, spear and harp. Policy No. 51111 in panel below. Issued in 1800. Manufactured and painted by Joseph Humpleby.

603. Copper. 7¼″ x 8½″. Seated figure of Britannia with shield, spear and harp. "London" raised in panel below. Issued about 1808.

604. Copper. 9⅞″ x 11⅝″. Raised "London Assurance Incorporated—A. D. 1720." Seated figure of Britannia raised on slightly convexed circular center. Issued about 1808.

605. Heavy tin. Oval. 8⅝″ x 7½″. Raised border and "London Assurance—A. D. 1720" gold on green background. Issued about 1825. From building in Constantinople, Turkey.

606. Tin. 9⅞″ x 11⅝″. Raised "London Assurance Incorporated—A. D. 1720" gold on black background. Seated figure of Britannia, raised, in gold, white, red and black on red circular center, convexed. Issued about 1835. From building in Istanbul, Turkey.

607. Tin. 9⅞″ x 11⅝″. Raised "London Assurance Incorporated—A. D. 1720" gold on black background. Seated figure of Britannia, raised, in gold, white, red and black on red circular center, convexed. Modern.

608. Heavy tin. 10″ x 11 9/16″. Raised "London Assurance Incorporated—A. D. 1720" gold on black background. Seated figure of Britannia, raised, in gold, white, red and black on red circular center, convexed. Varies in coloring and finish from other marks of this company.

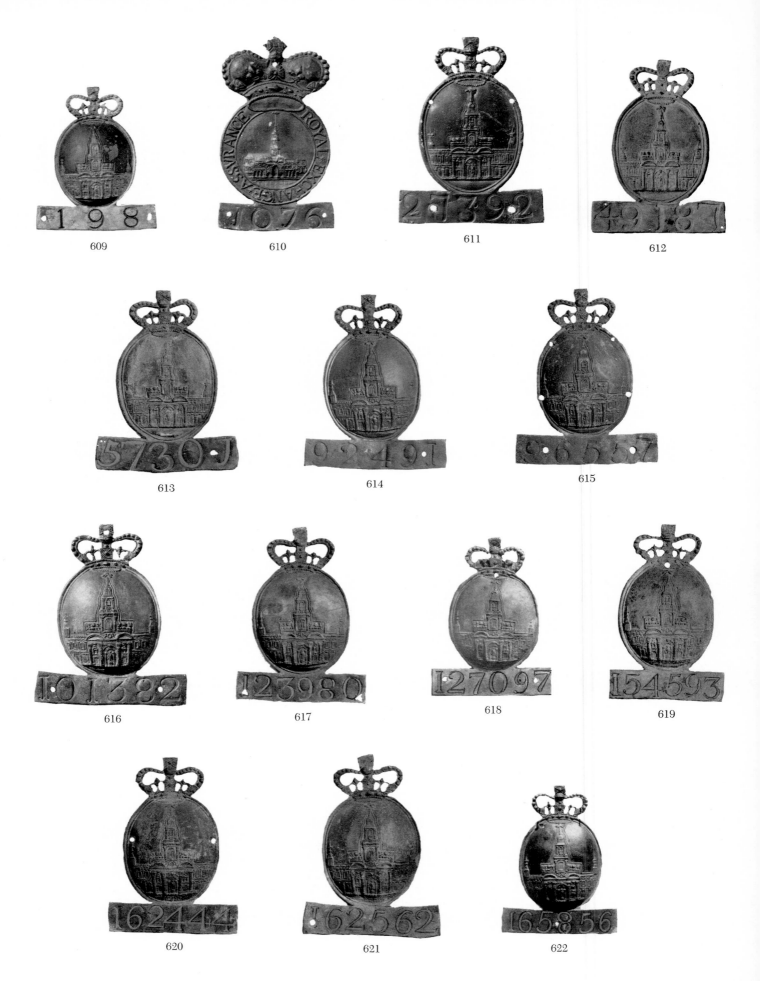

609

610

611

612

613

614

615

616

617

618

619

620

621

622

142

623

624

(609-637) ROYAL EXCHANGE ASSURANCE. LONDON, ENGLAND. 1720-

609. Lead. 7¾" x 9½". Raised Royal Exchange on convexed oval, open crown above and panel below with policy No. 198. Border, crown, building and panel gold. Oval red. Numerals black. Issued 1721.

610. Lead. 7⅛" x 13⅝". Raised Royal Exchange and "Royal Exchange Assurance" on circle with large closed crown above and panel below bearing policy No. 1076. Mark has been painted red. Issued between 1721 and 1723.

611. Lead. 7½" x 9⅝". Raised Royal Exchange on slightly convexed oval, open crown above and panel below with policy No. 27392. Issued 1729.

612. Lead. 7⅜" x 9½". Raised Royal Exchange on flat oval, open crown above and panel below with policy No. 49187. Issued 1776.

613. Heavy lead. 7" x 9¾". Raised Royal Exchange on flat oval, open crown above and panel below with policy No. 57301. Issued 1771.

614. Heavy lead. 7⅝" x 9½". Raised Royal Exchange on convexed oval, open crown above and panel below with policy No. 92491. Issued April 9, 1785 to John Lewis, baker, of the town and county of Monmouth (England) "on his dwelling house; furniture therein; utensils and trade in the same; on a house, tenant Richard Miles, joiner; on a malthouse and warehouse adjoining together; all the said buildings adjoin together, are brick, stone and tiled, situate in Church Street in Monmouth aforesaid. From April 7, 1785 to June 24, 1786."

615. Heavy lead. 7" x 9¾". Raised Royal Exchange on convexed oval, open crown above and panel below with policy No. 96557. Issued February 14, 1786 to John Wilmott, carpenter, of Chatham in the County of Kent (England) "on his dwelling house, brick, timber and plaster built and tiled, situate near the 3 Caps in Queen Street in Chatham, aforesaid; on household furniture therein; on a wash-house adjoining brick built and tiled. From February 13, 1786 to March 25, 1787."

616. Lead. 7¾" x 9⅜". Raised Royal Exchange on convexed oval, open crown above and panel below with policy No. 101382. Issued April 4, 1787 to "Elizabeth Smith of Littlemore in the Parish of Iffley in the County of Oxford on her Dwelling House stone built and slated situate in Littlemore aforesaid; on a House stone built and thatched situate in Littlemore aforesaid; Tenants William Jackson and Richard Bamton. From March 26, 1787 to March 25, 1788."

617. Heavy lead. 7" x 9¾". Raised Royal Exchange on convexed oval, open crown and panel below with policy No. 123980. Issued October 17, 1791 to Stephen Newcomer, farmer, of Billericay in the County of Essex "on a House in 2 Tenements, timber and tiled situate in the Parish of Tillingham in the County aforesaid in the occupation of himself and James Flack (?) and known by the Decoy House; on Furniture therein; on a Stable in the Yard belonging, timber and tiled; on a Barn and 2 Granaries adjoining called the Upper Barn, timber and thatched belonging; Utensils and Trade therein; etc. . . . From October 10, 1791 to December 25, 1792."

618. Heavy lead. 7" x 9⅜". Raised Royal Exchange on convexed oval, open crown above and panel below with policy No. 127097. Issued 1792 to William Spink of Whitby in the County of York "on a House brick or stone built and tiled situate in Grape Lane in Whitby aforesaid. Tenants Richard Skelton and Simon Bilsbro. Renewed from 115360. From March 17, 1792 to March 25, 1793."

619. Heavy lead. 6" x 9¾". Raised Royal Exchange on convexed oval, open crown above and panel below with policy No. 154593. Issued 1796.

620. Heavy lead. 7" x 9¾". Raised Royal Exchange on convexed oval, open crown above and panel below with policy No. 162444. Issued 1798 to "John MacPhail of Glasgow in the County of Lanark on a House, stone and slated, situate on the East Side of the Road leading from Bridge Town to Rutherglen Bridge, occupied as Weavers Shops below and Dwelling Houses above. . . . Warranted that no part of the Cotton Manufactory except Warping, Weaving or Cutting be carried on in the Premises. From June 5, 1798 to June 24, 1799."

621. Heavy lead. 7" x 9¾". Raised Royal Exchange on convexed oval, open crown above and panel below with policy No. 162562. Issued 1798.

622. Heavy lead. 7¼" x 9½". Raised Royal Exchange on convexed oval, open crown above and panel below with policy No. 165856. Issued 1798.

623. Lead. 6¼" x 7". Raised Royal Exchange and crown on convexed pear with panel below bearing policy No. 175206. Issued in 1800 to Oswald Brodie, cordwainer, of South Shields in the County of Durham "on a House, brick and tiled, situate in the Long Row in South Shields aforesaid, in the occupation of himself, George Brown and others. From June 27, 1800 to June 24, 1801."

624. Lead. 6⅛" x 7⅛". Raised Royal Exchange and crown on convexed pear with panel below bearing policy No. 185430. Issued 1801.

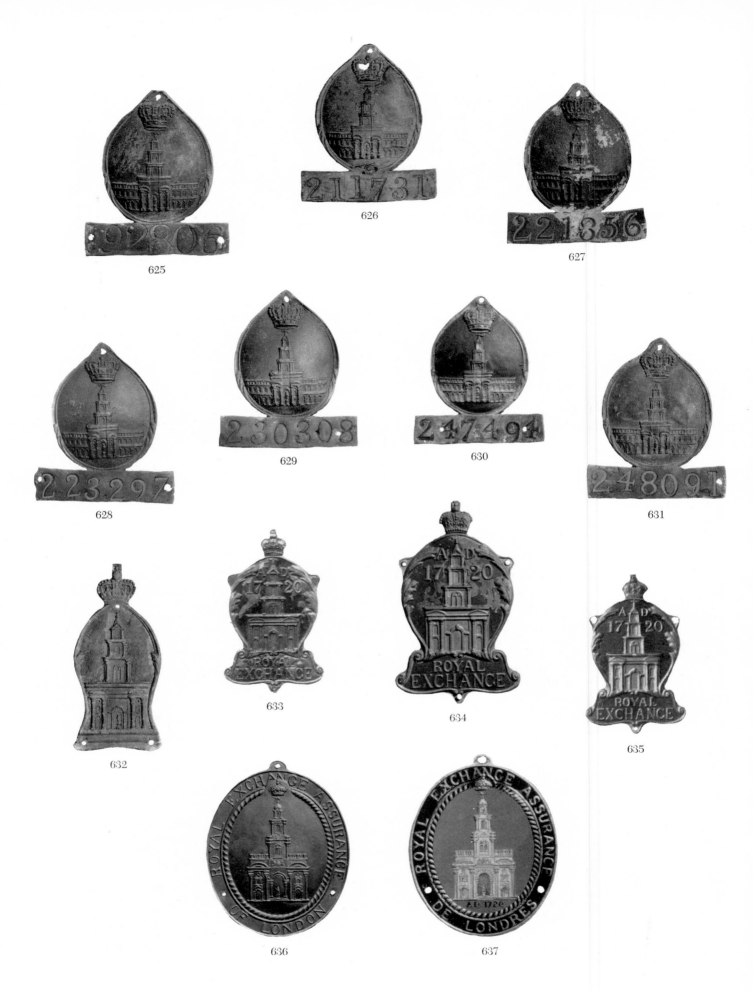

625

626

627

628

629

630

631

632

633

634

635

636

637

View of a fire in London March 3, 1791.

625. Lead. 6⅛″ x 7⅛″. Raised Royal Exchange and crown on convexed pear with panel below bearing policy No. 192806. Issued 1802.

626. Lead. 6⅛″ x 7⅛″. Raised Royal Exchange and crown on convexed pear with panel below bearing policy No. 211731. Issued in 1804 to Elisha Webb, farmer, of Beenham in the County of Berkshire "on Utensils and Trade in all or any of the Barns, Stables or other Buildings on his Farm situate at Beenham aforesaid including the Ricks, Stacks, Implements of Husbandry, Waggons, Carts and all Utensils in the Yards or on the Grounds thereunto belonging. . . . On his Dwelling House and Offices adjoining, brick and tiled, situate on the said Farm; on Furniture, Apparel, Plate and Printed Books therein; on a Barn called the Upper Barn, Stable and Outbuildings adjoining near; on a Barn called the Lower Barn, Stable, Granary and Outhouses adjoining near, on a Granary on Staddles near; on a Carthouse near; on a Carthouse and Cattlehouse adjoining near. . . . From November 20, 1804 to December 25, 1805."

627. Lead. 6⅛″ x 7⅛″. Raised Royal Exchange and crown on convexed pear with panel below bearing policy No. 221856. Issued 1806.

628. Lead. 6⅛″ x 7⅛″. Raised Royal Exchange and crown on convexed pear with panel below bearing policy No. 223297. Issued 1806.

629. Lead. 6⅛″ x 7⅛″. Raised Royal Exchange and crown on convexed pear with panel below bearing policy No. 230308. Issued 1807 to one "Pilgrim of Happisburgh in the County of Norfolk. On Furniture, Apparel, Plate and Printed Books in his Dwelling House, brick and tiled situate in Happisburgh aforesaid; on Utensils and Trade in a Stable and Hayhouse adjoining; on Utensils and Trade in the Wheat Barn; on Utensils and Trade in Stack Yard; on Utensils and Trade in a Barn called Burnt House, brick and thatched, all near and belonging. From May 1, 1807 to June 24, 1808."

630. Lead. 6⅜″ x 7¼″. Raised Royal Exchange and crown on convexed pear with panel below bearing policy No. 247494. Border, crown, building and panel gold. Background red. Numerals black.

631. Lead. 6⅛″ x 7⅛″. Raised Royal Exchange and crown on convexed pear with panel below bearing policy No. 248091. Issued 1809.

632. Lead. 4″ x 8⅞″. Raised Royal Exchange on elongated form with closed crown at top. Last type lead mark of this company. Issued about 1835.

633. Copper. 6¼″ x 10¼″. Raised Royal Exchange and "A. D. 1720—Royal Exchange" on ornate form with closed crown at top. Red with gold.

634. Copper. 6¼″ x 10¼″. Raised Royal Exchange and "A. D. 1720—Royal Exchange" on ornate form with closed crown at top. Green with gold.

635. Heavy tin. 6⅜″ x 10⅜″. Raised Royal Exchange and "A. D. 1720—Royal Exchange" in gold on dark blue background of ornate form with closed crown at top. Semi-modern type. From building in Martinique.

636. Aluminum. 6⅝″ x 7⅞″. Raised Royal Exchange with crown above, surrounded by roped design, and "Royal Exchange Assurance of London" on outer border. Green.

637. Heavy tin. Oval. 6⅜″ x 7⅞″. Raised yellow Royal Exchange on green background with gold crown above and "A. D. 1720" below surrounded by roped design of raised gold and black. Raised border and "Royal Exchange Assurance De Londres" gold on black background. Tab for hanging at top. Modern. Type of mark used in Palestine.

FOUR DECADES OF ROYAL ASCENDANCY
1760-1800

George III ascended to the throne in 1760, and a new era in English affairs began. In contrast to his grandfather, George II, who was crude, ponderous, and immoral, the new monarch was a true Englishman, clean thinking and genuinely religious. The people hailed his accession with much enthusiasm, which gave the King an opportunity to exercise his own ideas and prejudices with little opposition. While his intentions were sincere, his ambition was to restore to the throne a sort of absolutism and to deprive the Parliament largely of the power and the domination enjoyed under Whig control.

The monarch was so determined to restore the ancient privileges and power to the throne that he spent much of his own money to buy Tory elections for his agents, while at the same time he would suppress the Whigs. These tactics were evidently successful, for he soon achieved a majority support in the boroughs and in Parliament. With the defeat of the Whigs, who insisted upon the unconditional defeat of France, the King was then free to make peace and the Treaty of Paris was signed in February of 1763. Bribery in Parliament had won over patriotic opposition, but the peace was an unpopular one and the public was enraged by the concessions made to France. That business and commerce were showing a steady gain is evidenced by the repeated accusations that arms and goods were being sold to the enemy in large quantities. Still the economy, combined with the effects of the South Sea Bubble, had not yet reached a point where the people of London ventured to organize any new fire insurance companies.

However, the vital need for security and protection asserted itself again when, for the first time in over four decades, the Bath Fire Office was founded in the City of Bath in 1767. Its fire mark was in the form of the arms of the city, and as early as 1789 they advertised in support of agencies in Chippenham, Melksham, Tetbury, and Sarum. Possibly this is the very first place in which the phrase "Fireman, save my child!" was employed, for in the same advertisement the Bath Fire Office announces: "A reward of half a Guinea will be given to those who bring the first ladder capable of taking persons from the Windows of an Attic Story."

The Bristol Fire Office became very aggressive from its inception in 1769 in the city of Bristol. In Ireland the Dublin Insurance Company became a first for that area when it hung out its ornate sign in 1770. It was followed the next year by the organization of the Hibernian Fire Insurance Company whose fire mark so proudly displayed the crown and the harp of Erin. Also in 1771 the Manchester Fire Office was founded at Manchester, and three years later another rural underwriter came forth in Bristol—namely the Bristol Universal Fire Office. Some of these offices addressed their proposals to farmers. Indeed one could almost designate this period of new insurance ventures as an "agrarian era." As is common in most countries, national calamities affect the country districts the least and economically they are the first to recuperate from a disaster.

Chronologically we are rapidly approaching those years in English affairs which are of special interest to Americans because they deal largely with matters which were of joint importance to both countries. The citizenry in America was predominantly of English descent, and those coming to this new land were by tradition opposed to an absolute monarchy. In fact, parliamentary control was the order of the day in Britain at the time when large numbers emigrated to America. In the interim, the revival of royal ascendancy had become an accomplished fact under George III and the ideologies of the colonists were diametrically opposed to the new order in Britain. Then, too, the members of the assembly in the colonies were the truly elected representatives of the people and such things as corruption in politics and bribery were unheard of. In effect, the colonists had become genuinely self-governing and self-reliant. The situation was so contrary to that in the motherland, therefore, that almost any inflammatory situation might arise. Whatever the causes or their justifications, the natural differences in practical government were such as to make inevitable those hostilities which took place in New England in 1775.

The Whig party, which in the reign of Charles II had established the policy of parliamentary government as opposed to the divine right of kings, had also decried this war in America, and in effect the successful revolution was one of victory for the Whigs in the motherland. It was the liberal party, and had its members not always quarrelled among themselves, it could have taken over control of the government at the close of hostilities in America. Instead a coalition ministry was formed with internal strife and dissension prevailing.

Another revolution had visited England—an industrial one which had gained much ground between 1783 and 1800. During this period spinning and weaving, which were major endeavors in Britain, had passed from the peasant home to the factory where the newly invented flying shuttle, the spinning jenny, water frame, mule and power loom had all been placed in use. There were new wool-combing machines and an application of chlorine for bleaching. From water power these contrivances had passed to the steam engine and the entire process of manufacturing had been revolutionized. Home life was changed and the modern factory became a reality. Economics was not too seriously affected by the war, and with an increase in population, new buildings, and many new goods in the hands of the people there was created a need for more fire insurance.

Starting in 1776, fire insurance companies were founded in Bath, Liverpool, Leeds, Shrewsbury and also in Dundee, Scotland, and Dublin, Ireland. The original "Phoenix" or Fire Office which was founded in 1667 left no trace of itself. History did not follow the legend of the fabled bird and wait five hundred years to reappear, for according to Relton: "A movement was set on foot this year (1780), we believe at the instance of the London sugar bakers or refiners, for founding an insurance office which should meet the requirements of their trade. An application was made to Parliament for a charter of incorporation; but the then Attorney-General (afterwards Lord Kenyon) declined to recommend His Majesty to grant a charter; and the ground of his so declining was understood to be, that he considered the public as likely to be better served by voluntary associations of respectable individuals than by incorporated societies. In 1782 the New Fire Office was established chiefly by that class of traders. The name of the company was speedily changed to Phoenix Fire Office. The Engineers, Fireman, and Porters belonging to this Office are distinguished by a Uniform of Crimson Cloth, with a Silver Badge, the Emblem A PHOENIX rising from the flames—which is also the Office Mark." Often referred to as Phoenix No. 2, the footprints of this old concern have become a real distinguishing sign upon insured properties. Before the close of the century other companies were formed in Newcastle-Upon-Tyne, Worcester, Norwich, one in London, and two in Dublin, Ireland. These underwriting institutions were just forerunners of a large number of newcomers to be founded during the next half century, influenced more by industrial progress than any other cause.

639

638

640

(638-643)   BATH FIRE OFFICE. BATH, ENGLAND. 1767-1827.

638.   Lead.   6½″ x 8³⁄₁₆″.   Shield with scrolled border and panel below bearing policy No. 256. Bath Fire Office, also known as the "Old Bath" to distinguish from its competitor the "Bath Sun." It shows the Arms of the City of Bath. The wall in the base of the marks, and the water (wavy lines) commemorate Bath's origin as the Roman "Aqua Salus," health resort or spa. The sword in pale is of St. Paul and refers to the Abbey Church at Bath. It is to be found also in the City of London Arms and signifies how the saint met his death.

639.   Lead.   6¾″ x 8¼″.   Arms of the City of Bath on a shield with scrolled border and panel below bearing policy No. 2501.

640.   Lead.   6¾″ x 8¼″.   Arms of the City of Bath on a shield with scrolled border and panel below bearing policy No. 6417.

641

642

643

644

645

646

647

648

649

650

651

652

653

654

148

656

657

655

658

641. Lead. 6¾″ x 8⅛″. Arms of the City of Bath on a shield with scrolled border and panel below bearing policy No. 6515.

642. Lead. 6¾″ x 6¾″. Arms of the City of Bath on a shield with scrolled border. No policy panel below. (Courtesy of Licenses and General Insurance Company, Ltd.)

643. Copper. Oval. 7″ x 8¾″. Arms of the City of Bath raised in center with "Bath Fire Office" raised on border.

(644) BRISTOL FIRE OFFICE. BRISTOL, ENGLAND. 1769-1839.

Copper. 7⅛″ x 8¾″. Ribbon at top and scrolled panel below. The device is from the Bristol City Arms. A three-masted ship sailing out of the portway of a castle, which has two domed towers (each flying St. George's banner), and standing on a cliff by the sea. The City's ancient character of a fortified port.

(645-646) DUBLIN INSURANCE COMPANY. DUBLIN, IRELAND. 1770-About 1800.

645. Lead. 7½″ x 10¼″. Crest of City of Dublin with beaded edge on shield, bowknot at top and scrolled panel below bearing policy No. 3685.

646. Lead. 7½″ x 10¼″. Crest of City of Dublin with beaded edge on shield, bowknot at top and scrolled panel below bearing the name "Dublin." (Courtesy of Bertram Williams.)

(647-652) HIBERNIAN FIRE INSURANCE COMPANY. DUBLIN, IRELAND. 1771-1839.

647. Lead. 6⅜″ x 11″. Harp in raised form on oval with open crown above and panel below bearing policy No. 3636.

648. Lead. 7⅛″ x 10¼″. Harp in raised form on oval with open crown above and panel below bearing policy No. 3827.

649. Lead. 7⅛″ x 10¼″. Harp in raised form on oval with open crown above and panel below bearing policy No. 3951.

650. Lead. 6⅜″ x 10⅝″. Harp in raised form on oval with open crown above and panel below bearing policy No. 6213.

651. Lead. 6¼″ x 10½″. Harp in raised form on oval with open crown above and panel below bearing policy No. 9623.

652. Lead. 7½″ x 10⅝″. Harp in raised form on oval with open crown above and panel below bearing name "Hibernian."

(653-654) MANCHESTER FIRE OFFICE. MANCHESTER, ENGLAND. 1771-About 1788.

653. Lead. 9¼″ x 7½″. The lion passant, on a wreath is presumed to be from the arms of John O'Gaunt, Duke of Lancaster. "Manchester" and policy No. 2389 on panel below. Only type mark issued by this company.

654. Lead. 9⅝″ x 7⁹⁄₁₆″. Figure of standing lion, facing left with tail up, raised on circular portion of mark. "Manchester" and policy No. 4285 on panel below. Only type mark issued by this company.

(655-656) BRISTOL UNIVERSAL FIRE OFFICE. BRISTOL, ENGLAND. 1774 - ?

655. Lead. "Bristol Universal Fire Office" in oval in center flanked by two standing figures one holding a hook, and one an axe. Policy No. 336 in panel below. (Courtesy of Bertram Williams.)

656. Lead. "Bristol Universal Fire Office" in oval in center flanked by two standing figures with top of mark in cut out form. Has no policy panel below. (Courtesy of Bertram Williams.)

(657-660) BATH SUN FIRE OFFICE. BATH, ENGLAND. 1776-1838.

657. Lead. Arms of the City of Bath with sun at the top and panel below bearing policy No. 99. One of few British marks that contain "No." with policy number. (Courtesy of Licenses and General Insurance Company, Ltd.)

658. Lead. 6¾″ x 9⅞″. Sun at the top and panel below bearing policy No. 1169. The lead marks use the Bath City Arms (see "Bath Fire") but with sun in splendour in the chief (or upper third) to differentiate it from its Bath competitor, and to stress its name. Bath's origin was the Roman "Aqua Salus"—health resort or spa. The sword in pale, is of St. Paul, and refers to the Abbey Church at Bath. It is to be found also in the City of London Arms and signifies how the saint met his death.

659

660

661

662

663

664

665

666

667

668

669

670

671

672

673

659. Lead. Arms of the City of Bath with sun at the top and panel below bearing policy No. 4197. Numerals appear to have been picked out with a sharp pointed instrument instead of being incised or stamped. (*Courtesy of Bertram Williams.*)

660. Copper. 8½″ x 7⅜″. Sun with twenty wavy rays raised on convexed circular section of mark with raised "Bath—Sun—Fire" on semi-circular panel below.

(661) LIVERPOOL FIRE OFFICE. LIVERPOOL, ENGLAND. 1777-1795.

Lead. 6″ x 8″. Liver bird in high relief on circular section of mark. "Liverpool" and policy No. 5477 on panel below. The liver bird is taken from the arms of City of Liverpool. Heraldically they are described as "a liver (cormorant) with a branch of laver (seaweed) in its beak." (*Courtesy of J. A. D. Walsh.*)

(662) LEEDS FIRE OFFICE. LEEDS, ENGLAND. 1777-1782.

Lead. Raised design of three stars above ram, suspended, with "Leeds" and policy No. 170 below. Only type mark issued by this company. The devices are taken from the Leeds City Arms. A ram's fleece slewed up indicated the staple trade of the city— wool. The three stars or mullets are from the arms of Wm. Danby, High Sheriff of Yorkshire (1784), an old county family and local Lord of the Manor. (*Courtesy of Bertram Williams.*)

(663-665) GENERAL INSURANCE COMPANY OF IRELAND. DUBLIN, IRELAND. 1779-1824.

663. Lead. Rectangular. Raised border and phoenix with policy No. 698 on panel below. (*Courtesy of Bertram Williams.*)

664. Lead. Square. 7″ x 7″. Raised border and phoenix. Very rare.

665. Lead. Square. 7″ x 7″. Raised border and phoenix. The mould of the phoenix differs slightly from that of mark No. 664.

(666-671) SALOP FIRE OFFICE. SHREWSBURY, ENGLAND. 1780-1890.

666. Lead. 7⅛″ x 7⅝″. The Arms of Shrewsbury in high relief on circular section of mark. Policy No. 1213 on panel below. The three leopards' heads affrontee (called locally "longgerheads") are from the arms of Shrewsbury. They were adopted from the Royal Arms on a 13th century seal, an ancient heraldic charge believed to be the forerunner of the lion.

667. Lead. 7⅛″ x 7½″. The Arms of Shrewsbury in high relief on circular section of mark. Policy No. 1634 on panel below.

668. Lead. 7¼″ x 7¼″. The Arms of Shrewsbury in high relief on circular section of mark. Policy No. 3957 on panel below.

669. Lead. 7⅛″ x 7½″. The Arms of Shrewsbury in high relief on circular section of mark. Policy No. 5761 on panel below.

670. Lead. 7⅛″ x 7½″. The Arms of Shrewsbury in high relief on circular section of mark. Policy No. 14056 on panel below.

671. Copper. 7¼″ x 7⅝″. The Arms of Shrewsbury in relief on circular section of mark. "Salop" in panel below.

(672-673) DUNDEE INSURANCE COMPANY. DUNDEE, SCOTLAND. 1782-1826.

672. Lead. 6¾″ x 8″. Classic urn with three lilies, raised, on oval section of mark. "Dundee" and policy No. 2447 on panel below surrounded by beaded border. This mark is a reproduction. From the Dundee City Arms registered in 1673. The charge derives from the seal of the parish church (circa 1200) and dedicated to the Virgin Mary. They used to be called "Pig & Lilies;" "pig" being an old Scottish term for an earthenware pot.

673. Lead. Classic urn with three lilies, raised, on oval section of mark and panel below bearing "Dundee" and policy No. 4803. Entire mark has beaded border. (*Courtesy of Licenses and General Insurance Company, Ltd.*)

674

675

676

677

678

679

680

681

682

683

684

685

686

687

688

690

689

691

(674-687) PHOENIX ASSURANCE COMPANY, LIMITED. LONDON, ENGLAND. 1782-

674. Terra cotta. Rectangular. 12″ x 14⅝″ x 3³⁄₁₆″. Moulded emblem of the Phoenix with "Rebuilt—1790." End incised "Coade, Lambeth. 1790." Extremely rare.

675. Stone. Emblem of the Phoenix with "Rebuilt—1791." Extremely rare. (Courtesy of Bertram Williams.)

676. Lead. 7¾″ x 8½″. Border, figure of phoenix and "Protection" raised on convexed oval with panel below bearing policy No. 5800. Spear at angle; point missing. This well-known emblem is an imaginary bird whose origin is lost in antiquity. It is described as being like an eagle but with more beautiful plumage. An ancient writer describes how it "lives 500 years, and a little more, died and then becomes young again." It was used as a crest by Queen Jane Seymour. Queen Elizabeth I is said to have adopted it as a badge to signalize her recovery from smallpox.

677. Lead. 8⅛″ x 8½″. Border, figure of phoenix and "Protection" raised on convexed oval with panel below bearing policy No. 6581. Spear at angle; point missing. Detail of the phoenix on this mark beautifully executed.

678. Lead. 7⅝″ x 9¾″. Border, figure of phoenix and "Protection" raised on convexed oval with panel below bearing policy No. 7576. Spear at angle.

679. Lead. 7¼″ x 8½″. Border, figure of phoenix and "Protection" raised on convexed oval with panel below bearing policy No. 10919. Spear at angle; point missing.

680. Copper. 8″ x 9¼″. Border, figure of phoenix and "Protection" raised on oval with panel below bearing policy No. 266221. Spear at angle; point missing.

681. Copper. 7⅜″ x 9⅜″. Border, figure of phoenix and "Protection" raised on oval with panel below. Spear at angle; point missing.

682. Copper. 8¾″ x 9½″. Raised gold phoenix on red embers, background blue, border red. Panel below bears "Phoenix"

in gold on black background. Two tabs at top of mark for affixing to building.

683. Copper. 7½″ x 9⅝″. Raised gold border and figure of phoenix on black background of convexed oval. "Phoenix" black stamped into gold panel below. Gold spear at angle.

684. Copper. 7″ x 8⅛″. Border and figure of phoenix raised on convexed oval with panel below bearing the name "Phoenix." Spear at angle; point missing.

685. Tin. 9⅛″ x 10″. Figure of phoenix and "Estd. 1782—Phoenix—London" raised. From building in Greece.

686. Tin. Shield shape. 5¾″ x 7¼″. Slightly raised red and gold border. Gold phoenix on red embers and gold "Estd. 1782—Phoenix of London" slightly raised. Gold Chinese characters are flat. Background dark blue.

687. Tin. 9⁹⁄₁₆″ x 7¾″. Lithographed design and lettering. Brightly colored with red, yellow, blue and white. Modern.

(688-691) NEWCASTLE-UPON-TYNE FIRE OFFICE. NEWCASTLE-UPON-TYNE, ENGLAND. 1783-1859.

688. Lead. 7½″ x 7⅝″. Border and Arms of the City raised on oval with panel below bearing policy No. 391. City Arms consist of three silver towers each with three turrets. "New Castle" was applied to a stronghold erected there by Robert, eldest son of William the Conqueror who succeeded his father in the Duchy of Normandy. The castle was followed by one raised on the same site by Henry II, parts of which remain today.

689. Lead. 7½″ x 7½″. Border and Arms of the City raised on oval with panel below bearing policy No. 4336.

690. Lead. 7½″ x 7½″. Border and Arms of the City raised on oval with panel below bearing policy No. 5062.

691. Lead. 7½″ x 7½″. Border and Arms of the City raised on oval with panel below bearing policy No. 6509.

692

693

694

695

696

697

698

699

700

701

702

703

704

705

706

707

708

(692) ROYAL EXCHANGE OF IRELAND. DUBLIN, IRELAND. 1784-1823.

Lead. Border and City Hall of Dublin (which at time of organization was known as the Royal Exchange) raised on oval with open crown above and ornate tab below. This mark believed to be unique. *(Courtesy of Bertram Williams.)*

(693-696) WORCESTER FIRE OFFICE. WORCESTER, ENGLAND. 1790-1818.

693. Lead. Arms of the City on oval in center of cut-out mark with "Worcester" above and "Civitas In Bello In Pace Fidelis" below. Beneath is panel bearing policy No. 16. This sign is taken from the ancient and modern arms of the City—a silver tower with three turrets to commemorate Worcester Castle of which nothing remains. The city's modern arms include 3 black pears to mark a visit Queen Elizabeth made to the city when she planted a pear tree. These two arms are often combined and a close inspection of the marks will show the office has done this. The 3 black pears will be seen in the first quarter. The motto "Civitas In Bello In Pace Fidelis"—"In war and peace a faithful city." *(Courtesy of Bertram Williams.)*

694. Lead. Oval. 5¾" x 6¾". Arms of the City raised in center with "Worcester Fire Office" raised on border. Outer border also raised.

695. Lead. 5¾" x 8¼". Arms of the City raised in center with "Worcester Fire Office" raised on border. Outer border also raised. Panel below bears policy No. 2409. Tab at top for affixing to building.

696. Copper. 5⅛" x 8⅛". Arms of the City raised in center with "Worcester Fire Office" raised on border. Outer border also raised. Policy panel below. Had tab at top for affixing to building.

(697-705) NORWICH GENERAL ASSURANCE OFFICE. NORWICH, ENGLAND. 1792-1821.

697. Lead. 7⅝" x 9¾". Arms of the City in high relief on oval with raised border. "Norwich" raised on panel below. Policy No. 642 has been defaced on lower panel, possibly when policy was not renewed. The silver triple-towered castle, with a gold lion passant guardant, in the base, all on a red background are taken from the arms of the City of Norwich. These charges appeared on a 15th century seal of the city. The castle was built by King Stephen on the site of a fortress built by William I, and later became a

prison. In 1894 it was adapted for its present use as an Art Gallery and Museum.

698. Lead. 7⅝" x 9¾". Arms of the City in high relief on oval with raised border. "Norwich" raised on panel below. Policy No. 773 on lower panel.

699. Lead. 7½" x 9¾". Arms of the City in high relief on oval with raised border. "Norwich" raised on panel below. Policy No. 1634 on lower panel.

700. Lead. Arms of the City in relief on oval with "Norwich" and Policy No. 2465 raised on panels below. *(Courtesy of Bertram Williams.)*

701. Lead. 7⅝" x 9¾". Arms of the City in high relief on oval with raised border. "Norwich" raised on panel below. Policy No. 2942 on lower panel.

702. Lead. 7½" x 9¾". Arms of the City in high relief on oval with raised border. "Norwich" raised on panel below. Policy No. 3521 on lower panel.

703. Lead. 5¼" x 7¼". Arms of the City in high relief on shield with beaded border. "Norwich" raised on scroll beneath.

704. Copper. 7⅛" x 9½". Arms of the City in relief on octagonal. Decorative raised border. Policy No. 14909 on panel below and "Norwich" raised on lower panel.

705. Copper. 7⅛" x 9½". Arms of the City in relief on octagonal with decorative raised border. Policy panel does not contain a number. "Norwich" raised on lower panel.

(706-720) NORWICH UNION FIRE INSURANCE SOCIETY, LIMITED. NORWICH, ENGLAND. 1797-

706. Lead. 7½" x 9¼". Pair of clasped hands, raised, on oval with beaded border. Ornate festooning at top with two tabs for affixing mark to building and "Norwich" raised on scrolled ribbon below. Beneath is flat panel bearing the name "Union."

707. Copper. 7⅛" x 6⅞". Pair of clasped hands and "Union Society" raised on oval with beaded border. Below is panel with "Norwich" and border raised.

708. Copper. 7" x 8¾". Border, "Norwich" and sunburst raised on circular portion of mark with raised border and pair of clasped hands on panel below.

709

710

711

712

713

714

715

716

717

718

719

720

721

722

724

723

725

709. Tin. 6″ x 8″. Border, "Norwich Union" and sunburst raised on circular portion of mark with raised border and pair of clasped hands on panel below.

710. Copper. 7⅛″ x 10⅛″. Raised figure of Justice standing holding steelyard scale. "Norwich" raised in panel below. Borders raised.

711. Heavy tin. Rectangular. 8½″ x 11½″. Raised "Norwich Union" and design of seated figure of Justice holding scales. Pair of clasped hands in oval. An early type mark of this company.

712. Heavy tin. 7¾″ x 9½″. Seated figure of Justice facing left holding scales. Pair of clasped hands in oval. "Norwich" above and "Union" raised in panel below.

713. Seated figure of Justice facing left holding scales. Pair of clasped hands in oval. "Norwich" above and "Union" raised in panel below. Wreath varies from that on Mark No. 712. *(Courtesy of Bertram Williams.)*

714. Brass. 10¼″ x 14⅜″. Standing figure of Justice holding scales surrounded by ornate design and "Norwich Union" in panel below. All raised. This mark, known as the "Gaudiano plate" was named for the designer.

715. Copper. 7¾″ x 9⅞″. Seated figure of Justice facing right holding scales. Pair of clasped hands in oval. "Norwich" above and wreath at base of design, all raised, including border. "Union" raised in panel below.

716. Heavy tin. 7¾″ x 9½″. Seated figure of Justice facing right holding scales. Pair of clasped hands in oval. "Norwich" above and wreath at base of design, all raised, including border. "Union" raised in panel below.

717. Copper. 7¾″ x 10″. Seated figure of Justice facing right holding scales. Pair of clasped hands in oval. "Norwich" above and wreath at base of design, all raised, including border. "Union" raised in panel below.

718. Tin. 9½″ x 11″. Seated figure of Justice holding scales and pair of clasped hands in wreath. "Union" above and "Norwich" on scroll below design. Design and lettering raised. *(Courtesy of Licenses and General Insurance Company, Ltd.)*

719. Copper. 8¾″ x 10⅝″. Seated figure of Justice facing right holding scales. Pair of clasped hands in oval, gold on red background. "Norwich Union" gold on black background. Design, border and lettering raised.

720. Tin. 8¾″ x 10⅝″. Seated figure of Justice facing right holding scales. Pair of clasped hands in oval, gold on red background. "Norwich Union" gold on black background. Design, border and lettering raised.

(721-727) BRITISH FIRE OFFICE. LONDON, ENGLAND. 1799-1843.

721. Lead. Circular. 9¼″ in diameter. Design of lion with paw on shield, facing front, tail up, is raised on slightly convexed center of mark. "British Fire Office" and outer border raised.

722. Lead. Circular. 8″ in diameter. Design of lion with paw on shield, facing front, tail up, is raised on slightly convexed center of mark. "British" and outer border raised.

723. Lead. Circular. 8⅛″ in diameter. Design of lion with paw on shield, facing front, tail up, is raised on slightly convexed center of mark. "British" and outer border raised. Casting and detail are heavier than in mark No. 722.

724. Copper. Circular. 7⅞″ in diameter. Design of lion with paw on shield, facing front, tail up, is raised on slightly convexed center of mark. "British" and outer border raised.

725. Copper. Circular. 7⅞″ in diameter. Design of lion with paw on shield, facing left, tail down, is raised on convexed center of mark. "British" and outer border raised.

726

727

728

729

730

726. Copper. Circular. 8½″ in diameter. Design of lion with paw on shield, facing left, tail down, is raised. "British" and outer border also raised.

727. "British Fire Office—Strand.", raised on outer border. Unique specimen but unfortunately seriously damaged. (*Courtesy of Bertram Williams.*)

(728) COMMERCIAL FIRE INSURANCE COMPANY OF DUBLIN. DUBLIN, IRELAND. 1799-1827.

Lead. Circular. 7⅜″ in diameter. Ship and border raised. The ship is the famous "Ouzel Galley." A Dublin ship trading with the Mediterranean in the late 17th century. It sailed from Dublin in 1695 with a cargo for Smyrna. Captured by pirates the crew were held captive, and the ship used for piracy. The crew ultimately regained control and reached Dublin in 1700 with the pirates' loot on board. A dispute arose as to the owners of the cargo. After years of litigation the "Ouzel Galley Society" was formed to administer the funds. The Society was closely associated with the foundation of the Dublin Royal Exchange. It closed down in 1888 when its remaining funds were distributed amongst the City hospitals.

(729-730) SUFFOLK AND GENERAL COUNTRY AMICABLE INSURANCE OFFICE. BURY AND IPSWICH, ENGLAND. 1799-1849.

729. Lead. Rectangular. 10¾″ x 4¾″. "Insured Suffolk Fire Office" and border raised. The ram's fleece slewed up in the chief, and plough in base, stress the flourishing woolen industry for which Suffolk was famous in those days. With the introduction of machinery, and in consequence coal, the trade moved on to the coalfields of South Yorkshire. The plough indicates the "Agricultural" side of the Company's business.

730. Copper. Seven-pointed star in relief and "Suffolk" raised in panel below. (*Courtesy of Bertram Williams.*)

THE DECLINE OF GEORGE III
1800-1820

William Pitt, once Prime Minister, was again directing the policies of war against Napoleon. Under pressure from the throne The Peace of Amiens was concluded on March 25, 1802, in which Great Britain gave up all of her hard won conquests from France. Napoleon boasted that this was only a breather and that war was necessary to his existence so he cleverly contrived to have Britain again declare war on May 18, 1803. His attempt to invade England failed when Nelson was victorious at Cape Trafalgar, adding more glory to Britain's navy and forcing Napoleon to confine hostilities to the continent. During the first decade of this century there were the Peninsular War of 1808 and the Spanish Campaign of the same year which extended into 1809. It is little wonder that under these enormous pressures George III became totally blind and that insanity, which had been apparent earlier, finally closed in on him. In 1810 he passed into a state of physical and mental oblivion. The Prince of Wales became permanent Regent and wars continued to spread.

Other important forces were also at work in the land and the new inventions of the eighteenth century altered the entire mode of life of the people. London had once been the center of activity, but now, because of the factory movement, the density of population advanced to the midlands and to the north. The countryside was soon dotted with small villages and the older towns became crowded and cramped with this new influx of humanity. Twenty-five new fire insurance companies originated in this expanding area between 1800 and 1820, most of them filling the need occasioned by the new industrial development. Regardless of where the companies originated it is very evident, in reviewing the fire marks which they employed, that the arts of the period were most ably expressed. That was particularly true of the marks issued by the Essex and Suffolk, Kent, Hants Sussex and Dorset, British and Irish United, Birmingham, Glasgow, County, West of England, North British and Mercantile, Newport Association, and the Aylsham New Association. Each was distinctive in its own right and to a great extent was purely British in style.

Wars also had an influence upon everything symbolic, for when the French were popular in Germany during the eighteenth century, the Germans tried to imitate the French design. When the French were driven out of the country, the new art excluded anything of a French influence and followed a form of design fashioned on the crudities of the fifth century. Such wars, of course, not only had an effect upon the arts of a given period; they also affected the thoughts and habits of the people and so were influential in every department of life.

The art of war changed when Napoleon lost the battle at Waterloo on June 18, 1815, abdicated on the twenty-second and was banished by the British to imprisonment for life on the island of St. Helena. Domestically events were not progressing so successfully, for the industrial revolution had, in fact, dislocated the economy. Many new labor-saving devices had eliminated a large number of workmen, and a series of crop failures had discouraged the farmers. The depression had caused so much distress and deprivation among the people that popular disturbances were prevalent during 1816 and 1817. The smug Tories who were the dominant party, now that French influence was out of the way, merely passed repressive acts and used force to secure compliance instead of making an effort to readjust and ease the situation for the distressed. The Manchester Massacre was an example of this short-sighted policy. All of these acts tended to resolve in the minds and hearts of the people a determination to regain their freedom by means of a representative form of government. Symbolic of this era was the deterioration in the reign of George III who died an imbecile on January 29, 1820. His demise saw the end of the regency. By this time fire insurance had become so definitely entrenched into the economy and lives of the citizens that these changes in government had little effect upon their establishment and administration. Insurance had become a symbol of free enterprise.

731

732

733

734

735

736

737

738

739

740

741

742

743

744

160

745

746

(731-732) ESSEX & SUFFOLK EQUITABLE INSURANCE SOCIETY LIMITED. COLCHESTER, ENGLAND. 1802-1911.

731. Copper. 8¼″ x 6½″. Crest, "Essex Insurance" and border raised on convexed circular section of mark. Ribbon above and "Society" raised on panel below. Issued between 1802 and 1806 when company was known as "Essex Equitable Insurance Society." The Society originally used the Essex County Arms—three seaxes or ancient swords—the cutting edge upwards and is to be found in a number of Essex arms and devices. The design is attributed to the ancient Kingdom of the East Saxons. Middlesex County uses it with a crown added. It is based on the theory that the Saxons derived their names from this distinctive weapon—a notched sword.

732. Tin. Circular. 8″ in diameter. "Essex & Suffolk—1802" cream color and yellow. Red and gold crest in center encircled by gold "Equitable Insurance—England." Border gold. Background green.

(733-737) KENT FIRE INSURANCE COMPANY. MAIDSTONE, ENGLAND. 1802-1901.

733. Lead. 6⅝″ x 8¾″. Rampant horse in high relief on octagonal section of mark. Raised "Invicta" and stamped policy No. 74 on panel below. This is the famous white horse of Kent, the County Arms. It was reputed to be the steed of Odin and was displayed on the standard of the first Saxon Chieftain to invade Kent. He was accordingly called "The Horse"—"Hengist"—in the tongue of some of his followers, "Horsa" in that of others, hence the fable of the brothers Hengist & Horsa. In the mark the horse is salient, i.e., both hind legs on the ground and front legs together. An animal is rampant or in the case of horse—forcene—when rearing with one rear foot off the ground. May have been done deliberately to differentiate it from the County Arms—a mere detail—it is still Invicta!

734. Lead. 6½″ x 8½″. Rampant horse in high relief on octagonal section of mark. Raised "Invicta" on panel below.

735. Heavy lead. 6⅜″ x 7¾″. Rampant white horse in high relief on octagonal section of mark. "Kent" in panel below.

736. Copper. 6¾″ x 8¼″. Border, rampant horse on octagonal section of mark and "Kent" in panel below all raised. "Invicta" raised on small panel at top.

737. Copper. 6½″ x 7¾″. Rampant gold horse in high relief on octagonal section of mark. Gold "Kent" stamped in panel below. Background dark green.

(738) SUN INSURANCE COMPANY OF DUBLIN. DUBLIN, IRELAND. 1802-1804.

Lead. Circular. Raised border and sun with sixteen rays, alternating straight and wavy. (Courtesy of Bertram Williams.)

(739-740) GLOBE INSURANCE COMPANY. LONDON, ENGLAND. 1803-1864.

739. Tin. 7⅛″ x 7¾″. Extremely convexed globe with wide flat border and "Globe" raised below on border.

740. Copper. 6⅝″ x 9½″. Convexed globe with "Globe" raised in panel above and policy panel below.

(741-742) HANTS SUSSEX AND DORSET FIRE OFFICE. WINCHESTER, ENGLAND. 1803-1864.

741. Copper. Seated figure raised in center surrounded by "Sussex—Dorset—Hants." The figure is a representation of Vesta (Greek Hestia) the goddess of the hearth. She was a great Greek and Roman divinity who was protector of the home. She is shown seated on a throne with spear and shield, protecting the child at her feet. (Courtesy of Bertram Williams.)

742. Copper. Circular section, 6¼″ in diameter, shows design of seated woman holding staff in her right hand and wearing a shield on her left arm. "Hants—Sussex and Dorset" and borders raised. "Security" raised in panel below.

(743-751) IMPERIAL FIRE INSURANCE COMPANY. LONDON, ENGLAND. 1803-1902.

743. Copper. 8⅜″ x 8⅜″. Crown in relief with border and "Imperial" raised.

744. Copper. 9½″ x 8⅝″. Small crown in relief with border and "Imperial" raised.

745. Copper. 8⅛″ x 8⅛″. Crown in relief with "Imperial" raised. Slightly raised border.

746. Copper. 8″ x 8″. Crown in relief with "Imperial" raised. Narrow raised border.

161

748

749

747

750

752

751

753

754

755

756

757

758

759

760

761

762

763

764

747. Copper. 8¼″ x 8½″. Crown, border and "Imperial" raised.

748. Copper. 8¼″ x 8″. Crown in relief with "Imperial" raised in panel below. Border slightly raised.

749. Tin. 7¾″ x 8″. Red, gold and white crown, red border and gold "Imperial" raised. Black background.

750. Tin. 8⅜″ x 8⅜″. Red, gold and white crown, red border and gold "1803—Imperial" raised. Black background.

751. Tin. Rectangular. 9¾″ x 6⅞″. Border and "Imperial—London 1803" gold on black background. Crown red and gold in center of red shield. *(Courtesy of Licenses and General Insurance Company, Ltd.)*

(752-754) BIRMINGHAM FIRE OFFICE. BIRMINGHAM, ENGLAND. 1804-1867.

752. Copper. 8½″ x 9⅝″. Raised border and design of fireman standing by early hand pumper with "Birmingham" raised on band below. Fireman faces right. Rarest type mark of this company.

753. Copper. 11″ x 10″. Raised border and design of fireman standing by early hand pumper with "Birmingham" on band below. Fireman faces left.

754. Copper. 7¼″ x 6¼″. "Estd. 1805" raised on circular section of mark with "Birmingham" raised on panel below. Borders raised. Has two tabs for fastening to building.

(755) BRITISH AND IRISH UNITED. DUBLIN, IRELAND. 1804-1843.

Copper. Circular. 7⅞″ in diameter. Design of lion with paw on harp, facing front, tail up, is raised on convexed center of mark. "British and Irish United" and outer border raised.

(756) ALBION FIRE AND LIFE INSURANCE COMPANY. LONDON, ENGLAND. 1805-1828.

Cast iron. Circular. Border and "Albion Fire Office" raised. *(Courtesy of Bertram Williams.)*

(757-758) CALEDONIAN INSURANCE COMPANY. EDINBURGH, SCOTLAND. 1805-

757. Copper. 7⅝″ x 7″. Thistle raised on circular section of mark; "Caledonian" raised on scrolled ribbon beneath. Borders raised. The thistle, emblem of Scotland, has been the Company's emblem for many years. It is indicative of the Scottish character. The Scottish motto "Nemo me impune lacessit" is often used in conjunction with it. Translated into Scottish parlance "Wha dare meddle wi' me."

758. Tin. 8″ x 6⅞″. Thistle, "Caledonian" and borders raised gold on maroon background. Modern. Used in Martinique.

(759-760) GLASGOW INSURANCE COMPANY. GLASGOW, SCOTLAND. 1805-1841.

759. Lead. Border, design on oval of bird, tree, bell and fish, and "Glasgow" on panel below all raised. Represents the City Arms. The charges refer to incidents in the life of St. Mungo (known also as St. Kentigern) patron saint of the City. The Clyde was famous up to 18th century (before the industrial period) as a salmon river hence the fish. *(Courtesy of Bertram Williams.)*

760. Lead. Border, design on oval of bird, tree, bell and fish, and "Glasgow" on panel below all raised. *(Courtesy of Bertram Williams.)*

(761-765) COUNTY FIRE OFFICE. LONDON, ENGLAND. 1807-1906.

761. Copper. Rectangular. 6½″ x 8½″. Border, figure of Britannia facing front and "County" in panel below all raised. Britannia gold on red background. "County" black on gold.

762. Copper. Rectangular. 6¾″ x 9½″. Border, figure of Britannia facing left and "County" in panel below all raised. Britannia gold on red background. "County" gold on black.

763. Copper. 9¾″ x 11⅛″. Raised figure of Britannia facing front gold on black background surrounded by red garter with raised "County" in gold.

764. Copper. Rectangular. 6¾″ x 9½″. Border, figure of Britannia facing front and "County" in panel below all raised. Britannia gold on red background. "County" gold on black.

765

766

767

768

769

770

771

772

773

774

775

776

777

778

779

780

164

782

781

783

765. Copper. Rectangular. Border, figure of Britannia facing front and "County" in panel below all raised. (*Courtesy of Bertram Williams.*)

(766) EAGLE INSURANCE COMPANY. LONDON, ENGLAND. 1807-1917.

Iron. 7" x 8½". Eagle in relief. "Safety" raised in panel below.

(767-769) HOPE FIRE & LIFE ASSURANCE COMPANY. LONDON, ENGLAND. 1807-1826.

767. Tin. 6⅝" x 9". Vertical anchor in relief on oval with raised border and "Hope" on panel below.

768. Tin. 6¾" x 9". Slanted anchor in relief on oval with raised border and "Hope" on panel below.

769. Copper. Slanted anchor in relief on oval with raised border and "Hope" on panel below. (*Courtesy of Bertram Williams.*)

(770-774) WEST OF ENGLAND FIRE AND LIFE INSURANCE COMPANY. EXETER, ENGLAND. 1807-1894.

770. Copper. 7¼" x 9⅛". Standing figure of King Alfred in oval section of mark and "West of England" in panel above raised. Policy panel below.

771. Copper. 7¾" x 10". Standing figure in relief, cut out, with "West of England" raised in panels below.

772. Copper. Oval. 7⅞" x 9⅝". Standing figure, "West of England" and border raised.

773. Sheet iron. 7¼" x 9¼". Standing figure in relief on convexed oval section of mark. "West of England" raised on band above and "Exeter" raised on panel below.

774. Tin. 7⅜" x 9½". Standing figure in relief on convexed oval section of mark. "West of England" raised on band above and "Exeter" raised on panel below. Design gold, red, white and green on black background. Lettering black on gold.

(775) ANCHOR FIRE OFFICE. NORWICH, ENGLAND. 1808-1811.

Copper. Anchor in relief, beaded border and raised "Anchor Fire Office—Security" on octagonal section of mark. "Norwich" raised on scroll below. At base is policy panel. (*Courtesy of Bertram Williams.*)

(776-782) ATLAS ASSURANCE COMPANY, LIMITED. LONDON, ENGLAND. 1808-

776. Copper. Rectangular. 6⅜" x 10¾". Raised figure of Atlas supporting convexed globe. Gold, white and black design on red background. "Atlas" in gold. Raised border. Atlas or Atlantis was one of the Titans, giants of Greek mythology, sons and daughters of Uranus (Heaven) and Gaeo (earth). He assisted the Titans in an unsuccessful war against the Gods and was condemned by Zeus to bear the heavens or celestial globe upon his shoulders. The plural form Atlantes is the classical term in architecture for supporting columns taking the form of the figures of men.

777. Copper. Rectangular. 6¾" x 11". Raised figure of Atlas supporting convexed globe. Black, white, gold and blue design on red background. "Atlas" in black. Raised border.

778. Copper. Rectangular. 6⅝" x 10½". Raised figure of Atlas supporting convexed globe. Gold and black design on black background. Raised border.

779. Copper. Rectangular. 6½" x 10½". Raised figure of Atlas supporting convexed globe. Red, gold, black and white design on black background. "Atlas" in red. No border.

780. Tin. Oval. 6" x 9½". Raised figure of Atlas supporting convexed globe. Blue, gold, red and yellow design on black background. "Atlas—A. D. 1808" gold. Raised border.

781. Tin. Oval. 6" x 9½". Raised figure of Atlas supporting convexed globe. Design and "Atlas—A. D. 1808" gold on black background. Raised border.

782. Tin. Oval. 6" x 9½". Raised figure of Atlas supporting convexed globe. Green, gold, rose and yellow design on black background. "Atlas—A. D. 1808" gold. Raised border.

(783) SHEFFIELD FIRE OFFICE. SHEFFIELD, ENGLAND. 1808-1863.

Tin. Circular. Border, "Sheffield Fire Office" and center design raised. The sheaf of arrows is from the Sheffield City Arms in saltire (crosswise) and represents cutlery for which the city is famous throughout the world. (*Courtesy of Bertram Williams.*)

784

785

786

787

788

789

(784) HERCULES INSURANCE COMPANY. EDINBURGH, SCOTLAND. 1809-1849.

Tin. Border and "Hercules Fire Office" raised. *(Courtesy of Bertram Williams.)*

(785) NORTH BRITISH INSURANCE COMPANY. LONDON, ENGLAND. 1809-1862.

Tin. 6⅜" x 7½". Established at Edinburgh, Scotland. Raised figure of St. Andrew with cross and "North British" on panel below.

(786) NEWPORT ASSOCIATION. NEWPORT, ISLE OF WIGHT, ENGLAND. 1811 - ?.

Tin. Shield shape. Border, "Protected by the Newport Association" and center design of ship with "1811" raised. *(Courtesy of Bertram Williams.)*

(787) BRISTOL UNION FIRE AND LIFE INSURANCE COMPANY. BRISTOL, ENGLAND. 1814-1844.

Tin. Rectangular. 6⅝" x 9½". Design and bundle of fagots raised in center with "Bristol" raised on panel above and "Union" raised on panel below. Slightly raised border. Fascines or fagots the type used for military protection and coast erosion defences. Signifies union and protection. Differs from Roman fasces which has an axe protruding.

(788) AYLSHAM NEW ASSOCIATION. LONDON, ENGLAND. 1820 - ?.

Brass. Circular. 11½" in diameter. Castle raised in center with "Aylsham New Association" in relief around edge.

(789) BRITISH COMMERCIAL. LONDON, ENGLAND. 1820-1860.

Copper. Oval. Border, "British Commercial" and caduceus in center all raised. The caduceus is the wand attributed to Hermes the God of Commerce and Peace. Must not be confused with the rod of Aesculapius—medical. *(Courtesy of Bertram Williams.)*

AN ERA OF REFORM
1820-1837

In 1821 George IV, a sovereign as abhorrent as had yet reigned, succeeded to the throne. Shortly after his accession he attempted to divorce Queen Caroline, who was never crowned, but public sentiment stopped the proceedings. Regardless of his personal conduct, however, the Parliament and Cabinet were responsible for many humane advances, especially under William Huskisson who was president of the Board of Trade.

Huskisson was a free trader in principle. His influence brought about a partial release of duties and tariffs, thus providing for a greater flow of commerce between the colonies and European countries. He was also instrumental in lowering the taxes and in securing a modification in the "Sinking Fund" arrangement. The soundness and constructiveness of his policies were proven when the vast increase in trade and commerce more than offset the loss of taxes. This same man was responsible for bettering conditions for the working classes as well as fostering an almost modern concept of the relations between the employer and employee, another tribute to the progress which has always been made under the system of a free enterprise.

Transportation has always played an important part in the expansion and development of the fire insurance business. As has already been mentioned many American fire insurance companies had their

beginnings simultaneously with and along the same routes opened by the stagecoach and the building of railroads and canals. The story in Britain is quite similar. In 1813 the steamboat Comet began to ply its way on the Clyde. The Stockdale and Darlington Railroad commenced operations in 1825, and road construction received a great impetus. John McAdam discovered a new process of road surfacing known as "Macadamizing" which was readily adopted. The effect was to speed up transportation rapidly and make it so pleasant that the people in the provinces soon began to intermingle freely. As a result, trade and commerce thrived and once again a need for additional fire insurance facilities arose. In the cities and towns along these roads, railroads, and waterways, twenty-six new fire insurance companies were started from 1821 through 1825, each having left behind one or more various footprints or fire marks. These concerns individually played an important part in the expansion and progress of their respective communities, and since most of them followed the same sound and conservative investment policies for which British insurance is noted, they were an important asset to their locale.

This opening up of new vistas, the improvement in working conditions, and the lowering of taxes were the first real signs of the emancipation of the common people. Naturally, not all in England was rosy, for when vice and corruption have prevailed for many decades it requires time and patience to rid an entire nation of such practices. There were continued religious bickerings, but over all the evolution of English society was benefited at every turn. Disliked, unloved, and unregretted, King George IV, a monarch who gained little for himself during his few years at the helm of state, died on June 26, 1830.

Immediately after his death, William IV took the throne. Kindhearted in a rough and simple sort of way, the new King appealed to the masses and accordingly was acclaimed with enthusiasm. That these sentiments were warranted was proven by an action taken by the King in behalf of good government. For many years reformers had advanced the theory that Britain's government should be so revamped as to provide "the greatest happiness for the greatest number." Because of the shift in population as well as the change in capital control from large landowners to merchants and industrialists, an area with one million people had only nineteen representatives, while another area with about two hundred and fifty thousand had forty-four, most of whom were landowners. Under such a system graft and bribery thrived. The first reform bill was presented in 1831 but was defeated by the Lords. Another bill was prepared in 1832 and when there were evidences that the Lords would again defeat it, King William applied pressure at the right time and in the proper manner, and the act became law. It was the most progressive movement in behalf of humanity and freedom that England had yet made. Consequently the Cabinet now represented the majority in the House of Commons instead of being under the control of a sovereign who might not have the welfare of the people at heart. It provided for an electoral redistribution system which would give each population group proper representation not necessarily confined to the landowner type. The next year, in 1833, this Parliament passed another act abolishing slavery in the colonies, and for good measure approved the Factory Act which controlled child labor and provided for better working conditions for the workingman. Truly, a new and wonderful change had come to England as one social advance after another became a reality. William IV came to the throne at a mature age without benefit of any extensive education and under no circumstances did he appear great. Yet, when he died on June 20, 1837, he left a heritage to his peoples which no other sovereign had surpassed in any similar period of time.

In 1834 through 1836 to the city of London, to the factory cities of Nottingham and Birmingham, and to the rural areas of Leicestershire and York came new capital to form eight additional fire insurance companies. Without the new courage and representation which was provided by England's era of reform they might never have been established. With these changes they became an integral part of the nation's life and economy.

790

791

792

793

794

795

168

796

797

798

799

800

(790-791) BEACON FIRE INSURANCE COMPANY. LONDON, ENGLAND. 1821-1827.

790. Copper. Scene of burning building, woman and child and figure of Plenty raised with "Beacon" in relief in panel above. Borders raised. First type mark issued by company. (Courtesy of Bertram Williams.)

791. Copper. 8" x 9⅜". Scene of burning building, woman and child and figure of Plenty raised on circular section of mark with "Beacon" raised on panel above. Borders raised. Second type mark of this company.

(792-800) GUARDIAN ASSURANCE COMPANY, LIMITED. LONDON, ENGLAND. 1821-

792. Copper. Ornate shaped mark with raised border. Bust of Athene in relief on oval medallion and raised "Guardian" below. Figure of rope raised beneath lettering. Minerva (Pallas Athene) erect and fully armed as she sprang from the head of her father Zeus. She represents strength and wisdom, and a promoter of power and prosperity. The mark which shows a knot of rope at the base refers to the story of Arachne, a Lydian maid who excelled in the art of weaving. The goddess Athene challenged her to compete with the goddess in this art. As she could find no fault with the maid's finished work, Athene in anger tore it to pieces. Arachne in despair hung herself. Athene loosened the rope and saved her life. The legend declares that the rope was turned into a cobweb and Arachne herself into a spider. (Courtesy of Bertram Williams.)

793. Tin. Odd. Border, erect figure of Athene and "Guardian Brand" raised. Mark issued about 1875 for use in Denmark. (Courtesy of W. A. Osborne.)

794. Copper. 8½" x 9". Border, erect figure of Athene and "Guardian" in panel below all raised.

795. Copper. 8½" x 9". Border, erect figure of Athene and "Guardian" in panel below all raised. Lettering and impress varies from mark No. 794.

796. Copper. 7⅞" x 9¼". Border, erect figure of Athene and "Guardian" in panel below all raised.

797. Tin. 8⅛" x 9¼". Red border, erect figure of Athene in gold, silver and red and gold "Guardian" below all raised. Black background. Modern.

798. Tin. 8¼" x 9¼". Red border, erect figure of Athene in gold, white and red and gold "Guardian" below all raised. Background black. Modern. Used in Martinique.

799. Tin. 8⅞" x 10⅜". Six-pointed star with red background and gold border, Chinese characters and "Guardian 1821." Mark used in China.

800. Tin. 8⅞" x 10⅜". Six-pointed star with red background and raised border, "Guardian 1821" and Chinese characters gold. Modern. Mark used in China.

801

802

803

804

805

806

807

808

809

810

811

812

813

814

815

816

817

(801) INSURANCE COMPANY OF SCOTLAND. EDINBURGH, SCOTLAND. 1821-1847.

Copper. 7″ x 7¾″. Border, "Insurance Company of Scotland" and design raised.

(802-804) NATIONAL ASSURANCE COMPANY OF IRELAND. DUBLIN, IRELAND. 1822-1904.

802. Very heavy tin. 8½″ x 9⅜″. Green borders, gold, "National—1822" and green shamrock on gold background raised. Outer background red. Mark is slightly convexed.

803. Heavy tin. 8½″ x 9⅜″. Raised inner border and shamrock green on gold background. "National—1822" gold on red background. Red outer border raised. Mark is slightly convexed.

804. Tin. Rectangular. "National—Dublin" and design in center of harp, shamrocks and crown with "National Assurance Co. of Ireland" encircling it. (Courtesy of Bertram Williams.)

(805) READING INSURANCE COMPANY. READING, ENGLAND. 1822 - ?.

Copper. Circular. 9¼″ in diameter. Border, "Borough of Reading" and Arms of the Borough of Reading raised. Arms representing crowned head in centre is said to be King Edward (975-978) assassinated by jealous stepmother Aefthryth. In expiation she founded a nunnery (now St. Mary's Church) at Reading. This is represented on the arms by the remaining 4 heads. The Corporation has borne the arms since 1566.

(806-810) SALAMANDER FIRE OFFICE SOCIETY. LONDON, ENGLAND. 1822-1835.

806. Lead. 7″ x 8⅛″. Dates according to Williams. Recent research indicates assumption of this name between 1790 and 1802. Design of salamander enveloped in flames and beaded border raised on oval. "Secure in Flames" on ribbon above. Policy No. 838 in panel below.

807. Copper. 6⅝″ x 8⅛″. Design of salamander enveloped in flames and beaded border raised on oval. "Secure in Flames" on ribbon above. Policy No. 3467 in panel below. The salamander is usually shown as a lizard. In the Middle Ages it was believed to have the shape of a man and lived in the fire. The Greek derivation means a man who lives in the chimney or fire. It has been described

as "a small beast which lives in the fire, and at length, by its extreme cold puts out the fire."

808. Copper. 6⁷⁄₁₆″ x 6¼″. Design of salamander enveloped in flames and beaded border raised on oval. Ribbon broken off this mark. Policy panel below without number.

809. Brass. Design of salamander enveloped in flames and beaded border raised on oval. Ribbon above and policy panel below without number. (Courtesy of Bertram Williams.)

810. Copper. 7½″ x 8″. Design of salamander enveloped in flames and beaded border raised on oval. "Secure in Flames" raised on ribbon above. "Salamander" raised on band below.

(811) ROYAL IRISH ASSURANCE COMPANY. DUBLIN, IRELAND. 1823-1827.

Copper. Border, heraldic design and "1823—Royal Irish" raised. (Courtesy of Bertram Williams.)

(812) SHAMROCK FIRE AND LIFE. DUBLIN, IRELAND. 1823-1825.

Lead. Oval. Border and "Shamrock" raised. Has tabs for fastening to building. (Courtesy of Bertram Williams.)

(813-819) ALLIANCE ASSURANCE COMPANY, LIMITED. LONDON, ENGLAND. 1824-

813. Zinc. Circular. 8″ in diameter. Border, "Alliance" and design of woman and child being comforted by Plenty raised. Believed unique. Company has no record of issuance of this mark.

814. Copper. 7″ x 9⅛″. Castle on oval, "Alliance" in panel below and all borders raised. From building in Greece.

815. Copper. 8½″ x 9⅜″. Castle on oval, "Alliance" in panel below and all borders raised. Lettering and castle vary from other marks of this company.

816. Copper. 9″ x 9″. Castle on oval, "Alliance" in panel below and all borders raised.

817. Cast iron. 7″ x 6″. Borders, castle and lettering raised. (Courtesy of Licenses and General Insurance Company, Ltd.)

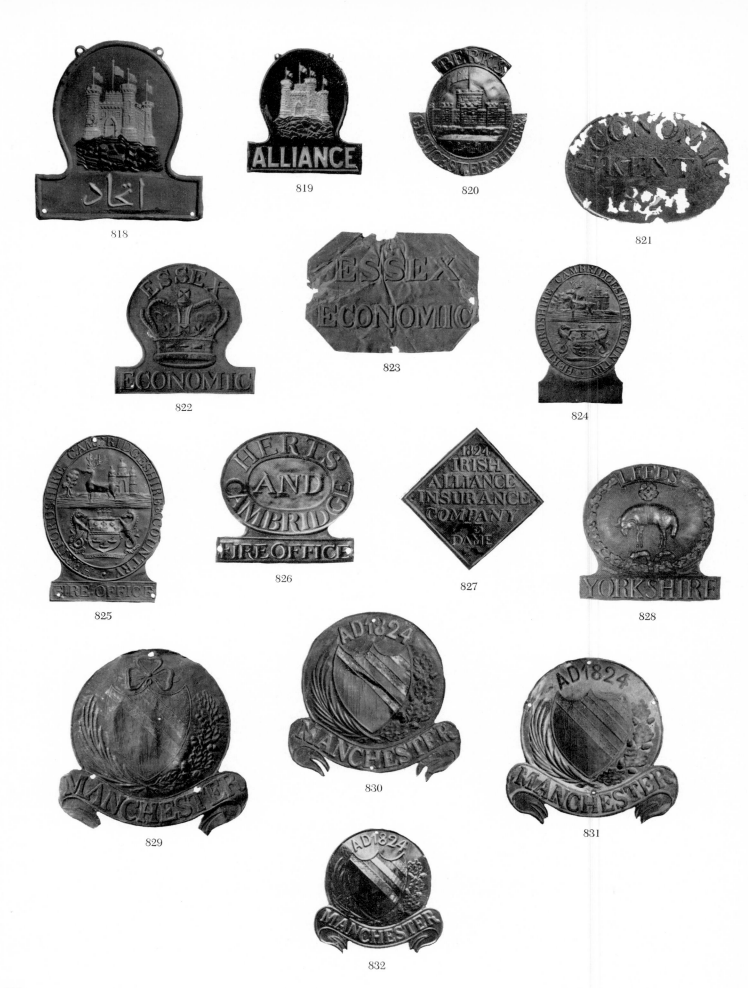

818

819

820

821

822

823

824

825

826

827

828

829

830

831

832

818. Copper. 9″ x 9¾″. Castle, Arabic characters below and border raised. Design yellow and green, characters yellow, background red.

819. Copper. 9″ x 9⅞″. Border, gold castle and "Alliance" raised. Background red.

(820) BERKSHIRE, GLOUCESTERSHIRE AND PROVIDENT LIFE AND FIRE. LONDON, ENGLAND. 1824-1831.

Copper. 9⅛″ x 10″. Raised castle and "Salus" on convexed oval section of mark with raised "Berks" on panel above and "Gloucestershire &c" on panel below. Only type mark of this company.

(821) ECONOMIC OF KENT. CANTERBURY, ENGLAND. 1824-1829.

Tin. Slightly convexed oval. 9″ x 6⅝″. Border and "Economic—Kent—1824" raised.

(822-823) ESSEX ECONOMIC FIRE OFFICE. CHELMSFORD, ENGLAND. 1824-1857.

822. Copper. Border, crown and "Essex Economic" raised. *(Courtesy of Bertram Williams.)*

823. Copper. Octagonal. 8¼″ x 5¾″. Border and "Essex Economic" raised.

(824-825) HERTFORDSHIRE, CAMBRIDGESHIRE AND COUNTRY FIRE OFFICE. LONDON, ENGLAND. 1824-1831.

824. Copper. Border, "Hertfordshire-Cambridgeshire & Country" and heraldic emblems raised on oval with policy panel below. The lower arms are those of Cambridge Borough which in past days derived much prosperity from coastal river-borne traffic—hence the three ships. Two roses (national emblem) and fleur-de-lys (Royal emblem) are in chief (upper third of shield)—a gold arched-bridge (a pun on the town's name) separates the ships from the other two emblems. The crest is a silver bridge on grassy mound supporters, two sea horses. The upper half or chief (and most important position) of the mark consists of a hart standing in water with a tree on left and castle with three domed towers in the right background. These are from an old seal of the Borough of Hertford and upon which the present Borough arms are based. The fact that the Hertford arms hold premier place in the mark clearly indicates where the Head Office lay. *(Courtesy of Bertram Williams.)*

825. Copper. 7⅛″ x 9¾″. Border, "Hertfordshire-Cambridgeshire & Country" and heraldic emblems raised on oval with "Fire Office" raised on panel below.

(826) HERTS AND CAMBRIDGE FIRE OFFICE. LONDON, ENGLAND. 1824-1831.

Copper. Raised "Herts and Cambridge" on oval and "Fire Office" on panel below. Borders raised. *(Courtesy of Bertram Williams.)*

(827) IRISH ALLIANCE INSURANCE COMPANY. DUBLIN, IRELAND. 1824-1826.

Copper. Diamond shape. Border and "1824—Irish Alliance Insurance Company—33 Dame" raised. Chief offices were at 33 Dame Street, Dublin. *(Courtesy of Bertram Williams.)*

(828) LEEDS AND YORKSHIRE ASSURANCE COMPANY. LEEDS, ENGLAND. 1824-1864.

Tin. Design of fleece and beribboned garland and "Leeds" raised on oval with "Yorkshire" raised on panel below. *(Courtesy of Bertram Williams.)*

(829-836) MANCHESTER FIRE INSURANCE COMPANY. MANCHESTER, ENGLAND. 1824-1904.

829. Copper. 9½″ x 9⅜″. Arms of the City of Manchester topped with bow raised on convexed circle; "Manchester" raised on scrolled ribbon beneath. The red shield and three gold bandlets enhanced (raised above the arms) are from the arms of the Lancashire family of Byron (relations of the poet), the sixth Lord Byron of Rochdale. It is now part of the Manchester City Arms.

830. Copper. 9½″ x 9½″. Arms of the City of Manchester and "A. D. 1824" raised on slightly convexed circle; "Manchester" raised on scrolled ribbon beneath. Arms are red, gold and green on blue background with all lettering gold.

831. Tin. 9½″ x 9½″. Arms of the City of Manchester and "A. D. 1824" raised on convexed circle. "Manchester" raised on scrolled ribbon beneath.

832. Tin. 10″ x 9¾″. Arms of the City of Manchester and "A. D. 1824" raised on convexed circle. "Manchester" raised on scrolled ribbon beneath. Arms are red, gold and green on blue background with date and name gold. "J. Eldred & Co., 21, Paternoster Square, London, E. C." in red on lower left-hand tip of ribbon.

833

834

835

836

837

838

839

840

841

842

843

844

845

846

847

848

849

833. Tin. Shield shape. 8⅛" x 10⅛". Background yellow, border and "Manchester Fire Assurance Company" red and designs green and red. Mark used in Orient.

834. Tin. Shield shape. 7⅞" x 9". Background yellow, raised "Estbd. 1824—Manchester" and Chinese characters red. Raised dragons green. Border raised. Mark used in China. *(Courtesy of Licenses and General Insurance, Ltd.)*

835. Tin. Shield shape. 7⅞" x 9³⁄₁₆". Background yellow, raised "Estbd. 1824—Manchester" and Chinese characters red. Raised dragons green. Border raised. Mark used in China.

836. Copper. Circular. 7½" in diameter. Gold Chinese characters raised on convexed black center surrounded by wide red border with raised gold "Manchester Fire Assurance 1824." Narrow borders raised.

(837-838) PALLADIUM FIRE INSURANCE COMPANY. LONDON, ENGLAND. 1824-1829.

837. Copper. 8" x 9¼". Border, design of seated figure and "Palladium" in panel below all raised. Minerva (Latin), Pallas Athene (Greek), always carried on her shield the head of Medusa, one of the three frightful maidens, the Gorgons. Athene changed Medusa's hair into serpents and it was said that everyone who looked on her turned to stone. An image of Athene was preserved in the citadel at Troy, known as the Palladium, as a pledge of the safety of the city. This image or statue was stolen by Ulysses (Odysseus) and Diomedes thus making the capture of the city possible. The altar indicates the importance of the charge to watch. The mask or head of Medusa is seen on the shield on the right of Pallas. The name was obviously adopted by the Office as a "protector of cities."

838. 4¾" x 5". Erect figure with armor cut out above panel bearing "Palladium." There is some question as to identity of this mark. *(Courtesy of Licenses and General Insurance Company, Ltd.)*

(839-848) PATRIOTIC ASSURANCE COMPANY, LIMITED. DUBLIN, IRELAND. 1824-

839. Lead. Oval. 9½" x 10¾". Border, center design and

"Patriotic—1824" all raised. Patriotism shielding the widow and orphans left helpless by fire. The building in background is the Bank of Ireland, formerly Irish Parliament House before the union (1800).

840. Copper. Oval. 9½" x 10¾". Border, center design and "Patriotic Assurance Company 1824" all raised.

841. Heavy tin. 9" x 9¼". Border, center design and "Patriotic —1824" all raised.

842. Tin. Oval. 6⅝" x 9". Border, design and "Patriotic" above all raised. From building in Greece.

843. Tin. Oval. 8⅞" x 10⅛". Painted design in center surrounded by raised "Patriotic Assurance Company—1824." From building in Greece.

844. Tin. Oval. 6⅝" x 9". Multi-colored design, raised, with gold border and "Patriotic" also raised. "1824" in gold at bottom.

845. Tin. Rectangular. 6¾" x 9⅛". Multi-colored design, raised, with gold border around oval and "Patriotic" also raised. "1824" in gold at bottom. Four corners are gold with a blue Chinese character in each. Mark used in China.

846. Tin. Circular. 7⅛" in diameter. "Patriotic" raised on scroll across face of sun. Blue background. Raised border. From building in Greece.

847. Tin. Circular. 7" in diameter. "Patriotic" raised on scroll across face of sun. Lettering and underside of scroll red. Sun is gold. Raised border.

848. Heavy tin plate. Rectangular. 6⅜" x 9". Border yellow and blue, background white, sun yellow and lettering blue and yellow. "Alfred Salzmann Co. Ltd.—Jerusalem" in blue in lower right-hand corner. Modern. From building in Jerusalem.

(849) ST. PATRICK (DUBLIN) LIFE, FIRE AND MARINE INSURANCE COMPANY. DUBLIN, IRELAND. 1824-1829.

Copper. 7¾" x 9¾". Border, "St. Patrick—1824" and erect figure of Saint Patrick in oval all raised.

850

851

852

853

854

855

856

857

858

859

860

861

862

863

A chromo of the Metropolitan Fire Brigade of London in action shortly before the turn of the century. The fire mark upon the wall is that of the Royal Insurance Company. This is one of the few fire scenes in which a mark is shown on a burning building.

864   865   866

(850-853) SCOTTISH UNION INSURANCE COMPANY. EDINBURGH, SCOTLAND. 1824-1878.

850. Copper. 9″ x 11⅞″. Red rampant lion, raised on gold center, surrounded by raised gold "Scottish Union—1824" on red background. Outer border raised gold. Crown at top red and gold.

851. Copper. 6¾″ x 7⅞″. Border, rampant lion in oval and "Scottish Union" in panel below all raised.

852. Heavy tin. 7½″ x 8⅝″. Rampant lion on very slightly convexed circle, "Scottish" in band above, "Union" in panel below and borders all raised.

853. Tin. 7½″ x 8⅝″. Rampant lion on circle, "Scottish" in band above, "Union" in apron below and borders all raised. (Courtesy of Licenses and General Insurance Company, Ltd.)

(854-858) YORKSHIRE INSURANCE COMPANY, LIMITED. YORK, ENGLAND. 1824-

854. Copper. 9¾″ x 11¾″. Borders, view of minster and "Fire—Yorkshire—Life—Established 1824" raised.

855. Copper. 7⅛″ x 9½″. Borders, gold minster on oval panel with "Yorkshire" above and "1824" on panel below all raised.

856. Tin. Shield shape. 7″ x 9½″. View of minster on white shield in center on black background. Raised border and "Yorkshire—1824" gold.

857. Heavy tin. Shield shape. 6½″ x 9½″. Border, crest and "Yorkshire—1824" raised. From building in Istanbul, Turkey.

858. Heavy tin. Shield shape. 7″ x 9½″. Raised crest red, white and gold on black background. Raised border and "Yorkshire—1824" gold. Modern.

(859) ABERDEEN ASSURANCE COMPANY. ABERDEEN, SCOTLAND. 1825-1852.

Lead. Oval. Border, "Aberdeen" and crest raised. Arms of the City of Aberdeen. The three towers represent the three local hills on the slopes of which early settlers built their homes—Castle Hill, Port Hill and St. Catherine's. (Courtesy of Bertram Williams.)

(860-861) LANCASHIRE INSURANCE COMPANY. MANCHESTER, ENGLAND. 1825-1901.

860. Copper. 10″ x 10″. Ornate shape. Red border, gold "Lancashire" with crown above and three lions below all raised.

861. Tin. 10⅛″ x 10″. Ornate shape. Border, "Lancashire" with crown above and three lions below all raised. The three lions guardant in pale are from the arms of John O'Gaunt, Duke of Lancaster. The crown signifies that the King or Queen in her own right is hereditary Duke, and is toasted as such in addition to that of King or Queen in the loyal toast at all public functions in the County.

(862) PROTECTOR FIRE INSURANCE COMPANY. LONDON, ENGLAND. 1825-1835.

Copper. 9⅝″ x 8¾″. Border, scene of burning building with waterman directing nozzle and "Protector" in panel below all raised.

(863) SURREY, SUSSEX AND SOUTHWARK FIRE AND LIFE. SURREY, ENGLAND. 1825-1826.

Copper. Emblem on shield, "Surrey" in panel above and "Sussex" in panel below all raised. The device between the two titles is known as "The Southwark Cross" and is the sign of the Bridge House the headquarters of the officers connected with London Bridge, the house having been anciently situated in Southwark on the south side of the river. (Courtesy of Bertram Williams.)

(864-866) DISTRICT FIRE OFFICE. BIRMINGHAM, ENGLAND. 1834-1864.

864. Copper. Circular. 7½″ in diameter. Borders, Arms of the City of Birmingham in center circle, "District" and two crossed axes below all raised. The arms of Birmingham City taken from the arms of the Midland branch of the De Berminghams who were local landowners. 5 golden Lozenges joined bendwise (across the arms) with ermine fess (centre strip) charged with gold mural crown.

865. Copper. 10″ x 9⅞″. Arms of the City of Birmingham in center circle surrounded by "District" and two crossed axes and "Fire Office" in panel below all raised. Borders raised.

866. Copper. 10″ x 10¼″. Raised Arms of the City of Birmingham surrounded by garter with raised "Birmingham." "District" raised on panel below.

867

868

869

870

871

872

873

874

875

876

877

878

879

880

881

(867) LEICESTERSHIRE FIRE AND LIFE INSURANCE COMPANY. LEICESTER, ENGLAND. 1834-1843.

Tin. Circular. Borders, design in center and "Leicester" raised. The cinquefoil (or flower) in the center is taken from the City Arms. It was originally from the arms of Robert FitzPernell, Earl of Leicester (d. 1204). It is said to be a canting (or pun) on the early family name; the flower is understood to be a pimpernel. (Courtesy of Bertram Williams.)

(868) YORK AND LONDON FIRE AND LIFE. LONDON, ENGLAND. 1834-1844.

Copper. Oval. Borders, seated figure and "York & London" raised. A representation of Britannia, seated holding an olive branch in the right hand and a sceptre in the left. Her left hand resting on an oval Union Jack shield. (Courtesy of Bertram Williams.)

(869-870) YORK AND NORTH OF ENGLAND. YORK, ENGLAND. 1834-1844.

869. Copper. Borders, crest and "York & North of England" raised. The arms of the City of York, the Red Cross of St. George with 5 gold lions of England. "These emblems are considered appropriate to the second city of England," says York. (Courtesy of Bertram Williams.)

870. Copper. 6⅝" x 9. Raised crest surrounded by garter with raised "York & North of England."

(871) NOTTINGHAM AND DERBYSHIRE FIRE AND LIFE ASSURANCE COMPANY. NOTTINGHAM, ENGLAND. 1835-1869.

Zinc. 8¾" x 10⅝". Raised crest on pebbled background surrounded by garter with raised "Notts and Derbys." Centre shield is taken from Nottingham City Arms—the ragged wooden cross and three open gold crowns, the lowest encircling the bottom limb of the cross, refer to the nearby Royal forest of Sherwood.

(872) LEGAL AND GENERAL ASSURANCE SOCIETY, LTD. LONDON, ENGLAND. 1836-

Tin. 8¼" x 8⅝". Temple Bar, date, "Legal & General" and border all raised, gold on blue background.

(873) LICENSED VICTUALLERS FIRE AND LIFE INSURANCE COMPANY. LONDON, ENGLAND. 1836-1857.

Copper. 9¾" x 11¾". Cluster of grapes raised on convexed oval surrounded by garter with raised "Licensed Victuallers."

(874-879) THE NORTHERN ASSURANCE COMPANY, LIMITED. LONDON, ENGLAND. 1836- (Established at Aberdeen, Scotland.)

874. Copper. 6½" x 8½". Raised shield with rampant lion and crown. "Northern" in panel below and borders raised. "Heaton —Birmm." in small raised letters at base of shield.

875. Copper. Rectangular. 6¾" x 9½". Raised shield with rampant lion and crown red and gold on black background. Border and gold "Northern—1836" raised.

876. Copper. Rectangular. 6¾" x 9½". Raised shield with rampant lion and crown red and gold on black background. Border and gold "Northern—1836" raised. Stamping and coloring differs from No. 875.

877. Heavy tin. Rectangular. 6⅝" x 9⅛". Raised shield with rampant lion and crown. "Northern" in panel below and borders raised.

878. Tin. Rectangular. 7" x 9⅜". Raised shield with rampant lion and crown red and gold on black background. Border and gold "Northern—1836" raised.

879. Tin. Rectangular. 7⅛" x 9½". Raised shield with rampant lion red and gold on black background. Border and gold "Northern—1836" raised.

(880) GENERAL LIFE AND FIRE ASSURANCE COMPANY. LONDON, ENGLAND. 1837-1893.

Tin. Shield with crown at top. Borders and "Fire—Life—General —A. D. 1837" raised. (Courtesy of Bertram Williams.)

(881) SHROPSHIRE AND NORTH WALES ASSURANCE COMPANY. SHREWSBURY, ENGLAND. 1837-1890.

Copper. 9½" x 9½". Prince of Wales' feathers in center surrounded by "Shropshire & North Wales" raised. Four scrolls on outer border.

THE VICTORIAN ERA

1837-1901

At the tender age of eighteen Alexandrina Victoria became Queen of England. This young lady had a dignity and poise which, together with rather inherent good sense, acquired for her the full respect of her subjects. She married Albert of Saxe-Coburg-Gotha who was made Prince Consort and who proved to be so reliable and sound in judgment that in the passing years he really filled the position of a king to his Queen. Though respected by all, Albert never became very popular because of his foreign birth.

Throughout the reign of Victoria there was a kaleidoscopic succession of ministers and a series of wars. During the American civil strife in the 1860's, England almost supported the cause of the South, but finally retained her neutrality. There were uprisings in Ireland, but even those were finally suppressed, and at least a temporary state of tranquility between Ireland and England existed.

One sore spot on the British scene for a great many decades was the enforced class consciousness of the working people. While the Reform Act of 1832 had provided for a redistribution of parliamentary representation it did not enfranchise the workingman. After the civil war in America, the colored man was permitted to vote, while the worker in Britain was deprived of that privilege unless he was a "ten-pound householder." After repeated struggles in the legislative chambers a bill was enacted and received the Queen's assent on August 15, 1867, extending enfranchisement to over a million new voters. This act also provided the ballot for every man who owned land at five pounds a year and every tenant whose annual rent reached twelve pounds. In the boroughs it gave the vote to every householder and also to each lodger who paid a yearly rent up to ten pounds for an unfurnished room. This may seem like a most restricted concession, but when viewed from the standpoint of steady progress in Britain toward a genuine democratic form of government it represented a momentous step forward. Only five years later the secret ballot was introduced, bringing another advance in representative government.

Because of the topography of the British Isles there arose a relocation of various endeavors. With such readjustments came a cleft between the peers and the masses. The reason that such a large group of working people concentrated in the north and west was that industry, of which textiles were a major product, liked the lowland country. Here in the wet and damp area, cotton thread was less apt to break, and weaving became more efficient. Here, too, were located the mines to supply the coal for power.

The evolution of each class group has had a definite effect upon the general economy and that in turn affected the organization and advance of fire insurance institutions and their security for the people. While in the early part of the Victorian era there was cheap labor, long hours, and exploitation of the young in mines and factories, the benefits of progressive legislative steps soon brought on improved conditions.

It is to the credit of Lord Ashly, with the assistance of Sir Robert Peel, that the first move was made to alleviate such conditions when they secured the passage of a regulatory bill for child and female labor in 1844. Family needs and greed were great and as late as 1870 there were two million children of school age who had no education whatever; the others were mostly in schools of a substandard variety. It was Benjamin Disraeli who in that year sponsored the bill which provided for a compulsory school attendance.

This is, of course, not a treatise upon labor or education, but those two factors have been of the greatest importance in the economic progress of Britain. Those leaders who were wise believed that to expand agriculture, industry, and commerce there had to be an emancipation of the workingman and a pronounced advance in educational standards. To that end they were supported by the Queen. It was a new era of humanitarianism and the people felt more responsibility for their neighbors' morals and welfare. The industrial revolution followed the same pattern as in America, and industry was completely transformed by the gigantic strides of chemistry, physics, and geology. Transportation of materials and communications through an improved postal service, and later by means of the telephone, telegraph, and cable, were responsible for a great increase in the manufacture of goods and their distribution. All of this once more created a demand for extended property insurance facilities. From 1837, at the start of Victoria's reign, until 1870 fire marks representing some twenty-seven new fire insurance companies are recorded. There may have been others who left no visual record of their existence. These companies were scattered throughout England and were formed mostly at points where additional facilities were required.

The influences of communication were making themselves felt, permitting a more centralized headquarters for industry. Of the thirty-one new fire insurance companies represented by fire marks between 1870 and the close of the Victorian era in 1901, a great percentage were domiciled in London. Just as the newly organized companies in America began their operations on the eastern seaboard, then spread across the country throughout the states, and finally receded again to the East, so the British organizations also changed their final course. Starting in London, then spreading throughout the counties of England, Ireland, and Scotland, they have once more retraced their steps and the control and supervision is now principally in the city of London.

Much has been said about Victorian art, but most authorities agree that it was not in good taste. If one compares the character of the fire marks of the Victorian period with those so vividly displayed during the earlier chapters on the British footprints of assurance, one at once recognizes the lack of artistic design. They were nevertheless truly representative in form, with the Shropshire and North Wales showing the plume of the Prince of Wales; the Church of England exhibiting the accouterments of the church; the several farmers' companies displaying a bundle of grain; the Queen and the Albert companies offering the busts of these respective leaders; and the Lion boasting the image of that monarch of the veldt.

Under the influences of a conservative Queen, a recognition of the importance of law, order, and self-control began. Patience, unselfishness, and self-restraint came to be highly praised virtues in society, morals, and religion. Of all the Victorian poets, Tennyson was perhaps most strongly impressed by these virtues, particularly those of law and moderation. In his two poems entitled "Locksley Hall" and "Locksley Hall Sixty Years After," he provides us with two portraits which hold a mirror to the era. The first portrays a young poet, impatient and idealistic like so many young men of his time, decrying the iniquity of social injustice and yearning for a great "Federation of the World." He visualizes rapid change and almost limitless human progress. His contrasting portrait, written more than forty years later, reveals the same man older, grayer, and more mature, but still believing in the inevitability of improvement though holding the opinion it will come not from unlimited self-expression but rather from self-discipline and gradual evolution through the slower but surer operation of law and order.

So, too, has it been with fire insurance. When one studies the histories of those companies whose fire marks remain one finds that those whose ambitions caused overenthusiastic acts, are referred to as having "wound up." The industry itself has in many respects been principally "Victorian" in its conduct. While there may not have been the exuberance of Tennyson's "Youth," the solidarity of British companies has been responsible for a soundness and security unaffected by the vicissitudes of political and governmental strife. Those attributes are a great tribute to the influences of the Victorian era and to the Queen who died on January 22, 1901, mourned by a people who had learned to love her especially for her interests in their welfare. In commerce it was the period when conservatism took root.

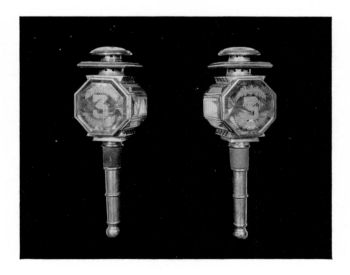

882

883

884

885

886

887

888

889

890

891

892

893

894

895

896

897

898

(882-883) CHURCH OF ENGLAND LIFE AND FIRE ASSUR-
ANCE INSTITUTION. LONDON, ENGLAND. 1840-1892.

882. Copper. Circular. 9″ in diameter. Crown, bishop's mitre,
sword and crosier raised on slightly convexed center. Borders and
"Church of England" raised. The Crown refers to the King as head
of the established Church. The Mitre—ecclesiastical power. The
Crook—pastor for shepherd of the flock (in saltire, crosswise) with
sword of St. Paul, City of London's saint.

883. Copper. Circular. Bishop's mitre, "Church of England"
and borders raised. (Courtesy of Bertram Williams.)

(884-885) FARMERS AND GENERAL FIRE AND LIFE IN-
SURANCE INSTITUTION. LONDON, ENGLAND. 1840-1843.

884. Copper. 8″ x 10″. Sheaf of wheat, "Farmers & General
Fire & Life Insurance" and "Institution" in panel at bottom all
raised. Borders raised.

885. Copper. 8″ x 10″. Sheaf of wheat, "Farmers & General
Fire & Life Insurance" and "Institution" in panel at bottom all
raised. Borders raised. Design of sheaf of wheat differs from mark
No. 884.

(886-887) SOUTH OF ENGLAND FIRE AND LIFE INSUR-
ANCE COMPANY. LONDON, ENGLAND. 1841-1847.

886. Copper. Circular. Border, crown, rose and "South of
England" raised. Charges are from the arms of the "County of
Southampton" i.e., Hampshire—Red rose, with Royal Crown above
it. The rose (of Lancaster) was granted to the County by John
O'Gaunt, a large landowner there, and is found on the 14th century shield. It is also in the present arms of Southampton. (Courtesy of Bertram Williams.)

887. Copper. Shield shape. 8¼″ x 10¼″. Crown and rose
surrounded by "Winchester. Hants & S. of England." Border raised.
(Courtesy of Licenses and General Fire Insurance Company, Ltd.)

(888-889) ROYAL FARMERS' AND GENERAL FIRE, LIFE
AND HAIL-STORM INSURANCE COMPANY. LONDON, ENG-
LAND. 1843-1888.

888. Copper. 8⅛″ x 10¼″. Sheaf of wheat in center oval,
"Fire & Life" across top and "Farmers" in panel at bottom all
raised. Borders raised.

889. Zinc. 8⅛″ x 10¼″. Sheaf of wheat in center oval, "Fire &
Life" across top and "Farmers" in panel at bottom all raised.
Borders raised.

(890) THE BONACCORD LIFE AND FIRE ASSURANCE
COMPANY. ABERDEEN, SCOTLAND. 1845-1849.

Lead. Figure of bishop on oval with policy No. 330 in panel
at bottom. (Courtesy of Bertram Williams.)

(891-901) ROYAL INSURANCE COMPANY, LIMITED.
LIVERPOOL, ENGLAND. 1845-

891. Copper. 10″ x 12″. Ornate shield with border, design
and lettering raised. Crown and liver bird gold on green background. "Royal" gold on red.

892. Tin. 12″ x 15″. Ornate shield with border, design and
lettering raised. Crown and liver bird gold on green background.
"Royal" gold on red.

893. Tin. Circular. 4½″ in diameter. Orange with gold border, crown and "Royal Liverpool" raised. Issued about 1860. Used
in America.

894. Sheet iron. Rectangular. 6½″ x 9¼″. "Royal Liverpool"
and large liver bird. (Courtesy of Licenses and General Insurance
Company, Ltd.)

895. Sheet iron. Rectangular. 6¼″ x 10″. Crown set within
outline of shield, "Royal" below. Border raised. (Courtesy of
Licenses and General Insurance Company, Ltd.)

896. Copper. 9¼″ x 12⅛″. Red, gold and silver crown atop
red shield with border and gold "Royal" raised.

897. Tin. Rectangular. 7″ x 2″. White "Royal" on dark blue
background. From agency at Defiance, Ohio.

898. Iron. Rectangular. 7⅝″ x 5½″. Convexed with flat border.
"Royal" and Chinese characters white on dark green enamel background. Mark used in China.

899

900

901

902

903

904

905

906

907

908

909

910

911

912

913

914

915

916

899. Heavy tin. Shield. 9″ x 12″. Red, gold and silver crown atop red shield with border and gold "Royal" raised.

900. Tin. Rectangular. 4⅝″ x 5⁵⁄₁₆″. Red with gold rampant lion and "Royal" raised. Identification questionable.

901. Heavy tin. 10″ x 12″. Ornate shield with border, design and lettering raised. Crown and liver bird had been gold on green background. "Royal" had been gold on red.

(902) STAR INSURANCE COMPANY. LONDON, ENGLAND. 1845-1853.

Copper. Circular. 9″ in diameter. Border and eight-pointed star of the Order of the Garter with "Star Insurance Company" raised.

(903-904) LIVERPOOL AND LONDON FIRE AND LIFE INSURANCE COMPANY. LIVERPOOL, ENGLAND. 1846-1864.

903. Thin copper. 7⅞″ x 9¹¹⁄₁₆″. Rust and green design of liver bird with "Liverpool" on green panel above and "& London" on green panel below all raised. Borders raised.

904. Tin. 8½″ x 9¾″. Design of liver bird with "Liverpool" on panel above and "& London" on panel below all raised. Borders raised.

(905-906) THE PRUDENTIAL ASSURANCE COMPANY, LIMITED. LONDON, ENGLAND. 1848-

905. Tin. 6″ x 9″. Border and "The Prudential Assurance Company Ltd. London" raised gold on blue background. Tinted picture of building raised with "Founded 1848" in gold below.

906. Tin. "Prudential Assurance Company Ltd. London" with heraldic emblem and "Founded 1848" below. Modern. (*Courtesy of Bertram Williams.*)

(907) ANCHOR FIRE AND LIFE. LONDON, ENGLAND. 1849-1857.

Tin. Upright anchor with "Anchor Fire & Life" and borders all raised. (*Courtesy of Bertram Williams.*)

(908) ATHENAEUM FIRE INSURANCE OFFICE. LONDON, ENGLAND. 1852-1856.

Porcelain. 8⅜″ x 11¾″. Blue and white porcelain finish showing head of Athene and "Athenaeum Fire Insurance Office" raised. This mark is a reproduction.

(909-911) QUEEN INSURANCE COMPANY. LIVERPOOL, ENGLAND. 1857-1891.

909. Copper. 8¾″ x 8⅝″. Bust of Queen Victoria raised gold on red circle with black background. Gold "Queen" on panel below. Borders raised with traces of red on upper border.

910. Copper. 9½″ x 10½″. Bust of Queen Victoria, borders and "Queen Insurance" raised gold on black background.

911. Tin. 8⅛″ x 11⅝″. Bust of Queen Victoria and "Queen" raised on slightly convexed shield in center of octagonal with raised crown at top. Raised border. From building in Greece.

(912-913) LONDON AND PROVINCIAL MARINE AND GENERAL INSURANCE COMPANY, LIMITED. LONDON, ENGLAND. 1860-

912. Tin. Circular. 7″ in diameter. Border, "London & Provincial" and two crossed flags raised.

913. Tin. Circular. 8″ in diameter. Black "1860" on red circle in center with raised gold "London & Provincial" on surrounding black band. Raised gold borders.

(914-919) COMMERCIAL UNION ASSURANCE COMPANY, LIMITED. LONDON, ENGLAND. 1861-

914. Tin. Circular. 10″ in diameter. Border, gold "Commercial Union" and flag with Union Jack described in a canton at the upper corner of red ensign, all raised.

915. Tin. Oval. 9⅞″ x 8¾″. Raised design of salamander in flames red, gold and green on black background with raised border and "Commercial Union" gold. Semi-modern.

916. Tin. Oval. 9⅞″ x 8¾″. Raised design of salamander in flames red, gold and green on black background with raised border and "Commercial Union" gold. Modern.

917

918

OSIGURAVA
COMMERCIAL UNION

919

920

921

922

923

LONDON AND LANCASHIRE.

925

924

927

926

928

929

930

931

932

935

933

934

917. Tin. Oval. 9⅞" x 8¾". Raised design of salamander in flames red, gold and green on black background with raised border and "Commercial Union" gold. Modern lithographed mark.

918. Tin. Oval. 9⅞" x 8¾". Raised design of salamander in flames red, gold and green on black background with raised border and Chinese characters gold. Modern. Mark used in China.

919. Iron. Rectangular. 7¹⁄₁₆" x 2¾". Border and "Osigurava—Commercial Union" light green on dark brown convexed background. Modern. From Yugoslavia.

(920-928) THE LONDON AND LANCASHIRE INSURANCE COMPANY, LIMITED. LONDON, ENGLAND. 1861-

920. Copper. 9½" x 10¼". "London & Lancashire" raised in panels on ornate shield with raised border. The arms of London, and the County of Lancashire—the Royal County, hence the Royal Arms (English).

921. Tin. 8⅜" x 6". Black and gold shields, ornate border and gold "London & Lancashire" all raised. Background black.

922. Copper. Shield shape. 8½" x 9¼". "London & Lancashire Fire" white, left shield red, white and gold, right shield red and gold, background black. Border, design and lettering raised.

923. Copper. 8½" x 9⁵⁄₁₆". "London & Lancashire Fire" gold, left shield white and gold, right shield red and gold, background blue. Border design and lettering raised.

924. Zinc. 9½" x 8½". Shields, panel and "London & Lancashire" raised.

925. Tin. Rectangular. 7" x 3¼". Border and "London and Lancashire." gold on black background. First type mark of this company used in America.

926. Tin. 10¾" x 9¼". Two shields and "Fire" raised on convexed center of mark with "London &" on ribbon panel above and "Lancashire" on ribbon panel below.

927. Tin. Shield shape. 8½" x 9¼". "London & Lancashire" gold, left shield red, white and gold, right shield red and gold, background blue. Border, design and lettering raised.

928. Tin. Octagonal. 8" x 7¾". Green and gold painted ornamentation with "London & Lancashire," Chinese characters and border painted gold on red background.

(929-940) NORTH BRITISH AND MERCANTILE INSURANCE COMPANY, LIMITED. LONDON, ENGLAND. 1862-

929. Copper. Circular, with panel. 10" in diameter. Borders, "North British & Mercantile," shield in center and "1809" in small panel below, all raised. Earliest type mark issued by this company under this title.

930. Tin. Rectangular. 7⅞" x 9⅝". Figure representing St. George killing dragon and "North British & Mercantile" raised. From building in Greece.

931. Tin. Rectangular. 7½" x 9¼". Border, figure representing St. George killing dragon and "North British & Mercantile—1809" raised.

932. Tin. Rectangular. 9¾" x 7". Border, "North British & Mercantile—A. D. 1809" and two shields, raised. From building in Greece.

933. Heavy tin. Rectangular. 7⅞" x 9⁹⁄₁₆". Raised border and "North British & Mercantile" gold. Raised figure representing St. George killing dragon gold, red and green on black background. Used in Martinique.

934. Tin. Rectangular. 7" x 3¼". Border and "Insured North British and Mercantile." gold on black background. Type of mark used upon entry to America.

935. Rectangular. Border, design of two shields and crown and "North British & Mercantile—A. D. 1809" lithographed. (Courtesy of Bertram Williams.)

936

937

938

939

940

941

942

943

944

945

946

947

948

188

949

950

951

936. Tin. Rectangular. 7⅝" x 10". Border and "North British & Mercantile—1809" gold with two shields and crown red and gold. Background black.

937. Tin. Rectangular. 9½" x 6⅞". Slightly raised shields and lettering. Left shield red, white and gold, right shield red and gold on black oval set on red background. Lettering gold. Outer border black and gold.

938. Tin. Rectangular. 10" x 7". Slightly raised shields and lettering. Left shield red, white and gold, right shield red and gold on black background. Borders and "North British & Mercantile—A. D. 1809" gold. Each corner bears a Chinese character painted in white.

939. Tin. Rectangular. 10⅜" x 7⅜". "North British & Mercantile Insurance Company" on oval band and figure of engine in center slightly raised. From building in Greece.

940. Tin. Rectangular. 10" x 7⅛". Slightly raised shields and lettering. Left shield red, white and gold, right shield red and gold on black background. Borders and "North British & Mercantile—A. D. 1809" gold.

(941) WESTERN FIRE INSURANCE COMPANY, LIMITED. LONDON, ENGLAND. 1863-1868.

Tin. Oval. Border and "Western Fire" raised. (Courtesy of Bertram Williams.)

(942) ALBERT INSURANCE COMPANY, LIMITED. LONDON, ENGLAND. 1864-1866.

Copper. Border, bust and "Albert" raised. (Courtesy of Bertram Williams.)

(943-947) LIVERPOOL AND LONDON AND GLOBE INSURANCE COMPANY, LIMITED. LIVERPOOL, ENGLAND. 1864-

943. Heavy copper. 8½" x 10¾". Raised design, with liver bird facing right, gold on red background. Raised "Liverpool & London & Globe" gold on black panels. Borders raised.

944. Copper. 8¹¹⁄₁₆" x 10⅞". Raised design, with liver bird facing left, gold on black background. Raised "Liverpool & London & Globe" and "1836" gold on red panels. Borders raised.

945. Tin. 7³⁄₁₆" x 10⅞". Raised design, with liver bird facing left, gold and black on red background. Raised "Liverpool & London & Globe" gold on black panels with Chinese characters in gold on panel extended below. Borders raised. Modern.

946. Tin. 7⁵⁄₁₆" x 9⁹⁄₁₆". Raised design, with liver bird facing left, gold and black on red background. Raised "Liverpool & London & Globe" gold on black panels. From agency at Mexico City, Mexico.

947. Tin. 7¼" x 9½". Raised globe encircled with band bearing company name gold and black on red background. Raised "Liverpool & London & Globe" gold on black. Borders raised. Modern.

(948) SCOTTISH COMMERCIAL FIRE AND LIFE INSURANCE COMPANY. GLASGOW, SCOTLAND. 1865-1880.

Copper. Oval. Border, design and "Scottish Commercial" raised. Figure of Charity with spear and Targe or Target (Scottish shield) for defence. (Courtesy of Bertram Williams.)

(949) SCOTTISH IMPERIAL FIRE AND LIFE INSURANCE COMPANY. GLASGOW, SCOTLAND. 1865-1883.

Copper. Rectangular. Lion rampant with "Scottish Imperial" above and "Insurance Co." below. (Courtesy of Bertram Williams.)

(950) THE ETNA. DUBLIN, IRELAND. 1866-1868.

"Etna" on shield. (Courtesy of Bertram Williams.)

(951) BRITANNIA FIRE INSURANCE COMPANY. LONDON, ENGLAND. 1868-1879.

Copper. 10⅛" x 12½". Erect figure of Britannia with lion behind her, borders and "Britannia" in panel below all raised.

952

953

954

955

956

957

958

959

960

961

962

963

965

966

964

968

967

(952-953) LONDON GUARANTEE AND ACCIDENT COMPANY, LIMITED. LONDON, ENGLAND. 1869-

952. Tin. Circular. 8″ in diameter. Crest and date on convexed center section of mark. Raised "London Guarantee & Accident Co. Ltd." on surrounding band with raised borders. From building in Greece.

953. Tin. Circular. 8″ in diameter. Red and white crest and white lettering on convexed red center with raised Greek lettering in gold on black band. Raised borders gold.

(954) GREAT BRITAIN FIRE INSURANCE COMPANY. LONDON, ENGLAND. 1871-1880.

Copper. Design in triangle with crown atop, "Great Britain Compy." and borders raised. (*Courtesy of Bertram Williams.*)

(955) EQUITABLE FIRE INSURANCE COMPANY. LONDON, ENGLAND. 1873-1890.

Copper. Rectangular. 6½″ x 8⅝″. Raised figure of Justice in colors on red background with raised "Equitable" in gold on black painted panel below. Border slightly raised.

(956) MIDDLESEX FIRE INSURANCE COMPANY. 1874-1877.

"Middlesex" and three scimitars, on shield-shape mark. (*Courtesy of Bertram Williams.*)

(957) THE SEA INSURANCE COMPANY, LIMITED. LIVERPOOL, ENGLAND. 1875-

Tin. Shield shape. 6½″ x 6¾″. Raised border and "Sea 1875" blue on red background.

(958-959) SCOTTISH INSURANCE CORPORATION, LIMITED. EDINBURGH, SCOTLAND. 1877-

958. Tin. Circular. 8⅞″ in diameter. Raised design of lion rampant with paw on axe and date "1877" gold on black center circle with gold garland on surrounding red band. Borders raised. No verification that this is a mark of the above company.

959. Tin. Circular. 10″ in diameter. Raised borders and lion with anchor gold on white background. Raised "Scottish Insurance Corporation Limited" black. Modern.

(960) NATIONAL FIRE INSURANCE CORPORATION, LIMITED. LONDON, ENGLAND. 1878-1888.

Copper. Rectangular. 7¾″ x 10⅝″. Bust of Britannia raised in circle with "National Fire Ins. Corpn. Ld." raised below. Border slightly raised. On border at bottom is barely discernible lettering, "The Anglo-Russian Iron & Tin Plate Co."

(961-962) SCOTTISH UNION AND NATIONAL INSURANCE COMPANY. EDINBURGH, SCOTLAND. 1878-

961. Rectangular. Border, "Scottish Union & National—Established 1824" and crest lithographed. (*Courtesy of Bertram Williams.*)

962. Rectangular. Border, "Scottish Union & National—Established 1824" and two crests lithographed. (*Courtesy of Bertram Williams.*)

(963-964) LION FIRE INSURANCE COMPANY. LONDON, ENGLAND. 1879-1902.

963. Copper. 6¾″ x 9¼″. Ornate border, reclining lion and "Lion" all raised. Background red.

964. Copper. Oval. 6⅞″ x 8⅞″. Raised ornate border, reclining lion and "Lion" gold on dark green background.

(965) THE EMPLOYERS' LIABILITY ASSURANCE CORPORATION, LIMITED. LONDON, ENGLAND. 1880-

Tin. 8⅝″ x 10″. Raised border, center design of Britannia with shield and "The Employers' London" red on green background. Raised "Liability Assurance Corporation Limited" green. Modern.

(966) CITY OF LONDON FIRE. LONDON, ENGLAND. 1881-1892.

Circular. Border, shield and "City of London" raised. (*Courtesy of Bertram Williams.*)

(967) RELIANCE MARINE INSURANCE COMPANY, LIMITED. LIVERPOOL, ENGLAND. 1881-

Tin. 8¼″ x 9¼″. Border, design and "Reliance" raised. Anchor and name gold. Border and anchor chain cream colored. Background dark green.

(968) ECONOMIC FIRE. LONDON, ENGLAND. 1886-1894.

Rectangular. "Economic" raised across face. (*Courtesy of Bertram Williams.*)

969

970

971

972

973

974

975

976

977

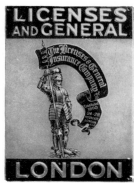

978

979

980

981

982

983

984

985

986

987

Many British concerns adopted for their fire marks a design emblematic of the heraldry developed in England over the centuries.

(969-973) PALATINE INSURANCE COMPANY, LIMITED. LONDON, ENGLAND. 1886-

969. "Palatine" raised on center oval with "Insurance Company Limited" raised on surrounding garter. Lancashire, a County Palatine since 1351, subsequently passed to John O'Gaunt and to the Royal Family in 1377. It is so called because the estate had a *Palace* with a Royal prerogative, and was outside the jurisdiction of the local and national law. The castle is Lancaster—the County town. It has always been closely identified with the Royal family. *(Courtesy of Bertram Williams.)*

970. Rectangular. Shield with castle in center, "Palatine" above and "Insurance" below. *(Courtesy of Bertram Williams.)*

971. Heavy tin. Rectangular. 9½" x 7¹⁄₁₆". Border, "Palatine Insurance" and castle raised. From building in Greece.

972. Tin. Rectangular. 9½" x 7". Outer border, lettering and design raised. Border gold with red stripe, "Palatine Assurance" black and gold, castle and trees, cream, gray and black. "Waterlow & Sons, Limited, London" in small letters in lower left-hand corner of picture.

973. Tin. Rectangular. 9½" x 7⅛". Outer border, lettering and design raised. Border gold with red stripe, "Palatine Insurance" black and gold, castle and trees, cream, gray and black. "Waterlow & Sons, Limited, London" in small letters in lower left-hand corner of picture. From agency in Palestine.

(974-975) WEST OF SCOTLAND INSURANCE OFFICE, LIMITED. GLASGOW, SCOTLAND. 1886-

974. Lead. Circular. Crown in center with "West of Scotland" on surrounding garter. *(Courtesy of Bertram Williams.)*

975. Lead. Circular. Crown in center surrounded by "West of Scotland." *(Courtesy of Bertram Williams.)*

(976) FEDERAL FIRE INSURANCE COMPANY. LONDON, ENGLAND. 1887-1889.

Rectangular. Border, crest in center of mark with "Federal" above and "London" below. *(Courtesy of Licenses and General Insurance Company, Ltd.)*

(977) PROPERTY FIRE OFFICE. 1887-1892.

Crossed anchor and key surrounded by "Property Fire Office" and raised border. *(Courtesy of Bertram Williams.)*

(978) THE LICENSES AND GENERAL INSURANCE COMPANY, LIMITED. LONDON, ENGLAND. 1890-

Tin. Rectangular. 7" x 9⅞". Black and gold design of knight holding banner bearing company's name, date and address, raised on red background with raised "Licenses and General" above and "London" below gold on black. Border gold.

(979) NATIONAL BENEFIT LIFE AND PROPERTY ASSURANCE COMPANY, LIMITED. LONDON, ENGLAND. 1890-1921.

Circular. Head with warrior's helmet surrounded by company name and date of establishment on ribbon. *(Courtesy of Bertram Williams.)*

(980-981) GENERAL ACCIDENT ASSURANCE CORPORATION, LIMITED. PERTH, SCOTLAND. 1891-1906.

980. Tin. 7" x 9⅛". Borders, crest and banner, and "General Accident Assce. Corpn." "Fire & Accident" all slightly raised. First mark of company under above title.

981. Tin. 8" x 9⅝". Borders, crest and banner and "General Accident Assce. Corpn." "Fire & Accident" all slightly raised. Crest had been red, white and black and lettering red on black background. Second type mark of this company; somewhat larger than first.

(982-983) THE STATE ASSURANCE COMPANY, LIMITED. LIVERPOOL, ENGLAND. 1891-

982. Tin. 6" x 7⅝". Shield, with crown at top and "The State Fire Insurance Co. Ltd., Liverpool, Eng." Raised border and "State" gold. Raised crown red, gold, black and white. Other lettering black and white. Background red. "Griffiths & Browett Ltd.—Makers—London & Birmingham" in small black letters at bottom of shield.

983. Tin. Shield shape. 8" x 8". Black border and gold and black "The State Assurance Company Limited" raised. Background red.

(984) LAW UNION AND CROWN FIRE AND LIFE INSURANCE COMPANY. LONDON, ENGLAND. 1892-1909.

Tin. Rectangular. 7" x 9". Gold and black border, yellow background, red shield with gold, black, red and yellow crown above. "Law Union & Crown Insurance Coy.—1825" black and white. "Founded" black and red on yellow panel. From building in Istanbul, Turkey.

(985-987) EXCESS INSURANCE COMPANY, LIMITED. LONDON, ENGLAND. 1894-

985. Tin. Shield shape. 5¾" x 5¾". Border and "The Excess—London E. C." raised. Flat letters, "Fire Insurance Co." barely discernible. From building in Istanbul, Turkey.

986. Nickel. Horseshoe, inverted. 3" x 3⅜". "Langeveldt-Schroder" in nickel letters on red incised background. Incised "Excess" black. Modern. Mark used on doors and autos in Dutch East Indies.

987. Nickel. Horseshoe. 3" x 3⅜". "Langeveldt-Schroder" in nickel letters on red incised background. Incised "Excess" black. Modern. Mark used on doors and autos in Dutch East Indies.

988

989

990

991

992

993

994

995

996

997

998

999

1000

1001

1002

(988-992) NATIONAL UNION SOCIETY, LIMITED. BEDFORD, ENGLAND. 1894-1907.

988. Tin. Rectangular. 7⅝" x 11⅜". Border, "National Union Insurance Office—Fire & Accident—Bedford" and figure with trident all raised. From building in Greece.

989. Rectangular. Border, center design and "National Union Fire Office—Bedford, England" raised. (Courtesy of Bertram Williams.)

990. Tin. Shield shape. 9⅞" x 10⅝". Border, red "National Union Insurance" and green and red center design of figure with two shields all raised. Background yellow. From building in Istanbul, Turkey.

991. Tin. Heart shape. 9⅜" x 10". Border, "National Union Insurance," Chinese characters and figure with two shields raised. (Courtesy of Licenses and General Insurance Company, Ltd.)

992. Tin. Shield shape. 10" x 10¾". Border, red "National Union Insurance," and red Chinese characters, green, red and gold center design of figure with two shields, all raised. Background yellow. Chinese characters indicate mark used in Orient.

(993) THE WORLD MARINE AND GENERAL INSURANCE COMPANY, LIMITED. LONDON, ENGLAND. 1894-

Heavy tin. Rectangular. 12¼" x 8¾". Lettering dark blue and cream color on light blue ground. Design of two globes and anchor in dark blue, light blue and cream color in cream color circle on dark blue ground. Ornamental border light blue on cream color. Outer border dark blue.

(994) EMPRESS. 1895-1898.

Copper. Rectangular. Bust of Queen Victoria within circle having crown at top and crossed sprays below. "Empress 1895" above circle. (Courtesy of Bertram Williams.)

(995) THE NATIONAL BRITISH AND IRISH MILLERS' INSURANCE CO. LTD. LONDON, ENGLAND. 1896-1912.

Tin. Rectangular. 7⅞" x 11¾". Border, "The National British & Irish Millers Insurance Co. Ltd. London" and windmill raised. From building in Greece.

(996) BRITISH DOMINIONS INSURANCE COMPANY, LIMITED. LONDON, ENGLAND. 1897-1911.

Oval. Border, "British Dominions" and two rosettes raised. (Courtesy of Bertram Williams.)

(997) THE NATIONAL INSURANCE COMPANY OF GREAT BRITAIN, LIMITED. LONDON, ENGLAND. 1897-

Heavy tin. Oval. 6¼" x 12⅛". Raised border, seated figure with trident and "The National Insurance Company of Great Britain Limited" gold on maroon background. From building in Greece.

(998) PROPERTY INSURANCE COMPANY, LIMITED. LONDON, ENGLAND. 1898-1913.

Tin. Circular. 9" in diameter. "Property Insurance Company Ltd." black on gold band. Rose of England, thistle of Scotland and shamrock of Ireland in colors of red, gold, green, and mauve with cream, black and gold tracery. Off-white background. Border black and gold.

(999) KING INSURANCE COMPANY. LONDON, ENGLAND. 1901-1915.

Tin. Oval. 6⅞" x 9⅛". Border, crest with wreath, and name raised. Crest, including crown, silver, red, brown and gold, wreath green, "King" gold, background brown.

(1000-1002) CENTRAL INSURANCE COMPANY, LIMITED. BIRMINGHAM, ENGLAND. 1902-

1000. Copper. Circular, convexed. 7¾" in diameter. Border, "Central London" and flaming brazier raised. From building in Greece.

1001. Tin. Circular, convexed. 7¾" in diameter. Border, "Central London" and flaming brazier raised. Traces of red and yellow on flames and gold on lettering. From building in Istanbul, Turkey.

1002. Tin. Circular, convexed. 7⅝" in diameter. Border, "Central London" and flaming brazier raised. Border and lettering dull gold, brazier dull gold with red and yellow flames. Background black. Modern.

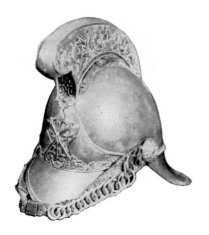

THE MODERN AGE
1901-1920

Edward VII, a man well acquainted with the general problems of the nation, ascended to the throne on January 22, 1901. He was well traveled and had quite an intimate knowledge of the conditions in Britain's colonies as well as those prevailing upon the continent. He associated with the monarchs and ambassadors of Europe, and insofar as any foreign problems were concerned they were mostly of a minor nature and were effectively handled by the ministry. There were, of course, the usual internal dissensions but none of especial note.

After a short reign Edward VII died on May 6, 1910, and was succeeded by George V, who was proclaimed King three days later. During his reign he was to witness a war of four and a half years' duration which was more completely mechanized than any yet engaged in. England was really unprepared for a war which began in August, 1914, and had to be conducted against such a well-equipped army as that of Germany, but our readers well know the final outcome of that conflict. Our previous chapters have outlined a constant forward march made by the people of the British Empire, a progress characterized by a conservatism and ruggedness inherited from the Victorian era. No one had ever seen these people in a total war, and no one realized what the sum of these latent attributes would be. Germany learned the answer early in the war, for shortly after hostilities got under way an article in *Der Tag* read: "We have been mistaken in so many of our calculations! We expected that the whole of India would revolt at the first sound of the guns in Europe; but, behold, thousands and tens of thousands of Indians are fighting with the British and against us. We expected that the British Empire would crumble away; but the British Colonies are one with the Mother-Country as never before. We expected a successful uprising in South Africa; but we see only a fiasco there. We expected disorders in Ireland; but Ireland is sending some of the best contingents against us. We believed that the peace-at-any-price party was all-powerful in England. We considered that England was degenerate and incapable of becoming a serious factor in the war; but she has proved our most dangerous enemy." We repeat that the greatly improved position of the people, along with the free-enterprise operations of merchants and manufacturers, had built a nation of citizens who with others of their kind erected an unbeatable barrier against teutonic aggression.

During the period of World War I many officers and soldiers who knew of the signevierists' interests in fire marks secured specimens from properties upon the continent. A number of these are included among the illustrations found on these pages. Of course, these marks of assurance were no longer being used in Great Britain. Since many English companies were obliged to issue them in the colonies and other foreign places, however, it is interesting to note that twenty new companies starting in business between 1901 and 1914 in Britain did use such plates. None was founded during the period of hostilities, but three newcomers in 1919 used a distinctive mark. Needless to say, practically all of the marks of the companies established in this twentieth century are issued for advertising purposes and also to allay the superstitions of property owners in lands where religions and beliefs vary from those of the European countries. These newer marks are all modern in design and appearance, but some five decades from now, if properly preserved, they will represent a definite era in the progress of British fire insurance. The development of this great industry in England, Scotland, and Ireland has consumed almost a century more time than in America, but when one considers the fact that the development has been in step with the progress made by commerce and labor, it must be recognized that both countries have achieved a tremendous success in the evolution of civilization. They have become bulwarks in the unfolding processes of the free-enterprise system and the economy of their nations.

1004

1005

1006

1003

1007

1008

1009

(1003) CAR AND GENERAL INSURANCE CORPORATION. LONDON, ENGLAND. 1903-

Tin. 6½" x 7⅞". Borders, beading, quatrefoil in center oval with "A. D. 1903" underneath, "Car & General Insurance Corporation Ltd.—De Londres" all raised. Tab for fastening to building at top.

(1004) PROVINCIAL INSURANCE COMPANY, LIMITED. LONDON, ENGLAND. 1903-

Tin. 8⅛" x 8½". Border, lettering and design raised. Border and "Provincial Insurance Office" red, crest red and white, wreath green. From Palestine.

(1005-1006) BRITISH GENERAL INSURANCE COMPANY, LIMITED. LONDON, ENGLAND. 1904-

1005. Tin. Oval. 7⅛" x 11¾". Multi-colored mark showing figure of Britannia holding staff of the Union Jack with reclining lion next to her. "British General" in surrounding band.

1006. Tin. Rectangular. 8" x 10". Multi-colored mark showing figure of Britannia holding staff of the Union Jack with reclin-

ing lion next to her. "British General Insurance Company Limited, London" below. Border yellow, background black.

(1007) THE CORNHILL INSURANCE COMPANY, LIMITED. LONDON, ENGLAND. 1905-

Tin. Rectangular. 8¼" x 6½". Raised border and "The Cornhill—London—Insurance Co. Ltd." gold on dark blue background. "101. Ligure, Lavor, Latta & Fre., Conserve, Genova, 1. p. d'Arena," maker, in lower left-hand corner on border. Modern. From agency in Palestine.

(1008-1009) GENERAL ACCIDENT, FIRE AND LIFE ASSURANCE CORPORATION, LIMITED. PERTH, SCOTLAND. 1906-

1008. Tin. 8" x 10⅛". Borders, crest and banner and "General Accident—Fire–& Life Assurance Corpn. Limited" all slightly raised. Crest red, black and gold, lettering and borders gold, background black.

1009. Tin. 8" x 10". Borders, crest and banner and "General Accident—Fire–& Life Assurance Corpn. Limited" all slightly raised. Crest red, black and gold, borders red, lettering gold, background black. From Cairo, Egypt, office of company.

1010

1011

1012

1013

1014

1015

1016

1017

1018

1019

1020

1021

1022

1023

1024

1025

(1010-1011) THE MOTOR UNION INSURANCE COMPANY, LIMITED. LONDON, ENGLAND. 1906-

1010. Tin. 7⅜″ x 9⅝″. Multi-colored design with "M U I" "Fire" in center, "The Motor Union Insurance Co. Ltd.—Head Office London" white on dark blue background. Borders light blue. Modern. Mark used in Saint Lucia.

1011. Shows design of automobile above shield with "M. U. I." Name of company on ribbon below. (Courtesy of Bertram Williams.)

(1012) BRITISH CROWN ASSURANCE CORPORATION, LIMITED. LONDON, ENGLAND. 1907-1918.

Tin. 10½″ x 9″. Red and gold crown in relief with raised "British Crown Assurance" on scrolled panel below. From building in Greece.

(1013) LEGAL INSURANCE COMPANY, LIMITED. LONDON, ENGLAND. 1907-

Tin. Shield shape. 7¼″ x 9¼″. Red border, heraldic emblems in blue, gold, red, white and black, and gold "Legal Insurance Co. Ld. of London" on dark blue background all raised.

(1014) MONARCH ASSURANCE COMPANY, LIMITED. LONDON, ENGLAND. 1907-1910.

Border, lion above crown and "Non Tariff—Monarch" all raised. (Courtesy of Bertram Williams.)

(1015-1016) NATIONAL GENERAL INSURANCE COMPANY, LIMITED. LONDON, ENGLAND. 1907-1914.

1015. Tin. 7⅛″ x 10⅛″. Crown atop shield, border, "National General—London" and design of rose, thistle and shamrock, all raised.

1016. Tin. Rectangular. 8″ x 10″. Crown, "National General," shield with design of rose, thistle and shamrock, and scrolls, all raised. Multi-colored. "Insurance Company—Chief Office—London, England." in flat letters at side and bottom of shield. From building in Greece.

(1017) NORTH-EASTERN INSURANCE COMPANY, LIMITED. 1907-1914.

Tin. Circular. Border, "North-Eastern Ins. Co. Ltd. Darlington" and design of engine raised. (Courtesy of Licenses and General Insurance Company, Ltd.)

(1018) THE BRITISH FIRE INSURANCE COMPANY LIMITED. LONDON, ENGLAND. 1908-

Tin. 9⅜″ x 10⅜″. Gold lion raised on convexed center circle. "The British Fire Insurance Company Limited" in red raised letters. Background black. Borders raised.

(1019) NATIONAL PROTECTOR INSURANCE COMPANY, LIMITED. LONDON, ENGLAND. 1908-1913.

Tin. Circular. 11¾″ in diameter. Border, "National Protector Insurance Co. Ltd." and helmet with two crossed axes raised. From building in Istanbul, Turkey.

(1020) REINSURANCE AND GUARANTEE INSURANCE COMPANY. LONDON, ENGLAND. 1908-1911.

Tin. Rectangular. 9⅛″ x 6½″. Border, center design and "Reinsurance & Guarantee Compagnia Inglese Assicurazioni Incendio" raised. Modern. From building in Greece.

(1021) LAW UNION & ROCK INSURANCE COMPANY, LIMITED. LONDON, ENGLAND. 1909-

Tin. Rectangular. 7″ x 8⅞″. "Law Union & Rock Insurance Company, Ltd." dark blue and white on light green background with design in dark blue, yellow and white. Border yellow.

(1022) UNITED COUNTIES INSURANCE COMPANY, LIMITED. LONDON, ENGLAND. 1909-1911.

Rectangular. "United Counties" in panel above figure in armor and "Insurance" in panel below. (Courtesy of Bertram Williams.)

(1023-1024) PEARL ASSURANCE COMPANY, LIMITED. LONDON, ENGLAND. 1914-

1023. Tin. Rectangular. 8″ x 5″. Raised silver border and white "Pearl Assurance" on green background.

1024. Tin. Rectangular. 9¾″ x 6⅞″. Border and lettering white on green background. Mark used in Palestine.

(1025) ECONOMIC INSURANCE COMPANY, LIMITED. LONDON, ENGLAND. 1914-

Tin. 12⅜″ x 8¾″. "Economic Insurance Company, Limited" in oval on band with "London England" in scrolled panel at base. From building in Greece.

1026

1027

1028

1029

1030

(1026-1027) EAGLE STAR AND BRITISH DOMINIONS INSURANCE COMPANY, LIMITED. LONDON, ENGLAND. 1917-

1026. Tin. Rectangular. 11⅜" x 6¾". Border, eagle and "1807—Eagle Star & British Dominions" painted. **Modern.** From building in Greece.

1027. Tin. Rectangular. 6⅝" x 4¹¹⁄₁₆". Border, eagle and "1807—Eagle Star & British Dominions" gold on black background. Modern. From agency in China.

(1028) THE ENGLISH INSURANCE COMPANY, LIMITED. LONDON, ENGLAND. 1919-

Tin. Shield shape. 8¼" x 9⅝". "The English Insurance Company Limited" on band across shield bearing lion rampant and rose. Modern. From building in Greece.

(1029) GUARDIAN EASTERN INSURANCE COMPANY, LIMITED. LONDON, ENGLAND. 1919-

Tin. 8⅛" x 9¼". Border, "Guardian Eastern" and design raised. Border and all lettering black. "(London)" painted at base. Design purple, black, ochre and blue.

(1030) THE WORLD AUXILIARY INSURANCE CORPORATION, LTD. LONDON, ENGLAND. 1919-

Heavy tin. Rectangular. 12¼" x 8¾". Border and "The World Auxiliary Insurance Corporation Limited" yellow on dark blue background. Design in dark blue, light blue, green, yellow and white.

200

THE UNRECORDED AND MISREPRESENTED

Britain, as a nation, has long distinguished itself by its meticulous preservation of historical records and identification of most material remains of the centuries past; it leads in anthropology, archaeology, and, in fact, in all matters retrospective. British signevierists, too, have performed a most unusual service in properly identifying the fire marks of so many companies no longer in existence. However, we have not learned of any proper identification for the mark of the Fife Insurance Company (1031) or the Sovereign Fire (1032), the latter mark having been removed for the author from a building in Istanbul, Turkey. Mark No. 1033, if it really is the mark of a fire insurance company, has never been identified. This item came to America without comment as a part of a large collection. With the natural penchant of those in England for uncovering and authenticating articles such as these, it is hoped that soon the full story of the marks can be permanently recorded.

Britain has been no different from other countries in that its signevierists are subjected to misrepresentation and fraud, possibly—if the author is allowed to indulge in literary license—a vocation of the descendants of some of the promoters of the South Sea Bubble fiasco. Their activities have continually infringed upon legitimate barter among collectors; consequently, for the unwary, we have illustrated five specimens of the faker's art. That of the Sun Insurance Office (1034) has rays unlike the standard design, while the numerals on the panel are raised, the entire appearance being so crude as to give evidence of its deception.

The Westminster Fire Office (1035) mark, illustrated here as being of cast iron, makes it quite evident that it is a misrepresentation, since that company never did use an iron plate. Also the crown and Prince of Wales' feathers are not the orthodox design. Never did the Phoenix Assurance Company (1036) issue a mark with two crossed spears (on close examination it was found that one of the spears was soldered on). The Suffolk and General (1037) mark shown was taken from a building where, in position, it looked like a genuine specimen. When closely examined, however, it was found to be made of wood, then coated with a plaster of paris-like composition and painted grey. There are so many specimens of County Fire Office (1038) marks that most collectors are generally aware of the fact that none ever contained a policy number. The one here illustrated was minutely examined, and it was discovered that the policy number panel had been cleverly soldered onto a genuine background. If this had been a new, original, and authentic sign its uniqueness would have made it almost priceless.

These references to the unrecorded, and particularly to the misrepresented, have been added to the narrative of British fire marks in the hope that they will be of assistance to those collectors who continue to search out marks not yet recorded and at the same time sharpen their judgment in detecting the spurious. In this manner signevierists in England will maintain a pace comparable to that enjoyed by the fire insurance industry of their land, perpetuating the principles of genuineness and integrity.

1031

1032

1033

1034

1035

1036

1037

1038

(1031) FIFE INSURANCE COMPANY.

Tin. Border, "Unitas" above three wreaths, and "Fife" in panel below gold on black background. There is no data available regarding this company. *(Courtesy of Bertram Williams.)*

(1032) SOVEREIGN FIRE. LONDON, ENGLAND.

Heavy sheet metal. Circular. 8¼″ in diameter. Borders, design and lettering raised. From building at Istanbul, Turkey. Mark is unique.

(1033) UNKNOWN.

Lead. 10″ x 15″. Ornate border, crest and No. "425" in relief.

(1034) SUN INSURANCE OFFICE, LIMITED. LONDON, ENGLAND. 1710-

Lead. 5″ x 6½″. The Sun never used raised policy numbers, nor did the Company use this design of "sun." Definitely a fake. *(Courtesy of Licenses and General Insurance Company, Limited.)*

(1035) WESTMINSTER FIRE OFFICE. LONDON, ENGLAND. 1717-

Cast iron. 7½″ x 10″. Company never issued a cast iron mark and the design of crown and Prince of Wales' feathers is not in the traditional style. A spurious mark. *(Courtesy of Licenses and General Insurance Company, Limited.)*

(1036) PHOENIX ASSURANCE COMPANY, LIMITED. LONDON, ENGLAND. 1782-

Copper. 7″ x 9⅞″. No Phoenix mark ever used two spears and the reverse side indicates that this is a product of the faker's art. *(Courtesy of Licenses and General Insurance Company, Limited.)*

(1037) SUFFOLK AND GENERAL COUNTRY AMICABLE INSURANCE OFFICE. BURY and IPSWICH, ENGLAND. 1799-

Wood, coated. 6⅝″ x 7¼″. A definite fake, rare in wood. *(Courtesy of Licenses and General Insurance Company, Limited.)*

(1038) COUNTY FIRE OFFICE. LONDON, ENGLAND. 1807-

Copper. 6⅝″ x 9″. Company never affixed numbers to its marks and to prove that it is a fake the reverse side indicates that the panel has been soldered onto the sign. *(Courtesy of Licenses and General Insurance Company, Limited.)*

PART FOUR

Foreign Fire Marks

FOREIGN FIRE MARKS

Because of the conditions prevailing in many of the foreign countries to which we will refer, the difficulties of research, and the limitation of space, our approach to this section must differ somewhat from that adhered to in both the American and British parts. Here, too, the general historical background of the respective nations has been one of the controlling factors in the founding and progress of the various fire insurance concerns. Although it is evident that in most cases the purposes for which fire marks were employed ran according to a fixed pattern in each of these countries, it is hoped that in the very brief sketches given in the following chapters the data presented regarding the usage of these devices will not appear too repetitious. The technically minded reader will, of course, appreciate the specific data in each instance.

Authentic source information pertaining to fire-fighting and insurance activities is not available in many instances, but we do believe that a picture of genuine historical value is presented in those countries where the record is clear. Fire-fighting methods and advances in Holland, France, Germany, and Italy formed a pattern adopted in most of the remaining countries of the world. Of course, this uniformity was due largely to the fact that so many of the places referred to existed as colonies of the sovereignties mentioned.

ALGERIA

Insurance has never attained any prominence as an independent factor in the economy of Algeria. The country's history dates back to the earliest days of civilization when twelve centuries before Christ the Phoenicians formed the first settlements. Four centuries later the Carthaginians reigned, and in 146 B.C. it became a Roman colony which was then followed by Christianity until 533 A.D. For a time Spain gained control but later gave way to the Turks. Finally, in 1830, Algeria became a French province.

Exports and commerce have never been a great factor in this Mediterranean country, and most fire insurance has been conducted by French and some British companies. The one fire mark of the *Afrique Française*, which was organized in 1887, is our sole evidence of local enterprise. Those foreign companies which operated in Algiers did use fire marks until about 1914 when the custom was discontinued. Later, the recent hostilities and need for scrap metal resulted in the disappearance of most of these marks.

1039

(1039) AFRIQUE FRANCAISE COMPAGNIE ANONYME D'ASSURANCES A PRIMES FIXES. ALGER, ALGERIA. 1887-

Tin. Rectangular. 6¹¹⁄₁₆″ x 5⁹⁄₁₆″. Raised tan letters and border on black background. Flat black letters on center panel.

ARGENTINA

The Charrua Indians were in possession of Argentina when the Spaniard, Juan Dias de Solis, landed there in 1516. At that time Argentina was the second largest country in South America. After many bloody wars and a vast increase in immigration, this Spanish colony developed into a vast producer of meats and cereals which were exported to Europe. The shipments were greatly increased later when maritime refrigeration became a reality. To this day these exports remain a prime factor in that country's economy.

From 1810 onward there had been efforts towards independence, but it was not until 1816 that the people declared one Payridon president of the new republic. A republic it has been ever since, though intermittent revolutions, counterrevolutions, and dissensions permeated its history. Such internal hostilities do not seem to have retarded the progress of the nation, for today the cities are populous and contain the same modern building construction and mechanical improvements to be found in North America and Europe. While the Argentine has furnished the outside world with foodstuffs, its imports have consisted largely of products from more industrial and mechanically productive nations.

Eight Argentinian fire insurance companies are known to have issued fire marks between 1865 and 1927. The practice of placing marks upon insured properties ceased to a great extent in 1900 for after that date a federal tax upon the owners of any property to which such a plate was affixed was imposed. This limited their use, even as an advertising medium, by foreign as well as domestic concerns.

1040 1041 1042

1043 1044

1045 1046 1047 1048

1049

(1040) LA ESTRELLA COMPANIA ARGENTINA DE SEGUROS. BUENOS AIRES, ARGENTINA. 1865-

Iron. Circular, convexed. 8½" in diameter. Brown five pointed star, blue center. Lettering in slightly raised brown letters on surrounding black background. Borders yellow.

(1041) AMERICA COMPANIA ARGENTINA DE SEGUROS. BUENOS AIRES, ARGENTINA. 1887-

Iron. Circular, convexed. 8½" in diameter. Yellow figure and lettering on blue. Borders white.

(1042) LA FRANCO ARGENTINA COMPANIA DE SEGUROS. BUENOS AIRES, ARGENTINA. 1896-

Tin. Circular. 8¾" in diameter. Vari-colored center having red surrounding band with raised gold lettering and borders.

(1043) LA GERMANO ARGENTINA COMPANIA DE SEGUROS. BUENOS AIRES, ARGENTINA. 1915-

Iron. Rectangular, convexed. 7⅞" x 5⅞". Lettering and border slightly raised in white on dark blue background.

(1044) LA ARGENTINA COMPANIA DE SEGUROS. BUENOS AIRES, ARGENTINA. 1909-1929.

Iron. Rectangular. 8¹¹⁄₁₆" x 6¹⁄₁₆". Top and bottom: white letters on light blue background. Center: light blue letters on white background. Mark bears lead tax seal of city of Buenos Aires in upper left-hand corner.

(1045-1046) COMPANIA ASEGURADORA ARGENTINA. BUENOS AIRES, ARGENTINA. 1918-

1045. Metal composition. Circular, convexed. 2⅞" in diameter. Vari-colored center design with silver lettering and borders on black band. Mark is door plate type.

1046. Alloy plate. 3½" x 4¾". Company crests at top, and center design vari-colored. Background silver. Lettering in silver on blue background. Silver and blue border. Used as door and auto plate.

(1047) LA HOLANDO SUDAMERICANA COMPANIA DE SEGUROS. BUENOS AIRES, ARGENTINA. 1921-

Alloy plate. 2¼" x 3½". Center design blue, white and gold. Name dark blue on gold. Initials dark blue on gold and white. Used as door and auto plate.

(1048) EL PLATA COMPANIA DE SEGUROS GENERALES. BUENOS AIRES, ARGENTINA. 1924-

Alloy plate. 2⅞" x 3½". Old sailing vessel and "El Plata" in white. Border and "Seguros" metal color. Background light and dark blue. Used as door and auto plate.

(1049) MERCURIO SOCIETE ANONIMA DE SEGUROS GENERALES. BUENOS AIRES, ARGENTINA. 1927-

Border, name and emblems raised. (*Courtesy of Chartered Insurance Institute.*)

AUSTRIA

The first fire mark referred to in this section represents a company formed in 1824; the last one belongs to a company formed in 1925. Austria, a powerful empire up to the third quarter of the nineteenth century, was greatly reduced by nineteenth-century revolutionary movements and by the rising power of Prussia. After World War I its population area was reduced to little more than the original archduchy of Austria, a direct result of land reallocation which involved the creation of the present Czechoslovakia, Hungary, and Yugoslavia.

Fire marks have been used in Austria to identify insured properties for the benefit of fire-fighting brigades since the founding of its first company. Their need disappeared at about the same time as in America and Britain, however, and the later issues were used principally for publicity purposes. They were also adopted for distribution in the Mediterranean area.

Versichert
bei
Wechselseitige Brandschaden
und Janus

Gegründet 1824

1050

Versichert
bei
Tiroler Landes-
Brandversicherung.

1051

1052

Landes
Brandversicherung

1054

Landes
Brandversicherung

1055

1053

1056

Wechselseitige
Brandschaden
Versicherungs-
Anstalt
in Graz
GEGRÜNDET 1828

K.k.priv.
wechselseitige
Brandschaden-
Versicherungs-Anstalt
in
Graz.

C.k.priv.
vzajemna
zavarovalnica
proti požarnej škodi
v
Gradcu.

1057

PHÉNIX AUTRICHIEN

FONDÉ À VIENNE EN 1860

1058

PHÉNIX

AUTRICHIEN

FONDÉ EN 1860

1059

ALLGEMEINE
VERSICHERUNGS-
GESELLSCHAFT
PHÖNIX

1061

ALLGEMEINE
VERSICHERUNGS-
GESELLSCHAFT
PHÖNIX

1062

K.k.priv.Oesterreich.
Versicherungs-Gesellschaft
"DONAU"
in WIEN.

1063

ΦΟΙΝΙΞ
1860
ΒΙΕΝΝΗΣ

1060

Versichert
"DONAU"

1064

Ο ΔΟΥΝΑΒΙΣ
1867
ΑΣΦΑΛΕΙΑΙ

1065

DANUBE
GENERAL INSURANCE COMPANY LTD

1066

VERSICHERT
BEI
ANGLO-ELEMENTAR

1067

ANGOL-
ELEMI
BIZTOSÍTÓ R.T.

1068

ANGLO
-
ELEMENTAR

1069

Kärntner
Landes-Brandschaden

1070

208

1071

(1050) WECHSELSEITIGE BRANDSCHADEN UND JANUS ALLGEMEINE VERSICHERUNGS-ANSTALT AUF GEGENSEITIGKEIT. VIENNA, AUSTRIA. 1824-

Tin. 7″ x 5″. Raised cream lettering and border on green ground.

(1051-1055) TIROLER LANDES BRANDSCHADEN VERSICHERUNGS ANSTALT. INNSBRUCK, AUSTRIA. 1825-

1051. Brass. Rectangular. 7⅞″ x 4″. Figure, border, and slightly raised lettering polished brass. Black background.

1052. Brass. Rectangular. 7⅞″ x 2⅜″. Figure, border, and slightly raised lettering polished brass. Black background.

1053. Brass. Triangular. 8¾″ x 7″. Red letters, border and figure cut into plate on black background.

1054. Iron. Triangular. 7⅛″ x 5½″. Black lettering and red figure on white background.

1055. Iron. Triangular. 8½″ x 7″. Black lettering and red figure on white background.

(1056-1057) WECHSELSEITIGE BRANDSCHADEN VERSICHERUNGS ANSTALT IN GRAZ. GRAZ, AUSTRIA. 1829-

1056. Tin. 6⅞″ x 9¾″. Raised cream, black and red lettering and emblem on dark green background. Raised cream and red border.

1057. Tin. 10″ x 7″. Border, raised silver lettering and crest on dark green background.

(1058-1062) ALLGEMEINE VERSICHERUNGS GESELLSCHAFT PHONIX. VIENNA, AUSTRIA. 1860-

1058. Heavy tin. Rectangular. 11⅜″ x 8⅞″. Raised border, lettering and figure. From building in Greece.

1059. Tin. Rectangular. 6⅝″ x 9″. Raised lettering, figure and border. From building in Istanbul, Turkey.

1060. Tin. 10″ x 6¾″. Raised cream colored lettering and border on dark green ground.

1061. Tin. Rectangular. 5¾″ x 7¾″. Raised red lettering and circular emblem on cream ground. Rolled outer border. Inner border red.

1062. Tin. Rectangular. 5¾″ x 7¾″. Raised cream lettering and circular emblem on bright green background. Rolled outer border. Inner border cream.

(1063-1066) DONAU ALLGEMEINE VERSICHERUNGS AKTIEN GESELLSCHAFT. VIENNA, AUSTRIA. 1867-

1063. Tin. Rectangular. 7¼″ x 10⅛″. Raised lettering, border and crest.

1064. Tin. Rectangular. 7″ x $5\frac{1}{16}$″. Lettering and border in raised white on green background.

1065. Tin. Oval. 9½″ x 6⅞″. Raised white border and lettering on blue background.

1066. Tin. Rectangular. 11″ x $7\frac{13}{16}$″. Red and black on white background. Lettering and design red, black and white on white background.

(1067-1069) ANGLO ELEMENTAR VERSICHERUNGS AKTIEN GESELLSCHAFT. VIENNA, AUSTRIA. 1897-

1067. Tin. Rectangular. 8⅞″ x 6¼″. Raised red border and lettering on white background.

1068. Aluminum. Rectangular. 6¾″ x 4⅝″. Natural metal background. Black lettering and border.

1069. Tin. Rectangular. 6¾″ x 4¾″. Raised white letters and border on blue background.

(1070) KARNTNERISCHE LANDES BRANDSCHADEN VERSICHERUNGS ANSTALT. KLAGENFURT, AUSTRIA. 1899-

Iron. Triangular. 9″ x 7¼″. Black lettering, black, yellow, orange and white crest and orange border on white background.

(1071) STEIRER VERSICHERUNGS AKTIEN GESELLSCHAFT. GRAZ, AUSTRIA. 1902-Reorganized in 1923.

Tin. 5⅞″ x 5⅛″. Raised cream letters, crest and border on bright green background.

1072

1073

1074

(1072) ANGLO DANUBIAN LLOYD ALLGEMEINE VER-
SICHERUNGS AKTIEN GESELLSCHAFT. VIENNA,
AUSTRIA. 1918-

Heavy tin. 6⅜″ x 5⅜″. Cream border, trademark and lettering
raised on blue background.

(1073) VERSICHERUNGS AKTIENGESELLSCHAFT
"GLOBUS." VIENNA, AUSTRIA. 1920-

Tin. Rectangular. 5½″ x 4¾″. Blue and white globe, deep
yellow lettering with "Globus" raised. White border. Blue background.

(1074) BURGENLANDISCHE VERSICHERUNGSANSTALT.
EISENSTADT, AUSTRIA. 1925-

Tin. Rectangular. 8⅝″ x 6½″. Raised red border and lettering
with slightly raised vari-colored emblem on light grey background.

AZORES

The three islands comprising the Azores group
were probably first visited by the Carthaginians
whose coins were discovered on the island of Corvo.
Pedro Alvarez Cabral reached this island in 1432. In
1444 he took possession of the island of St. Michael
in behalf of Portugal. In their early days, these islands
were the grand rendezvous for various fleets of ships
on their voyages home from the Indies. Portuguese
inhabitants predominate, but because of the frequent
visits of the ships there was also an admixture of
Flemish, Moors, English, Scotch, and Irish which
provided a heterogeneous population. That, too, was
true of the variation of fire insurance companies
which provided security for the inhabitants of these
islands. The one domestic exception, whose fire mark
is depicted here, is the Acoriana, headquartered at
Ponta Delgada on the island of St. Michael. There
were two good reasons for this dearth of fire insurance institutions: one was the limited population and
its minor industries, and the other was an inherent fire
hazard. In 1522 the capital of St. Michael's as well as
its good citizens was buried by a volcanic eruption.
Additional volcanic convulsions and earthquakes visited the island in 1630, 1652, 1656 and every century
thereafter, providing a discouragement to even the
most optimistic insurance underwriter.

1075

(1075) COMPANIA DE SEGUROS ACORIANA. PONTA
DELGADA, AZORES. 1892-

Tin. Rectangular. 6¾″ x 9½″. Gold lettering, trademark and
border on blue background.

BELGIUM

Considering that at the start of the century Belgium ranked only sixteenth in point of area among the European countries, we begin to seek out the reasons for the widespread use of fire marks by at least twenty-two insurance companies which began business between 1819 and 1917. The Kingdom of Belgium is one of the world's most densely populated areas and has ranked relatively high in world significance. Well-nourished land through which flows the Scheldt, its principal river, an abundant forest, and mineral resources contribute to the success of its industries and commerce.

In 1830 Belgium proclaimed its independence and established a constitutional hereditary monarchy. A well-organized assembly, truly representative of the people, was responsible for favorable internal conditions. In this stable atmosphere the *Compagnie Belge D'Assurances Générales* was founded in 1830 and enjoyed an uninterrupted success. Under the most competently regulated of all of the monarchies of Europe, this country was able to maintain a solid front in agriculture, industry, and commerce, including the establishment of sound and continuous fire insurance concerns. In like manner, fire fighting and extinguishment became an advanced art in Belgium sixty years before the forming of its first fire insurance plan. Both under French domination, prior to her independence, and following it, the use of fire marks was the custom. Even during the period of recent wars these marks could still be seen on buildings in Belgium's cities. Some of those shown upon these pages were secured by American soldiers.

1077

1078

1079

1076

1080

(1076-1077) COMPAGNIE D'ASSURANCE D'ANVERS SECURITAS SOCIETE ANONYME. ANTWERP, BELGIUM. 1819-

1076. Lead. Oval. 7″ x 9″. Raised figure and lettering in gold on black background. Rolled border.

1077. Tin. Oval. 7⅜″ x 9⅜″. Raised figure and lettering in gold on black background. Rolled border.

(1078-1079) COMPAGNIE DE BRUXELLES SOCIETE ANONYME POUR L'ASSURANCE A PRIMES CONTRE L'INCENDIE, LA FOUDRE ET LES EXPLOSIONS. BRUSSELS, BELGIUM. 1821-

1078. Tin. 8¾″ x 11⅛″. Raised gold center figure and lettering on black background. Raised border.

1079. Tin. 9″ x 11⅛″. Raised center figure and lettering in gold on black background. Raised border. Stamping not as deep as mark No. 1078.

(1080) COMPAGNIE D'ASSURANCE DE L'ESCAUT SOCIETE ANONYME D'ASSURANCES MARITIMES CONTRE L'INCENDIE & LES ACCIDENTS. ANVERS, BELGIUM. 1821-

Tin. Oval. 9¼″ x 7″. Raised border, raised gold lettering and center figure on black background. Gold trim inside border.

P. R.

1081

1082

BELGISCHE VEREENIGING
UNION BELGE

1083

VEREENIGING
UNION

1084

A. G.
BRUXELLES

1085

LA BELGIQUE

1086

LA BELGIQUE

1087

LOYD BELGE
ANVERS

1088

LES
PROVINCES RÉUNIES
1887
ASSURANCES
BRUXELLES

1089

DE
VEREENIGDE
PROVINCIEN
VERZEKERINGEN
1887
BRUSSEL

1090

U.P.B.
BRUXELLES

1091

LE GLOBE
ASSURANCES

1092

LA
PATRIE

1093

LA SAUVEGARDE
BRUXELLES

1094

LA SAUVEGARDE
BRUXELLES

1095

LA SAUVEGARDE
BRUXELLES

1096

PATRIOTIQUE
Antwerpen

1097

ASSURANCES
PRÉVOYANCE AGRICOLE
AMORTISSEMENT

1098

PREVOYANCE SOCIALE
ASSURANCES   BRUXELLES

1099

Versichert
GARANTIE FÉDÉRALE

1100

(1081) COMPAGNIE DES PROPRIETAIRES REUNIS. BRUSSELS, BELGIUM. 1821-

Tin. Rectangular. 11½" x 7¾". Border, initials and design raised gold on black background.

(1082) ESPERANCE BELGE. BRUSSELS, BELGIUM. 1924-

Zinc. Rectangular. 9¹¹⁄₁₆" x 6⅝". Border, anchor and lettering raised. From building in Greece.

(1083-1084) L'UNION BELGE SOCIETE ANONYME D'ASSURANCES CONTRE L'INCENDIE LES EXPLOSIONS & LE CHOMAGE. BRUSSELS, BELGIUM. 1824-

1083. Tin. Oval. 7¹⁄₁₆" x 9⅛". Raised gold lettering, clasped hands and arrows on black background. Raised border.

1084. Tin. Oval. 7⅛" x 9⅛". Raised gold lettering, clasped hands and arrows on black background. Raised border.

(1085) COMPAGNIE BELGE D'ASSURANCES GENERALES CONTRE LES RISQUES D'INCENDIE SOCIETE ANONYME. BRUSSELS, BELGIUM. 1830-

Tin. Rectangular. 11" x 8¼". Lettering in raised gold with black background. Border raised.

(1086-1087) LA BELGIQUE SOCIETE ANONYME COMPAGNIE D'ASSURANCES. BRUSSELS, BELGIUM. 1855-

1086. Zinc. Rectangular. 9" x 6⅝". Lettering, crown and border raised.

1087. Tin. Rectangular. 9" x 6⅝". Raised gold letters and oval. Crown red and gold. Pale blue background. Border raised.

(1088) LE LLOYD BELGE SOCIETE ANONYME D'ASSURANCES. ANTWERP, BELGIUM. 1856-

Tin. Rectangular. 11¼" x 8". Lettering and border in raised gold with black background.

(1089-1090) LES PROVINCES REUNIES COMPAGNIE ANONYME D'ASSURANCES. BRUSSELS, BELGIUM. 1887-

1089. Tin. Rectangular. 9¹³⁄₁₆" x 7⅞". Green border, lettering in gold and green with black background.

1090. Tin. Rectangular. 9¹³⁄₁₆" x 7⅞". Green border, lettering in gold and green with black background.

(1091) UNION DES PROPRIETAIRES BELGES. BRUSSELS, BELGIUM. 1890-

Tin. Rectangular. 8⅜" x 5¾". Border and raised lettering cream with dark blue background.

(1092) LE GLOBE COMPAGNIE BELGE D'ASSURANCES SOCIETE ANONYME. MONS, BELGIUM. 1898-

Tin. 9¹⁄₁₆" x 6⁵⁄₁₆". Raised gold lettering and border with black background.

(1093) LA PATRIE, CIE AN. D'ASSURANCES ET DE REASSURANCES. BRUSSELS, BELGIUM. 1901-

Tin. Rectangular. Raised border, oval and name. *(Courtesy of Chartered Insurance Institute.)*

(1094-1096) LA SAUVEGARDE COMPAGNIE BELGE D'ASSURANCES. BRUSSELS, BELGIUM. 1904-

1094. Tin. Oval. 9¹³⁄₁₆" x 7⅜". Raised gold border with raised cream and gold lettering. Gold, cream and black trademark raised in center. Blue background. "4,000,000 Francs" painted.

1095. Tin. Oval. 9¹³⁄₁₆" x 7⅜". Raised gold border and raised cream and gold lettering. Gold, cream and black trademark raised in center. Blue background. "Capital 5,000,000" painted.

1096. Tin. Oval. 9¹³⁄₁₆" x 7⅜". Raised gold border and raised white and gold lettering. Gold, white and black trademark raised in center. Blue background. "Capital 6,000,000" painted.

(1097) PATRIOTIQUE SOCIETE ANONYME. ANTWERP, BELGIUM. 1906-

Tin. Rectangular. 9¾" x 6¾". Raised white lettering with blue background. Blue and white border.

(1098) LA PREVOYANCE AGRICOLE. BRUSSELS, BELGIUM. Prior to 1907.

Zinc. Rectangular. 11⅞" x 8¾". Raised gold lettering. Green center oval with raised gold edge on black background. Border raised.

(1099) LA PREVOYANCE SOCIALE SOCIETE COOPERATIVE D'ASSURANCES. BRUSSELS, BELGIUM. 1907-

Iron. Rectangular, convexed. 11½" x 19⅜". Design blue, orange, black and white. Blue and white borders. White lettering.

(1100) LA GARANTIE NATIONALE SOCIETE ANONYME BELGE D'ASSURANCES. BRUSSELS, BELGIUM. 1909-

Tin. Rectangular. 8⅛" x 5⅝". Raised border, horse and lettering.

1101

1102

1104

1103

(1101) UNION DES ASSUREURS COMPAGNIE D'ASSURANCES SOCIETE ANONYME BELGE. BRUSSELS, BELGIUM. 1910-

Iron. 9¾" x 13¾". Red bordered shield of dark blue with red, white and blue lettering on light blue background. Lettering below, red and white. Border white.

(1102) LA MINERVA DE BELGIQUE SOCIETE ANONYME. ANTWERP, BELGIUM. 1913-

Lead. Diamond shape. 16½" x 9¾". Raised oval border and lettering. From a destroyed residence at Locre near Bailleul, Belgium, February, 1917.

(1103) LE PHENIX BELGE SOCIETE ANONYME D'ASSURANCES ET DE REASSURANCES. ANTWERP, BELGIUM. 1913-

Zinc. Rectangular. 9" x 10¾". Borders, phoenix and lettering raised.

(1104) NIVEZE PREVOYANCE SOCIETE COOPERATIVE D'ASSURANCES CONTRE L'INCENDIE ET LA FOUDRE. NIVEZE-SPA, BELGIUM. 1917-

Iron. Rectangular. 6⅜" x 4¼". Raised white lettering on dark blue background.

BRAZIL

To most of us Brazil means that greatest of all rivers, the Amazon. It also means coffee, castor beans, rice, cotton, cocoa, wheat, and sugar cane, all in abundant quantities. This land was discovered in 1499 by a companion of Columbus, Vincent Yanez Pincon, who took possession in the name of the Spanish government. The next year, however, Cabral, a Portuguese, claimed it for his country.

Brazil was administered by the Portuguese who saw it through a gold rush and the discovery of diamond mines until its declaration of independence as a Brazilian Empire in 1822 after which Dom Pedro II reigned as emperor. This ruler was universally loved and respected, particularly for his affectionate interest in the welfare of his subjects. Under his lead-

ership the immigration to Brazil increased, and the population multiplied ten times. During Dom Pedro's reign five of the fourteen Brazilian fire insurance companies listed in this chapter were formed. They were brought into existence because of the great commercial progress of the period.

Those who wanted a republic, together with the army, caused an overthrow of the monarchy. A constitutional government was set up in 1889 and was effective until 1930 when the revolution placed the country under a provisional president. The record of companies whose marks are shown here takes us up to 1920, at which time a tax was imposed by the municipalities upon companies utilizing such a sign. Consequently the practice was abandoned.

1105

1106

1107

1108

1109

1110

1111

1112

1113

(1105) COMPANHIA INTERESSE PUBLICO SEGURO CONTRA FOGO BAHIA. SALVADOR, STATE OF BAHIA, BRAZIL. 1853-1928.

Tin. Oval. 11½" x 8½". Borders, building and lettering raised.

(1106-1107) COMPANHIA ALLIANCA DA BAHIA DE SEGUROS MARITIMOS E TERRESTRES. SAN SALVADOR, STATE OF BAHIA, BRAZIL. 1870-

1106. Tin. 11½" x 8½". Design and lettering raised gold on black background. Ornate raised border had been colored.

1107. Iron. Oval, convexed. 11½" x 7½". Red lettering on white center panel. White border and lettering on blue background.

(1108) PREVIDENTE CIA DE SEGUROS MARITIMOS E TERRESTRES. RIO DE JANEIRO, BRAZIL. 1872-

Tin. Rectangular. Raised gold border and lettering on black background. (Courtesy of V. R. Willemson.)

(1109-1110) COMPANHIA DE SEGUROS PARAENSE. BELEM, STATE OF PARA, BRAZIL. 1878-1925.

1109. Iron. Shield shape. 5½" x 9¼". Red background, white border and lettering.

1110. Iron. 6" x 6¾". Yellow and white lettering. Yellow, orange, blue, black and white pattern. Yellow border. Black background.

(1111-1112) COMPANHIA DE SEGUROS COMMERCIAL DO PARA. BELEM, STATE OF PARA, BRAZIL. 1882-

1111. Iron. Oval. 6½" x 8¼". Black background with gold lettering—red center shield shape, and anchor in white. Raised gold border and lettering. Shield with raised border and anchor in red, white and gold. Black pebbled background.

1112. Iron. Oval, convexed. 6½" x 8½". Blue background, white border and lettering, center shield brick red with white.

(1113) COMPANHIA "UNIAO" DE SEGUROS MARITIMOS E TERRESTRES. STATE OF RIO GRANDE DO SUL, BRAZIL. 1891-

Iron. Oval. 4¼" x 2¾". White background, black lettering and design.

215

1114   1115   1116   1117

1118   1119   1120

1121   1122

(1114)   COMPANHIA DE SEGUROS LEALDADE. BELEM, STATE OF PARA, BRAZIL.   1893-1920.

Iron.   7¼″ x 7¼″.   Border, lettering and lion raised.

(1115)   AMAZONIA COMPANHIA DE SEGUROS TERRES-TRES E MARITIMOS. BELEM, STATE OF PARA, BRAZIL. 1894-1925.

Iron.   9″ x 11½″.   Brick red background with white lettering. Castle and flames at top. Shield slightly convexed.

(1116)   LLOYD PARAENSE. BELEM, STATE OF PARA, BRAZIL.   1899-

Tin.   Shield shape.   7½″ x 9½″.   Border, lettering and crest raised.

(1117)   BRAZIL SEGURADORA EDIFICADORA. BELEM, STATE OF PARA, BRAZIL.   1910-1931.

Iron.   Oval, slightly convexed.   7⅞″ x 6½″.   Red, white and blue oval with white border and lettering.

(1118)   LLOYD AMAZONESE. MANAOS, STATE OF AMAZONAS, BRAZIL.   1910-1917.

Iron.   Shield shape, slightly convexed.   8¾″ x 10″.   White background with brick red lettering.

(1119)   COMPANHIA AMERICANA DE SEGUROS. SAO PAULO, BRAZIL.   1918-

Tin.   Rectangular.   7¹⁵⁄₁₆″ x 5¹³⁄₁₆″.   Blue background with raised gold crest, border and lettering. Flat black lettering at bottom.

(1120-1121)   COMPANHIA INTERNACIONAL DE SEGUROS. RIO DE JANEIRO, BRAZIL.   1920-

1120.   Tin.   Rectangular.   11½″ x 4⅛″.   Gold border and lettering with red background.

1121.   Iron.   Rectangular, convexed.   11⅞″ x 4¾″.   Blue with white lettering and blue silhouette of mountain scene on white.

(1122)   SAGRES COMPANHIA DE SEGUROS. RIO DE JANEIRO, BRAZIL.   ? -

Tin.   Oval.   7¼″ x 9½″.   Slightly raised gold border, gold lettering and vari-colored crest. Scrolled ribbon blue with black letters.

BRITISH GUIANA

Britain's sole possession in South America proper is the Crown Colony of British Guiana. First settled by the Dutch during the seventeenth century, this possession was ceded to the English at the close of the Napoleonic wars. Two fire insurance companies have remained active there for many years. Originally they purchased the fire-fighting equipment for the towns in the colony and also provided two fire boats. They have continued to contribute substantially to the maintenance of this apparatus, and as a consequence the fire brigades have quite naturally given preference to properties insured by them. That is one of the reasons for the continued use of fire marks in British Guiana, holding inviolate the traditions of the past.

1123

1124

1125

1126

1127

(1123) THE HAND-IN-HAND MUTUAL GUARANTEE FIRE INSURANCE COMPANY OF BRITISH GUIANA, LIMITED. GEORGETOWN, BRITISH GUIANA. 1865-

Tin. Oval. 6⁹⁄₁₆″ x 5¹⁄₁₆″. Raised red border, lettering and clasped hands. Raised black letters on raised red ribbons.

(1124-1125) THE BRITISH GUIANA MUTUAL FIRE INSURANCE COMPANY, LTD. GEORGETOWN, BRITISH GUIANA. 1880-1923.

1124. Copper. Raised borders, lettering and design of old company trademark. Three tabs for affixing to building. (*Courtesy of V. R. Willemson.*)

1125. Copper. Circular. 7⅛″ in diameter. Raised borders, lettering and design of old company trademark. Three tabs for affixing to building. Much heavier stamping than No. 1124.

(1126-1127) THE BRITISH GUIANA AND TRINIDAD MUTUAL FIRE INSURANCE COMPANY, LTD. GEORGETOWN, BRITISH GUIANA. 1923-

1126. Tin. Shield shape. 4⅞″ x 7″. Red and white lettering on green background with red and white torches. White "Protection" and borders on red band. Shield border red.

1127. Aluminum. Circular. 7″ in diameter. Raised borders, lettering and design black on silver ground.

BULGARIA

Linguistically the Bulgarians are related to the eastern branch of the Slavic people. The main body of the country's population is descended from people who migrated from the region between the Volga and the Urals in the seventh century of our era. The people are industrious and the land is productive, especially of juice fruits, but progress has been re-strained by an endless succession of international conflicts and internal political strife. The numerous fire marks issued by the companies formed in the three decades which straddle the turn of the century indicate an aggressive commerce during that period, a condition which now is controlled principally from outside sources.

1128

1129

1130

1131

1132

1133

1134

1135

1136

1137

1138

1139

1140

1141

1142

1143

(1128-1130) BULGARIA PREMIERE SOCIETE BULGARE D'ASSURANCES. SOFIA, BULGARIA. 1891-

1128. Tin. Oval. 9⅜" x 5⅞". Lettering and figure raised.

1129. Tin. Oval. 10⁵⁄₁₆" x 6¾". Raised lettering, characters and figure. From building in Istanbul, Turkey.

1130. Tin. Oval. Border, lettering and crest slightly raised. *(Courtesy of V. R. Willemson.)*

(1131-1134) SOCIETE NATIONALE D'ASSURANCES BALKAN INCENDIE ET TRANSPORTS. SOFIA, BULGARIA. 1895-

1131. • Tin. Oval. 13" x 9". Border and lettering raised.

1132. Tin. Oval. 10" x 7⅛". Raised borders, lettering, characters and figure.

1133. Tin. Oval, slightly convexed. 10⅛" x 7¼". Raised border, lettering, characters and branches of oak leaves had been gold. Black background.

1134. Tin. Rectangular. 9¾" x 6½". Vari-colored crest with raised silver letters on dark green center oval. Cream background. Raised border red and dark green.

(1135) SOCIETE COOPERATIVE D'ASSURANCES ET D'EPARGNE DES FONCTIONNAIRES BULGARES. SOFIA, BULGARIA. 1905-

Tin. Oval. 10" x 7". Deep yellow lettering and border, and vari-colored design on dark blue background, all raised.

(1136-1137) OREL SOCIETE BULGARE D'ASSURANCES GENERALES. SOFIA, BULGARIA. 1914-

1136. Tin. Rectangular. 12⅛" x 8³⁄₁₆". Raised yellow border, lettering and design. Black panel on blue background.

1137. Tin. Rectangular. 8¼" x 6". Raised yellow border, lettering and design. Black panel on blue background. *(Courtesy of V. R. Willemson.)*

(1138-1139) LE PHENIX BULGARE SOCIETE ANONYME D'ASSURANCES. SOFIA, BULGARIA. 1917-

1138. Tin. Oval. 10" x 7⅛". Raised red border, gold phoenix with colored flames, and cream lettering on dark green background.

1139. Tin. Oval. 9⅞" x 6⅞". Raised gold border and phoenix, raised cream letters. Dark blue background.

(1140) RODINA SOCIETE BULGARE D'ASSURANCES GENERALES. SOFIA, BULGARIA. 1917-

Tin. Oval. 10" x 6¹⁵⁄₁₆". Raised black border and lettering on yellow background.

(1141-1142) L'EUROPE SOCIETE BULGARE D'ASSURANCES GENERALES. SOFIA, BULGARIA. 1918-

1141. Tin. 5⅛" x 5⅛". Pale gold border, lettering and beading. Circle oyster-white with tan and blue design. Brown lettering flat. Blue background. Border, gold lettering and design raised.

1142. Tin. 9½" x 6¾". Gold border, lettering and beading. Oval cream color with tan and blue design. Brown lettering flat. Blue background. Border, lettering and design raised.

(1143) SILA COMPAGNIE BULGARE D'ASSURANCES GENERALES. SOFIA, BULGARIA. 1918-

Tin. Oval. 5¾" x 4". Border and lettering white on green background.

The historic and economic conditions of Canada, that good neighbor of the United States, have in many instances paralleled those within the United States and contributed to the establishment of fire insurance companies in the Dominion. Almost nowhere else in the world do the people of two governments correspond so closely in their habits of living, their ideals, and their economics as they do in these two countries.

Until recent years most Canadians did not believe that the custom of attaching fire marks to buildings was followed in their country. However, in the archives of the Quebec Fire Insurance Company in the city of Quebec are records to substantiate the fact that one of that city's first fire pumpers was owned by this insurance concern. It was used for the benefit of their policyholders and the fire mark of that company shown here was adopted to identify the insured buildings to the members of this company-operated brigade. The engine was lost in the great fire on Sault-au-Matelot in lower town on April 10, 1826.

Conflagrations were frequent in this port city but the greatest occurred on May 28, 1845, when over three thousand houses were destroyed and twenty thousand persons were made homeless. According to the history of the Quebec fire department submitted by that brigade's Director K. Beaulieu, other insurance companies also employed their own brigades until 1866 when fire fighting became a municipal establishment. With this change the need for fire marks in this community lost their original significance.

Of those Canadian marks illustrated here only two came from local communities; the remainder were used by Canadian insurance representatives in distant countries. The customs of those who emigrated from both England and France, lead all to suspect that fire marks followed the national customs throughout the older cities of the Dominion. It is hoped that additional new marks of local companies will still come to light. The distant places disclosing those presently recorded should produce more unique specimens.

1144

1145

1146

1147

1148

1149

1150

1151

(1144) QUEBEC FIRE ASSURANCE COMPANY. QUEBEC, P. Q., CANADA. 1818-

Lead. Oval. Border, design and lettering raised. *(Courtesy of V. R. Willemson.)*

(1145-1147) BRITISH AMERICA ASSURANCE COMPANY. TORONTO, ONTARIO, CANADA. 1833-

1145. Tin. Odd shape. Lettering and border raised. *(Courtesy of V. R. Willemson.)*

1146. Tin. 5″ x 6″. Border and lettering cream on dark blue background.

1147. Tin. Diamond shape. 6½″ x 6½″. Raised border, lettering and Chinese characters gold on light green background.

(1148-1150) WESTERN ASSURANCE COMPANY. TORONTO, ONTARIO, CANADA. 1851-

1148. Copper. Arrowhead shape. 6½″ x 10¼″. Gold and black lettering, gold date and black borders raised. Red background. Black panel.

1149. Tin. Arrowhead shape. 6¾″ x 10⅛″. Border and lettering raised. From building in Greece.

1150. Tin. Arrowhead shape. 6⅞″ x 10¼″. Border and lettering raised. Painted characters. From building in Greece.

(1151) AGRICULTURAL INSURANCE COMPANY, LIMITED. REGINA, SASKATCHEWAN, CANADA. 1920-

Tin. Rectangular. Border and lettering painted. *(Courtesy of V. R. Willemson.)*

CHINA

China is one of the most ancient countries of the Far East. A succession of revolutions has affected her life and enterprise systems from the earliest times up to our own day. China's origins are lost in the mists of pre-history. Her legendary history takes us back to the period of the Five Rulers (2852-2255 B.C.) but the first Chinese dynasty definitely established by archaeology is the Shang-Yin (1766-1154 B.C.). By the time of the Shang-Yin dynasty the basic structure of the Chinese language as we now know it had been established, and Chinese handicrafts had reached a high state of perfection. The legendary Five Rulers are probably as well known to the Chinese people as any others in their long history and this mainly through the writings of the great philosopher Confucius (551-478 B.C.) who selected two of these rulers, Yao and Shun, as examples of the sage king who rules by moral suasion and not by force. Confucius left for the Chinese people a pattern of life and conduct which has had tremendous influence on them ever since.

As far back as 1835, Chinese fire insurance companies issued marks. The many ornate plates on these pages register the high development of their decorative arts. While used to identify insured properties for the fire brigades the popularity of these marks was due to their presumed ability to keep away the evil spirit of fire. Most signs contain characters which denote "good luck," a device which induces even the modern householder to demand a fire mark.

1152

1153

1154

1155

1157

1158

1159

1156

1161

1162

1163

1160

1164

1165

1166

1167

1168

1169

(1152-1153) UNION INSURANCE SOCIETY OF CANTON, LIMITED. HONGKONG, CHINA. 1835-

1152. Tin. Circular. 8¼" in diameter. Black borders, black lettering and gold design raised. Convexed inner circle blue with surrounding gold band.

1153. Tin. 7" x 9½". Raised gold borders, lettering and Chinese characters on black and red background.

(1154) NORTH CHINA INSURANCE COMPANY, LTD. SHANGHAI, CHINA. 1863-

Tin. Circular. 8" in diameter. Raised gold borders, lettering and Chinese characters. Vari-colored center design raised.

(1155) THE BRITISH TRADERS INSURANCE COMPANY, LIMITED. HONGKONG, CHINA. 1865-

Tin. 7¼" x 8½". Borders, lettering and Chinese characters raised gold. Background black and red.

(1156-1157) HONGKONG FIRE INSURANCE COMPANY, LTD. HONGKONG, CHINA. 1868-

1156. Copper. Circular. 8¼" in diameter. Red and gold raised design and gold Chinese characters on black center circle. Raised gold lettering and Chinese characters on surrounding red band. Raised borders red.

1157. Tin. 8½" x 6¾". Slightly raised black and white lettering and Chinese characters, vari-colored design and red and black border. Red background.

(1158-1159) CHINA FIRE INSURANCE COMPANY, LIMITED. HONGKONG, CHINA. 1870-

1158. Tin. Raised border, lettering and Chinese characters. (Courtesy of V. R. Willemson.)

1159. Tin. 7½" x 6½". Company name and characters raised gold on red background. Raised Maltese Cross dark green.

(1160) YANGTSZE INSURANCE ASSOCIATION, LIMITED. SHANGHAI, CHINA. 1889-

Tin. Circular. 6⅝" in diameter. Raised white Chinese characters on red inner circle. Raised white lettering on blue band. Raised gold border.

(1161-1162) THE WAH AN FIRE AND MARINE INSURANCE COMPANY, LIMITED. SHANGHAI, CHINA. 1906-

1161. Tin. Rectangular. 6¼" x 8¾". Green, gold and silver design and gold Chinese characters raised on red background. Raised border.

1162. Tin. 4¾" x 6⅞". Red, green, yellow design and gold lettering and Chinese characters raised on black background. Natural tin border.

(1163-1164) THE CHINA UNION FIRE AND MARINE INSURANCE COMPANY, LTD. SHANGHAI, CHINA. About 1907-1915.

1163. Tin. Rectangular. 9" x 6¼". Gold lettering and Chinese characters and vari-colored emblem raised on black background. Raised border.

1164. Tin. Rectangular. 9" x 6¼". Gold lettering and Chinese characters and vari-colored emblem raised on black background. Raised border. Lettering differs from No. 1163.

(1165-1166) LUN TAI MUTUAL FIRE AND MARINE INSURANCE COMPANY, LTD. SHANGHAI, CHINA. 1910-

1165. Iron. Shield shape. 6¼" x 7¼". Border and Chinese characters white on blue background.

1166. Tin. 6" x 7". Vari-colored design. Raised white characters on red band, raised red lettering on white and raised gold borders.

(1167) YEUNG SHING FIRE INSURANCE AND INVESTMENT COMPANY, LTD. CANTON, CHINA. 1912-

Tin. Rectangular. 8½" x 6¼". Raised border, lettering and characters had been black. Raised vari-colored flags. Background had been green.

(1168-1169) WING ON FIRE & MARINE INSURANCE COMPANY, LIMITED. HONGKONG, CHINA. 1915-

1168. Tin. Rectangular. 6⅝" x 6⅞". Natural tin background with gold-trimmed blue shield having gold characters, red lettering and black and white design.

1169. Tin. Shield shape. 6½" x 6¾". Raised gold border on blue shield having raised gold characters and red lettering with black and white emblem.

1170

1171

1172

1173

1174

1175

1176

1177

1178

1179

1180

1181

1182

1183

1184

1185

1186

1187

(1170) THE FAR EASTERN INSURANCE COMPANY, LIMITED. SHANGHAI, CHINA. 1917-

Tin. Circular. 6⅝″ in diameter. Dark blue center with raised white characters. Surrounding red band with raised white letters and gold border.

(1171) SHANGHAI INSURANCE OFFICE. SHANGHAI, CHINA. 1921-

Iron. Shield shape. 6½″ x 9⅛″. Crown and Cross above. Lettering and characters black with gold trimmings on red background.

(1172) TUNG YIH TRUST COMPANY, LIMITED. SHANGHAI, CHINA. 1921-

Iron. Oval. 6⅞″ x 5″. White Chinese characters and circle on dark blue background.

(1173-1174) AMERICAN ASIATIC UNDERWRITERS FEDERAL INC., U. S. A. SHANGHAI, CHINA. 1923-

1173. Tin. Rectangular. 7⁷⁄₁₆″ x 5⅞″. Red border and letters raised on yellow background. Red characters flat.

1174. Tin. Diamond shape. 6⁷⁄₁₆″ x 6⁷⁄₁₆″. White letters and characters on bright blue background. Border blue and white.

(1175) AN PING INSURANCE COMPANY, LIMITED. SHANGHAI, CHINA. 1927-

Tin. Circular. 6¼″ in diameter. Globe light and dark green with orange and white characters. Border dark green and white.

(1176-1177) THE EASTERN INSURANCE OFFICE. SHANGHAI, CHINA. 1930-

1176. Iron. Rectangular, slightly convexed. 7″ x 5″. White Chinese characters and border on blue background.

1177. Iron. Convexed. 7⅛″ x 5¼″. White Chinese characters and lettering on blue background.

(1178-1179) INTERNATIONAL ASSURANCE COMPANY, LIMITED. SHANGHAI, CHINA. 1931-

1178. Tin. Rectangular. 7″ x 5″. Black and white lettering and shield on orange background.

1179. Tin. Rectangular. 7″ x 5″. Black, blue and white lettering and Chinese characters on orange background.

(1180) CHINA INSURANCE COMPANY, LIMITED. SHANGHAI, CHINA. 1931-

Tin. Circular. 6¾″ in diameter. Rolled edge, raised monogram and Chinese characters vari-colored.

(1181) ARNHOLD BROTHERS, LIMITED. SHANGHAI, CHINA. ?

Iron. Diamond shape, convexed. 8½″ x 7¼″. Blue with white letters and Chinese characters.

(1182) BUTTERFIELD & SWIRE. SHANGHAI, CHINA. ?

Tin. Shield shape. 8½″ x 9″. Colored flag, gold Chinese characters, initials and border all raised. Black background.

(1183) THE EASTERN TRADING COMPANY, LIMITED. SHANGHAI, CHINA. ? - 1933.

Iron. Rectangular, convexed. 7⅛″ x 5¼″. White Chinese characters on blue background.

(1184-1185) THE FOOK ON ASSURANCE COMPANY, LIMITED. HONGKONG, CHINA. ?

1184. Zinc. Rectangular. 8⅞″ x 6¼″. Black with raised gold characters and lettering. Vari-colored flags crossed in center, and border also raised.

1185. Tin. 7⅛″ x 4⅞″. Blue and white globes with slightly raised black lettering and characters. White border. Deep yellow background.

(1186) RAYNER HEUSSER & COMPANY. SHANGHAI, CHINA. ?

Tin. Shield shape. 5⅞″ x 6⅞″. Name red and gold, characters black. "Fire & Marine" red and blue, borders blue. Background cream color.

(1187) THE VENUS FIRE AND MARINE INSURANCE COMPANY, LIMITED. SHANGHAI, CHINA. ? - 1928.

Tin. Oval. 6¾″ x 4⅝″. Gold star, lettering, Chinese characters and border all raised. Background blue.

COLOMBIA

New Granada, as Colombia was first known, was geographically isolated during the colonial era. Consequently, she was neglected by her mother country, Spain, and by the end of the eighteenth century the people had become noticeably discontented. In 1811 the country rose in open revolt against Spanish rule and almost incessant warfare continued until 1824. Throughout this struggle the people were led by their great national hero Símon Bolívar, whose efforts proved instrumental in founding the Republic of New Granada in 1831. But intermittent civil war constantly beset the country—even after she was officially known as The United States of Colombia—until the early twentieth century when the country was finally unified.

The fact that the sole local fire insurance company in Colombia has been in business for over three quarters of a century is a tribute to the business acumen of its citizens. Their intelligence and industry have placed Colombia second in the world's production of coffee and fourth in the production of petroleum in the western hemisphere.

1188

(1188) COMPANHIA COLOMBIANA DE SEGUROS. BOGOTA, COLOMBIA. 1874-

Tin. 6¾" x 9⁹⁄₁₆". Gold border, company name in black and green trademark raised. Black inner border. Cream colored background.

COSTA RICA

The most southerly of Central American states is Costa Rica, whose National Bank is engaged in the fire insurance business. That institution issues a fire mark to publicize its endeavor even though insurance is one of its monopolies. Insurance-wise, free enterprise does not exist in this country.

1189

(1189) ASEGURADO BANCO NACIONAL DE SEGUROS. SAN JOSE, COSTA RICA. 1924-

Tin. Oval. Raised border and lettering. *(Courtesy of V. R. Willemson.)*

226

Largest island in the Caribbean, Cuba was discovered by Columbus in 1492. Except for a brief British occupation three centuries later, it was a Spanish colony until after the Spanish-American War. The Republic, created in 1902, was under a temporary protectorate of the United States but is now fully sovereign. Havana, one of the world's finest and safest harbors, is the capital of this "Pearl of the Antilles," from which is exported Cuba's abundant crop of sugar and tobacco.

Fire marks as originally adopted were utilized in Cuba by foreign insurance companies and also by *El Iris*, the one local concern existent prior to 1902. Since that date these plates have been used in isolated localities or for advertising purposes. Recent inquiries disclose that marks no longer appear on buildings.

1190

1191

1192

1193

1194

(1190-1191) EL IRIS COMPANIA DE SEGUROS MUTUOS CONTRA INCENDIO. HAVANA, CUBA. 1855-

1190. Tin. Rectangular. 9½″ x 6½″. Words "El Iris" and "Habana" beneath. Lettering and design raised.

1191. Iron. Oval, convexed. 10½″ x 7¾″. Blue border. Red, black and blue lettering on white background.

(1192) LA COMERCIAL COMPANIA GENERAL DE SEGUROS. HAVANA, CUBA. 1918-

Tin. Circular. 8½″ in diameter. Emblem raised on brass center circle with raised brass lettering on surrounding red band. Red and brass borders.

(1193) LA ALIANZA COMPANIA DE SEGUROS CONTRA ACCIDENTES DEL TRABAJO SOCIETA ANONIMA. HAVANA, CUBA. 1919-

Tin. Rectangular. 11½″ x 5⅛″. Raised cream and black lettering on raised blue center panel. Cream colored background with raised border.

(1194) UNION HISPANO AMERICANA DE SEGUROS, S.A. HAVANA, CUBA. ?

Tin. Oval. Raised border and lettering. (*Courtesy of V. R. Willemson.*)

Woodrow Wilson's most notable political achievement at the close of World War I was the creation of Czechoslovakia as a new republic. Bound together for a few short years as an independent nation, Czechoslovakia fell victim to Nazi aggression in 1938 but rose again after World War II. Noted for its splendid products of iron, steel, glass, porcelain, and textiles, Czechoslovakia has once again fallen under foreign domination and is currently obscured by a curtain of iron.

A review of the numerous Czechoslovakian fire marks with reference to organization dates of issuing companies ranging from 1827 through 1923 is impossible here because of the limitations of space. Many of these concerns were originally formed under Austrian and Hungarian influence as well as German, and they continued to operate under the new republic. In some instances their marks were required to include the house number on the plate as well as the concern's trade sign. These footprints of assurance had been quite widely used until the most recent political reorientation.

1195

1196

1197

1198

1199

1200

1201

1205

1202

1203

1204

1206

1207

1208

1209

1210

(1195-1196) PRVNI CESKA VZAJEMNA POJISTOVNA. PRAGUE, CZECHOSLOVAKIA. 1827-

1195. Tin. Rectangular. $6\frac{13}{16}''$ x $4\frac{3}{4}''$. Blue background with raised red border and cream lettering. Red and cream shield. Inner border cream.

1196. Iron. Rectangular, convexed. 7" x 5". Blue, red and black with white and red lettering.

(1197-1198) MORAVSKOSLEZSKA VZAJEMNA POJISTOVNA V BRNE. BRNE, CZECHOSLOVAKIA. 1829-

1197. Tin. $7\frac{1}{16}''$ x $5\frac{1}{8}''$. Blue background with raised cream lettering and blue outer border. Inner border cream.

1198. Tin. $7\frac{1}{8}''$ x $5\frac{1}{8}''$. Dark green background with raised cream lettering and green outer border. Inner border cream.

(1199) PRAZSKA MESTSKA POJISTOVNA. PRAGUE, CZECHOSLOVAKIA. 1865-

Iron. Rectangular, convexed. $7\frac{7}{8}''$ x $4\frac{3}{4}''$. Black and white crest, white lettering and border on red background.

(1200) SCT. FLORIAN WECHSELSEITIGE VERSICHERUNGS ANSTALT FUR DEUTSCHE BEZIRKE UND GEMEINDEN. EGER, CZECHOSLOVAKIA. 1867-

Tin. 7" x $9\frac{3}{4}''$. Border, lettering and figure raised. Lettering white, yellow and black, figure multi-colored. Background black.

(1201) CONCORDIA ALLGEMEINE VERSICHERUNGS AKTIEN GESELLSCHAFT IN REICHENBERG. REICHENBERG, CZECHOSLAVAKIA. 1867-

Tin. $6\frac{1}{4}''$ x $4\frac{3}{8}''$. Raised company name and border cream on blue background.

(1202) ROLNICKA VZAJEMNA POJISTOVNA. PRAGUE, CZECHOSLOVAKIA. 1869-

Aluminum. Rectangular. $6\frac{3}{8}''$ x $4\frac{5}{8}''$. Green background with raised polished aluminum lettering and border.

(1203-1204) SLAVIA VZAJEMNA POJISTOVACI BANKA. PRAGUE, CZECHOSLOVAKIA. 1869-

1203. Iron. Convexed. $6\frac{5}{8}''$ x $5\frac{1}{8}''$. Dark blue background with white lettering slightly raised.

1204. Iron. Convexed. $7\frac{1}{8}''$ x $5\frac{3}{16}''$. Blue background with white lettering slightly raised.

(1205-1206) KORUNA AKCIOVA POJISTOVNA. PRAGUE, CZECHOSLOVAKIA. 1899-

1205. Iron. Rectangular, convexed. $6\frac{5}{8}''$ x $6\frac{5}{8}''$. Blue background with white house number and company name slightly raised.

1206. Iron. Rectangular, convexed. 7" x $5\frac{1}{16}''$. Dark blue background with white lettering slightly raised.

(1207) HASICSKA VZAJEMNA POJISTOVNA V BRNE. BRNE, CZECHOSLOVAKIA. 1900-

Iron. Convexed. 7" x 3". Red background with white lettering and border. Center decoration red, white and blue slightly raised.

(1208-1209) LIDOVA POJISTOVNA CECHOSLAVIA AKCIOVA SPOLECNOST. PRAGUE, CZECHOSLOVAKIA. 1919-

1208. Iron. Convexed. $6\frac{5}{8}''$ x $5\frac{1}{16}''$. Red background with white lettering slightly raised.

1209. Iron. Convexed. $6\frac{5}{8}''$ x $5\frac{1}{16}''$. Red background with white lettering slightly raised.

(1210) SLOVANSKA POJISTOVNA AKCIOVA SPOLECNOST V PRAZE. PRAGUE, CZECHOSLOVAKIA. 1919-

Tin. Rectangular. $7\frac{1}{16}''$ x $5\frac{1}{8}''$. Blue background with raised cream lettering. Raised cream and red border.

1211

1212

1213

1215

1216

1214

1217

1219

SLOVENSKÁ
POISTOVNA ÚC. SPOL.
SZLOVÁK
BIZTOSITÓ R.T.

1218

POJIŠTĚNO U UNION

1221

1220

(1211) POJISTILA VSEOBECNA POJISTOVNA AKCIOVA SPOLECNOST. BRNE, CZECHOSLOVAKIA. 1920-

Iron. Convexed. 7³⁄₁₆″ x 4¹³⁄₁₆″. Red background with white lettering slightly raised.

(1212) KARPATIA ROLNICKA A DRUSTEVNA POJIS-TOVNA UC SPOLECNOST. BRATISLAVA, CZECHOSLO-VAKIA. 1920-

Tin. Rectangular. 6⅞″ x 5″. Dark blue background with red, white and blue crest, white lettering and border, all raised.

(1213) LLOYD AKCIOVA POJISTOVNA V PRAZE. PRAGUE, CZECHOSLOVAKIA. 1920-

Tin. 6¾″ x 5″. Light blue background with raised cream lettering and border.

(1214-1215) LEGIE AKCIOVA POJISTOVNA. PRAGUE, CZECHOSLOVAKIA. 1921-

1214. Iron. Rectangular, raised. 7″ x 5¹⁄₁₆″. Red background with white lettering slightly raised.

1215. Iron. Convexed. 7⅛″ x 4¾″. Red background with white lettering slightly raised.

(1216-1217) MOLDAVIA GENERALI AKCIOVA POJIS-TOVNA. PRAGUE, CZECHOSLOVAKIA. 1921.

1216. Tin. Rectangular. Raised border and lettering. *(Cour-tesy of V. R. Willemson.)*

1217. Tin. 6¾″ x 4¾″. Light blue background with raised cream lettering and border.

(1218-1220) SLOVENSKA POJISTOVNA UC. SPOLECNOST. BRATISLAVA, CZECHOSLOVAKIA. 1921-

1218. Tin. Rectangular. 5⅝″ x 3¾″. Raised red border and raised blue lettering with cream background. Blue inner border. Red, cream and blue center crest raised.

1223

1222

1224

1219. Tin. Rectangular. 5⅞" x 3⅞". Raised red border and raised blue lettering with cream background. Red, cream and blue center crest raised.

1220. Tin. Rectangular. 5⅞" x 3⅞". Raised red border and raised blue lettering with white background. Red, white and blue center crest raised.

(1221-1222) UNION POJISTVACI AKCIOVA SPOLECNOST. PRAGUE, CZECHOSLOVAKIA. 1922-

1221. Iron. Triangular, convexed. 7⅛" each side. Red background with slightly raised white lettering. White border.

1222. Iron. Triangular, convexed. 7⅛" each side. Black background with slightly raised white lettering. White border.

(1223) MERKUR AKCIOVA POJISTOVNA V PRAZE. PRAGUE, CZECHOSLOVAKIA. 1923-

Iron. Convexed. 7⅛" x 5⅛". Yellow background with blue lettering slightly raised.

(1224) ASSEKURANZVEREIN DER ZUCKERINDUSTRIE. PRAGUE, CZECHOSLOVAKIA. 1861-

Tin. Rectangular. Raised border, emblem and lettering. (*Courtesy of Chartered Insurance Institute.*)

DUTCH EAST INDIES

All of the marks of assurance shown in this section were issued when Sumatra, Java, Madura, Celebes, the Moluccas, and central and southern Borneo formed the Dutch East Indies, an area now referred to as the Republic of Indonesia. In addition to their chief products—home of rubber, tar, and sugar—the islands produce 90 per cent of the world's quinine, 85 per cent of its pepper, and 80 per cent of its cocaine. Their fire insurance companies and the general agencies which issued fire marks in the past century all showed the effect of Dutch control, though the buyers of insurance were composed of two classes, the native East Indians and the Chinese.

Of the East Indians the Secretary of the Council of Fire Insurance Companies in the Netherland Indies has written from Batavia that: "The general use of fire marks has become a thing of the past in this country (1938). Originally the Companies considered fire marks as an effective way of advertising . . . however, . . . the population here took it as a sort of 'djemat' which means 'a talisman against malicious influence and evil spirits.' Consequently, after some time such marks were nailed to the worst imaginable fire risks, such as native houses of bamboo with dry leaf roofing, and old tumbled-down shacks. You can readily understand why the Insurance Companies here did not regard this use of fire marks as an efficient manner of advertising, on the contrary this was the cause of much ridicule! During one of my travels in Java I saw a horse-shoe mark of the Excess Insurance Co. Ltd., nailed to a creaking cart drawn by Buffalos!"

About the Chinese he says: "Companies are still using fire marks being of the opinion, that Chinese clients are keen on them, and that it is a help in acquiring Chinese business." The belief still prevails among many of these people that such a mark, with its "good-will—good luck" symbols, will ward off the evil spirits of fire. Such a belief is unquestionably of psychological benefit to any insurance company issuing these marks of assurance, even though their value as advertisements has been questioned.

231

1225

1226

1227

1228

1229

1230

1231

1232

1233

1234

1235

(1225-1226) EAST INDIA, BATAVIA AND JAVA SEA AND FIRE INSURANCE COMPANIES NETHERLAND LLOYD. BATAVIA, DUTCH EAST INDIES.

1225. Tin. 9″ x 7″. Black background with raised gold lettering and raised red, green and gold center crest. Border raised.

1226. Tin. 9″ x 7″. Black background with raised gold lettering and raised red, green and gold center crest. Border raised.

(1227) BATAVISCHE ZEE EN BRANDASSURANTIE MAATSCHAPPIJ. BATAVIA, DUTCH EAST INDIES. 1843-

Tin. Circular. 5⅞″ in diameter. Cream colored background with blue crest, lettering and borders.

(1228-1229) JAVASCHE ZEE EN BRANDASSURANTIE MAATSCHAPPIJ. BATAVIA, DUTCH EAST INDIES. 1861-

1228. Tin. Rectangular. 8″ x 5″. Red background with black crest, lettering, characters and borders.

1229. Tin. Oval. 9″ x 6⅜″. Black background. Chinese characters in white on upper portion, white lettering on red band across the center and gold lettering on lower portion. Dove white. Border gold.

(1230) SAMARANGSCHE ZEE EN BRANDASSURANTIE MAATSCHAPPIJ (1866) EN TWEEDE SAMARANGSCHE ZEE EN BRANDASSURANTIE MAATSCHAPPIJ (1886). SAMARANG, DUTCH EAST INDIES.

Tin. Rectangular. 6¹⁄₁₆" x 8¹⁄₁₆". White lettering on light blue background. Vari-colored design.

(1231) COMBINATIE SLUYTERS & COMPANY. BATAVIA, DUTCH EAST INDIES. 1875-

Tin. Rectangular. 6⅞" x 4¾". Black background with slightly raised crest in gold, red, white and green. Lettering and border raised gold.

(1232) N. V. HANDEL MAATSCHAPPIJ GUNTZEL & SCHU-MACHER. MEDAN, SUMATRA, DUTCH EAST INDIES. 1906-

Iron. Circular, slightly convexed. 5¼" in diameter. Light green center with vari-colored ornamentation and black lettering on white panel. White lettering and black characters on surrounding red band. White border.

(1233-1234) N. V. INDISCHE LLOYD ALGEMEENE VER-ZEKERING MAATSCHAPPIJ. SAMARANG, DUTCH EAST INDIES. 1916-

1233. Tin. 8⅞" x 7⅜". Raised and flat gold lettering and characters with gold, black and white emblem raised. Black background. Gold border.

1234. Iron. Shield shape. 3½" x 3½". Yellow and white with black monogram.

(1235) ALGEMEENE VERZEKERING MAATSCHAPPIJ DE ATLAS. BANDOENG, JAVA, DUTCH EAST INDIES. 1920-1935.

Tin. Rectangular. 5⅛" x 2⅜". Black lettering, borders and figure of Atlas on brass finish.

EGYPT

Land of the Nile, the Sphinx, and the Pyramids, Egypt has contributed for six thousand years to the history of civilization. Americans often think that land irrigation is a modern development in its western areas; yet it is a fact that it began in Egypt in 5000 B.C. and assumed great importance under King Menes in about 4000 B.C. A perfection of the system makes it possible for Egypt to grow vast crops of cotton which comprise about 80 per cent of its exports. This nation of the Nile became a British protectorate in 1914, altering its status by treaty in 1936. Modern fire marks were used between these dates by local companies, although the older signs were issued in Egypt by foreign companies throughout the nineteenth century. The marks of that period seem to have passed into oblivion.

1236

1237

1238

1239

(1236-1237) NATIONAL INSURANCE COMPANY OF EGYPT. ALEXANDRIA, EGYPT. 1900-

1236. Tin. Rectangular. Raised border, lettering and center figure. (Courtesy of Chartered Insurance Institute.)

1237. Iron. Rectangular, convexed. 7" x 10⅜". Yellow figure, lettering and border on blue background.

(1238) THE ALEXANDRIA INSURANCE COMPANY SO-CIETE ANONYME EGYPTIENNE. ALEXANDRIA, EGYPT. 1928-

Iron. Rectangular. 6" x 9". Yellow design and lettering on blue background.

(1239) SOCIETE MISR D'ASSURANCES GENERALES SO-CIETE ANONYME EGYPTIENNE. CAIRO, EGYPT. 1934-

Tin. Rectangular. 6⁵⁄₁₆" x 8¼". Yellow and black figure with raised black and white lettering and characters on green background. Black and white border.

From the time of Peter the Great until World War I the area which formed Estonia was known as the German Provinces of Russia though the people are not Germanic. Their language is related to Livonian and Finnish. In 1918 the Esths declared their independence but were again absorbed by their former Russian masters in 1940. With two exceptions, all of Estonia's fire insurance companies were established under the influence of the republic. The marks illustrated here are a pleasant reminder of an only too short period of freedom so dearly earned by these people.

1241

1240

1242

1243

1244

1245

1246

(1240) ESIMENE EESTI KINDLUSTUSE SELTS MAJA "EEKS-MAJA." TALLINN, ESTONIA. 1866-

Tin. Diamond shape. 10½" x 6⅝". Center panel yellow with raised dark blue lettering. Background dark blue with raised white lettering. Yellow border.

(1241) KINDLUSTUSSELTS EESTI. TARTUS, ESTONIA. 1907-

Tin. Shield shape. 5½" x 6⅞". Yellow border, yellow eagle and black and white lettering raised. Blue, black and white background panels.

(1242) EESTI LLOYD KINDLUSTUSE SELTS. TALLINN, ESTONIA. 1919-

Tin. Oval. 8⅞" x 5⅞". Raised blue lion on white center with raised white lettering on surrounding band of darker blue.

(1243) EESTIMAA KINNITUS AKTSIA SELTS EKA. TALLINN, ESTONIA. 1920-

Tin. 6⅞" x 3¾". White lettering, design and border raised on red background.

(1244) HANSA EESTI KINNITUS AKTSIA-SELTS. TALLINN, ESTONIA. 1920-

Tin. Rectangular. 7⅛" x 4¼". Raised lettering gold and black. Flat lettering black. Border gold and black. Background light blue.

(1245) OMA EESTI OMAVALITSUSTE JA UHISTEGELISTE ASUTUSTE KINDLUSTUS AKTSIA SELTS. TARTU, ESTONIA. 1920-

Tin. 7⅝" x 5¼". Raised white lettering on blue center panel and surrounding black band. White borders raised.

(1246) POLARIS EESTI KINDLUSTUSE SELTS. TALLINN, ESTONIA. 1920-

Tin. Rectangular. Lettering raised slightly. (*Courtesy of V. R. Willemson.*)

FINLAND

The people of Finland are a hardy group of northerners with a code of ethics and an integrity outstanding in this age of wars and cynicism. Her heroic efforts to reimburse America for a debt owed between the years of the two world wars will always inspire the admiration and appreciation of a sympathetic people. Small in area and somewhat limited in its industries, this country's wealth lies in its forests and their products. Fire insurance companies have never used a mark upon insured buildings, but there is one known example of a fire mark issued by a concern which insured forests against loss by fire. Notice of its security was posted upon a tree in the insured area. This fire mark constitutes the only example of this particular custom found in any country. It bears evidence of the fire consciousness of a prudent people.

1247

(1247) SUOMEN METSANOMISTAJAIN KESKINAINEN VAKUUTUSYHTIO METSAPALO. HELSINKI, FINLAND. 1916-

Tin. Oval. 12⅛" x 9⅝". Raised black and white lettering on green background. Raised black border. Mark posted in insured forests.

FRANCE

It was in 1699 that Sieur du Perier obtained from the King of France an exclusive privilege to construct fire engines of his own invention. In 1716 an ordinance of the King directed that a large number of these be distributed to various parts of the city of Paris. In 1829 French fire engines had advanced greatly in design and were as up-to-date in style and construction as contemporary hand-pump machines used anywhere else in the world. In France fire extinguishment has always seemed to be a public responsibility, and there is no record that insurance companies maintained their own equipment or brigades.

Fire insurance in this land of the ancient Gauls was almost coincidental with the development of fire engines. In 1686 Louis XIV signed a decree establishing the *Compagnie Générale pour les Assurances Grosses Aventures de France* (General Company for Insurances and Bottomry Bonds of France) in the city of Paris. A year after the King's ordinance for the distribution of engines was ordained, the *Bureau des Incendies* was started in 1717 to come to the aid of victims of fire; it was sustained exclusively by private charity.

There were several reorganizations and new decrees by the monarchs of France regarding the *Assurances Générales*. The General Fire which was dedicated in 1753 was "comprised first of all by the Perier Brothers, directors of the 'Company of the Water Works of Paris' who requested of the King authorization to negotiate insurances against fire, alleging that they were naturally fitted to be entrusted with the authorization which they requested, since they had already organized at great expense relief in case of fire." In other words, if they had invented the fire engine and established public water works, why not culminate these achievements with security from loss by fire? The King granted the authorization and the concern became the *Compagnie Générale d'Assurances contre les incendies.* Fire marks are referred to as *plaques* in France, and regarding this early company it is recorded "The Company invented the insurance plaque, arranging on the facade of each building which it insured a plaque in the form of an escutcheon, numbered, bearing the letters M.A.C.L. (*maison assuré contre l'incendie,* house insured against fire)."

The use and development of the fire insurance plaque have been long and prolific as can be seen in the wide variety of these French marks. With the defeat of Napoleon in 1815, private enterprise commenced on a long succession of advances, especially

in the fire insurance field. In 1817 the fire mark was first illustrated, to be followed by those of the new, long-lived and successful *Compagnie d'Assurances Générales* of 1819. The latter was a perfect example of the soundness of what they term "fixed premium insurance," a plan that weathered revolutions and wars throughout France's romantic, yet stormy career. The names of most French companies were imprinted upon their plaques, but these marks also featured a distinctive style which sets them apart from those of other nations.

1248

1249

1250

1251

1252

1253

1254

1255

1256

1257

1258

1259

1260

1261

1262

1263

1264

1265

(1248) ANCIENNE MUTUELLE DE LA SEINE-INF. ET DE L'EURE. ROUEN, FRANCE. 1817-

Tin. Rectangular. Raised border, crest and lettering. *(Courtesy of Chartered Insurance Institute.)*

(1249-1250) COMPAGNIE D'ASSURANCES GENERALES CONTRE L'INCENDIE ET LES EXPLOSIONS. PARIS, FRANCE. 1819-

1249. Tin. Oval. Slightly convexed. 9″ x 6¾″. Raised gold lettering. Center had been red. Outer band black. Borders raised, inner border gold. From building in Greece.

1250. Tin. Oval. Slightly convexed. 9″ x 6¾″. Raised gold lettering on red center and surrounding black band. Borders raised, inner border gold.

(1251-1255) COMPAGNIE FRANCAISE DU PHENIX ASSURANCE CONTRE L'INCENDIE. PARIS, FRANCE. 1819-

1251. Zinc. Rectangular. 7¾″ x 6⅝″. Phoenix, oval border and lettering raised gold. Outer border raised. Background had been black. Found in Hilterfingen, Lake Thun, Switzerland.

1252. Zinc. Rectangular. 10⅞″ x 9″. Phoenix, borders and lettering raised gold. Background black. From building in Greece.

1253. Tin. Rectangular. 10¾″ x 9⅛″. Phoenix, oval border and lettering raised gold. Outer border raised. Background had been black. Removed from building in Salonika, Greece.

1254. Tin. Rectangular. 10⅞″ x 9″. Phoenix, borders and lettering raised.

1255. Tin. Rectangular. 8″ x 6¾″. Phoenix, oval border and lettering raised gold. Outer border raised. Background black. Removed from building in Istanbul, Turkey.

(1256) ANCIENNE MUTUELLE DU CALVADOS ASSURANCE CONTRE L'INCENDIE. CAEN, FRANCE. 1820-

Tin. Rectangular. Black background and painted border and lettering. *(Courtesy of V. R. Willemson.)*

(1257-1260) LA NATIONALE COMPAGNIE D'ASSURANCES CONTRE L'INCENDIE ET LES EXPLOSIONS. PARIS, FRANCE. 1820-

1257. Tin. Rectangular. 11⅝″ x 7⅜″. Slightly convexed oval in center. Border and lettering had been gold on black background.

1258. Tin. Rectangular. 11¾″ x 7⅞″. Raised gold lettering and oval border on black background. Raised outer border.

1259. Aluminum. Rectangular. 8⅜″ x 6⅝″. White border, characters and date raised on green background. Used in Bulgaria.

1260. Tin. Rectangular. 9¹⁄₁₆″ x 9⅝″. Borders, date and characters in yellow and black. From building in Greece.

(1261) COMPAGNIE ROYAL. FRANCE.

(Courtesy of Chartered Insurance Institute.)

(1262) LA MUTUELLE DE VALENCE SOCIETE D'ASSURANCES MUTUELLES CONTRE L'INCENDIE. VALENCE-SUR-RHONE, FRANCE. 1826.

(Courtesy of Chartered Insurance Institute.)

(1263) LA MUTUELLE DU MANS SOCIETE D'ASSURANCE ET DE REASSURANCE A PRIMES LIMITEES. LE MANS, FRANCE. 1828-

Tin. Rectangular. 9½″ x 7″. Raised gold lettering on red center and black background. Oval border raised gold. Outer border raised red.

(1264-1269) L'UNION COMPAGNIE D'ASSURANCES CONTRE L'INCENDIE, LES ACCIDENTS ET RISQUES DIVERS. PARIS, FRANCE. 1828-

1264. Tin. Rectangular. 9¾″ x 6⅝″. Blue center oval with raised gold figures and lettering—black background. Oval border raised black. Outer border raised red.

1265. Tin. Rectangular. 9¾″ x 6⅝″. Lettering, figures and borders raised. Oval slightly convexed. From building in Greece.

1266

1267

1268

1269

1270

1271

1272

1273

1274

1275

1276

1277

1278

1279

1280

1281

1282

1283

1284

1285

1286

1287

1288

1266. Tin. Rectangular. 10⅜″ x 7″. Lettering, figures and borders raised. Oval slightly convexed. From building at Istanbul, Turkey.

1267. Tin. Rectangular. 10¼″ x 7″. Slightly convexed blue center oval with raised gold figures and lettering. Black background. Oval border and outer border raised black. Inner border red.

1268. Tin. Rectangular. 10½″ x 7″. Blue center oval with raised gold figures and lettering. Black background. Oval border raised black. Outer border raised red.

1269. Tin. Rectangular. 10½″ x 7⅛″. Blue center oval with raised gold figures and lettering. Black background. Borders raised black.

(1270-1272) COMPAGNIE DU SOLEIL SOCIETE ANONYME D'ASSURANCE CONTRE L'INCENDIE LA FOUDRE ET LES EXPLOSIONS. PARIS, FRANCE. 1829-

1270. Copper. Rectangular. 7½″ x 6″. Border, design and lettering raised.

1271. Tin. 10″ x 8″. Design and lettering gold on black background. Border raised.

1272. Brass. Rectangular. 10¼″ x 8¼″. Raised design and lettering gold on black background. Border raised.

(1273-1274) LA FRANCE COMPAGNIE D'ASSURANCES CONTRE L'INCENDIE. PARIS, FRANCE. 1837-

1273. Zinc. Rectangular. 14″ x 10″. Raised gold figure and border on blue center oval. Raised gold lettering on black background. Raised outer border had been gold.

1274. Tin. Rectangular. 8¼″ x 6¼″. Raised gold figure and border on dark blue center oval. Raised gold lettering on black background. Raised outer border red.

(1275) LA FRATERNELLE PARISIENNE STE. D'ASSURANCE MUTUELLE CONTRE L'INCENDIE. PARIS, FRANCE. 1837-

Tin. Rectangular. Raised clasped hands and lettering. (Courtesy of Chartered Insurance Institute.)

(1276) LA MUTUELLE DE POITIERS SOCIETE D'ASSURANCES MUTUELLES MOBILIERES ET IMMOBILIERES CONTRE L'INCENDIE. POITIERS, FRANCE. 1838-

Tin. Rectangular. 11⅛″ x 8⅝″. Gold lettering and border on black background.

(1277) LA PROVIDENCE COMPAGNIE D'ASSURANCES CONTRE L'INCENDIE. PARIS, FRANCE. 1838-

Tin. 8½″ x 6″. Rectangular. Blue oval with raised gold lettering and emblem. Black background. Borders raised.

(1278-1280) L'URBAINE COMPAGNIE ANONYME D'ASSURANCES L'INCENDIE. PARIS, FRANCE. 1838-

1278. Brass. Rectangular. 8⅝″ x 6⅛″. Raised gold crown and lettering. Raised border. Black background. From building in Constantinople, Turkey.

1279. Tin. Rectangular, slightly convexed. 8½″ x 6″. Raised gold crown and lettering. Raised border. Black background.

1280. Tin. Rectangular, slightly convexed. 12½″ x 9¼″. Raised gold crown and lettering. Raised border. Black background.

(1281-1285) LE NORD COMPAGNIE ANONYME D'ASSURANCE ET DE PROTECTION CONTRE L'INCENDIE LES ACCIDENTS LE VOL ET AUTRES RISQUES. PARIS, FRANCE. 1840-

1281. Brass. Rectangular. 9⅛″ x 6½″. Lettering and border raised. From building in Greece.

1282. Tin. Rectangular. 10⅛″ x 7³⁄₁₆″. Lettering and border raised. From building in Greece.

1283. Tin. Rectangular. 8³⁄₁₆″ x 6⅜″. Raised gold lettering on black background. Raised border. Type used in Martinique.

1284. Tin. Rectangular. 8½″ x 6½″. Raised gold lettering on black background. Raised border.

1285. Tin. Rectangular. 8½″ x 6¼″. Raised gold lettering and black and gold border on black background.

(1286-1288) L'AIGLE COMPAGNIE ANONYME D'ASSURANCES A PRIMES FIXES CONTRE L'INCENDIE. PARIS, FRANCE. 1843-

1286. Copper. Rectangular. 7½″ x 9⁵⁄₁₆″. Raised eagle and lettering had been gold on black background. Border raised.

1287. Brass. Rectangular, slightly convexed. 10⁵⁄₁₆″ x 8⁵⁄₁₆″. Raised gold lettering and eagle on black background. Raised border.

1288. Tin. Rectangular. 9½″ x 7¾″. Raised gold lettering and border on black background.

1290

1291

1292

1289

1293

1294

1297

1295

1296

L'ABEILLE

1298

1299

1300

1302

1301

1303

1304

1305

1306

240

A group of fire marks of foreign fire insurance companies other than Great Britain.

1307

1308

1309

(1289-1291) LA PATERNELLE COMPAGNIE ANONYME D'ASSURANCES A PRIMES FIXES CONTRE L'INCENDIE, LES ACCIDENTS ET RISQUES DE TOUTE NATURE. PARIS, FRANCE. 1843-

1289. Tin. 11½" x 8⅝". Raised figure, lettering and border.

1290. Tin. 11⅜" x 8½". Raised gold figure and lettering and blue clouds on black background. Raised border.

1291. Tin. Rectangular. 8½" x 6⅛". Raised gold building and lettering on black background. Raised border.

(1292-1296) LA CONFIANCE COMPAGNIE D'ASSURANCES CONTRE L'INCENDIE ET LES EXPLOSIONS. PARIS, FRANCE. 1844-

1292. Zinc. Rectangular. 13⅝" x 9¾". Raised border, design and lettering.

1293. Zinc. Rectangular. 10¾" x 7⅞". Raised lettering and characters had been gold on black background. Borders raised. From building in Greece.

1294. Tin. Rectangular. 9¾" x 6⅞". Raised border, dots and lettering. From building in Greece.

1295. Tin. Rectangular. 10¾" x 8". Oval center, raised gilded figure, raised gold letters on black background. Raised borders. From building in Istanbul, Turkey.

1296. Tin. Rectangular. 9⅛" x 11⅝". Oval center with raised figure and border. Lettering, characters and outer border raised. From building in North Africa destroyed during war, 1943.

(1297-1300) L'ABEILLE SOCIETE ANONYME D'ASSUR-ANCES CONTRE L'INCENDIE. PARIS, FRANCE. 1857-

1297. Tin. Rectangular. 10¼" x 8¼". Raised borders, lettering and beehive with bees.

1298. Brass. Rectangular. 9¾" x 6¾". Raised gold inner border, raised gold bee and lettering on black background. Outer border raised.

1299. Tin. Rectangular. 9¾" x 6¾". Bee, lettering and borders raised.

1300. Tin. Rectangular. 9⅝" x 6½". Painted yellow border, bee and lettering on black background. From building in North Africa destroyed during war, 1943.

(1301-1302) CIE LE MONDE D'ASSURANCES CONTRE L'INCENDIE. PARIS, FRANCE. 1864-

1301. Tin. Rectangular. 13⅜" x 9⅝". Raised lettering, dots and borders. From building in North Africa destroyed during war, 1943.

1302. Tin. Rectangular. 9⅞" x 6⅞". Oval center. Raised gold lettering. Black background. From building in Istanbul, Turkey.

(1303-1306) LA PRESERVATRICE COMPAGNIE ANONYME D'ASSURANCES A PRIMES FIXES CONTRE LES ACCIDENTS ET LES RISQUES DE TOUTE NATURE. PARIS, FRANCE. 1864-

1303. Tin. Circular. 7³⁄₁₆" in diameter. Vari-colored center with surrounding red band. Raised gold letters and borders.

1304. Alloy. Circular. 3" in diameter. Raised silver lettering, cream center and borders with dark blue surrounding band.

1305. Alloy. Circular. 3" in diameter. Raised silver lettering and borders. Dark green center with maroon surrounding band.

1306. Alloy. Circular. 3" in diameter. Raised metal color lettering, border and center. "Unfalle" red. Surrounding band blue.

(1307) L'UNION GENERALE DU NORD. LILLE, FRANCE. ? - ?

Tin. Rectangular. Raised border and lettering. *(Courtesy of V. R. Willemson.)*

(1308) L'INDUSTRIELLE DU NORD CIE D'ASSURANCES CONTRE LES RISQUES DE TOUTE NATURE STE. AN. LILLE, FRANCE. 1871-

Tin. Rectangular. 9¼" x 6¼". Company name in silver on black background. "Incendie" black on silver panel. Border silver. From building in Greece.

(1309) LE JURA SOCIETE D'ASSURANCE. LONS-DE-SAUNIER, FRANCE. ? - ?

Tin. Rectangular. Painted lettering and crest. *(Courtesy of V. R. Willemson.)*

1310

1311

1312

1313

1314

ASSURANCES
REMOISES

1315

ASSICURAZIONI
LA
MÉTROPOLE
CONTRO L'INCENDIO

1316

1317

LA FLANDRE
ROUBAIX

1318

LA MUTUELLE
A.M.
DE LIMOGES

1319

ALSATIA

1320

"L'ÉCLAIR"
ASSICURAZIONI
FIRICI GENOVA

1321

1322

LA CONCORDE
ASSURANCES
INCENDIE

1323

INSURE IN THE BEE HAIL
INSURANCE COMPANY

1324

CGR
ASSURANCES

1325

ASSURANCES
LA PROTECTRICE
ACCIDENTS · INCENDIE
GRÊLE · VOL

1326

LA
SÉCURITÉ FRANÇAISE
INCENDIE

1327

LA
COMMERCIALE

1328

(1310-1314) LA FONCIERE COMPAGNIE ANONYME D'AS-SURANCES CONTRE L'INCENDIE. PARIS, FRANCE. 1877-

1310. Zinc. Rectangular. 9⅝″ x 6⅝″. Raised border, lettering and dots. From building in South of Europe.

1311. Tin. Rectangular. 11¼″ x 8⅜″. Border, lettering and characters raised. From building in Istanbul, Turkey.

1312. Tin. Rectangular. 9⁷⁄₁₆″ x 6½″. Raised lettering and border. From building in Greece.

1313. Tin. Rectangular. 9⅝″ x 6¹¹⁄₁₆″. Raised gold lettering and inner border on black background. Raised black outer border with red stripe.

1314. Tin. Rectangular. 9⅝″ x 6¾″. Raised gold lettering and inner border on black background. Raised black outer border. Type used in Martinique.

(1315) CIE. GENERALE DES ASSURANCES REMOISES STE. AN. D'ASSURANCES CONTRE L'INCENDIE. RHEIMS, FRANCE. 1879.

Tin. Rectangular. Raised borders and letters. (Courtesy of Chartered Insurance Institute.)

(1316) LA METROPOLE CIE D'ASSURANCES MOBILIERES ET IMMOBILIERES CONTRE L'INCENDIE. PARIS, FRANCE. 1879-

Tin. Rectangular. 11″ x 7½″. Red oval, black background. Gold lettering and oval border raised. Outer border raised.

(1317) RHIN ET MOSELLE COMPAGNIE GENERALE D'ASSURANCE OF STRASBOURG. STRASBOURG, FRANCE. 1925-

Rectangular. Raised border, rosettes and monogram. (Courtesy of Chartered Insurance Institute.)

(1318) LA FLANDRE COMPAGNIE FRANCAISE D'ASSUR-ANCES SOCIETE ANONYME. ROUBAIX, FRANCE. 1888-

Tin. Rectangular. 9¾″ x 6⅝″. Raised gold lettering on black background. Raised border with red stripe.

(1319) LA MUTUELLE DE LIMOGES SOCIETE D'ASSUR-ANCES MUTUELLES A COTISATIONS FIXES. LIMOGES, FRANCE. 1896-

Iron. Rectangular. 9⅞″ x 6⅝″. Gold lettering and border on black background.

(1320) L'ALSACIENNE CIE. D'ASSURANCES CONTRE LES ACCIDENTS ET RISQUES DIVERS. STRASBOURG, FRANCE. 1820-

Tin. Rectangular. Raised border, crests and lettering. (Courtesy of Chartered Insurance Institute.)

(1321) L'ECLAIR CIE. AN. D'ASSURANCES ET DE RE-ASSURANCES. PARIS, FRANCE. 1898-

Tin. Rectangular. Raised border and lettering. (Courtesy of Chartered Insurance Institute.)

(1322) LA MUTUELLE D'ORLEANS SOCIETE D'ASSUR-ANCES. ORLEANS, FRANCE. 1899-

Alloy. Triangular. 3⅞″ x 3⅞″. Blue, yellow and gold.

(1323) LA CONCORDE COMPAGNIE D'ASSURANCES CONTRE LES RISQUES DE TOUTE NATURE. PARIS, FRANCE. 1905-

Tin. Rectangular. 9⁷⁄₁₆″ x 6⁵⁄₁₆″. Gold lettering on black background.

(1324) L'ABEILLE SOCIETE ANONYME D'ASSURANCES CONTRE LA GRELE ET DE REASSURANCES. PARIS, FRANCE. 1906-

Tin. Circular. 8″ in diameter. Red center, raised yellow bee. Raised black lettering on yellow border. Black stripe around red center.

(1325) COMPAGNIE GENERALE DE REASSURANCES SO-CIETE ANONYME D'ASSURANCES ET DE REASSURANCES. PARIS, FRANCE. 1906-

Brass. Rectangular. 10¼″ x 8¼″. Raised gold lettering and trademark on black background. Outer border raised.

(1326) LA PROTECTRICE COMPAGNIE ANONYME D'AS-SURANCES CONTRE LES ACCIDENTS, L'INCENDIE, LA GRELE ET LE VOL. PARIS, FRANCE. 1911-

Tin. Rectangular. 9¾″ x 6⅞″. Raised and flat black and white lettering on pale blue background. Raised border with white stripe.

(1327) LA SECURITE FRANCAISE COMPAGNIE ANO-NYME D'ASSURANCES A PRIMES FIXES CONTRE L'INCEN-DIE ET LES ACCIDENTS. PARIS, FRANCE. 1912-

Iron. Rectangular. 10⅝″ x 5¾″. Gold lettering on black background. Red border.

(1328) LA COMMERCIALE DE FRANCE. PARIS, FRANCE. 1912-1937.

Tin. Rectangular. 9¾″ x 6½″. Raised gold lettering on black background. Raised border.

1329

1330

1331

1332

1333

(1329) L'ALLIANCE REGIONALE DE FRANCE. PARIS,
FRANCE. 1919-

Tin. Rectangular, slightly convexed. 9½" x 6¾". Red center
oval, raised gold lettering, dark green background. Raised red border. Mark used in Martinque.

(1330-1331) LA PREVOYANCE COMPAGNIE D'ASSUR-
ANCES ET DE REASSURANCES CONTRE L'INCENDIE ET
AUTRE RISQUES. PARIS, FRANCE. 1920-

1330. Tin. 9" x 6½". Flat lettering and border. Background
had been dark blue. From building in Greece.

1331. Iron. Rectangular. 9⅟₁₆" x 6½". Yellow lettering and
border on black background.

(1332) LE CONSORTIUM DES MUTUELLES DE PROV-
INCE COMPAGNIE ANONYME DE REASSURANCES ET
D'ASSURANCES. LIMOGES, FRANCE. 1924-

Tin. Rectangular. 9⅜" x 6¾". Red center oval, gold lettering,
green background. Red border.

(1333) CHAMBLY MUTUELLE LAVAL & JACQUES
CARTIER. FRANCE. ? - ?

Tin. Rectangular. Painted border and lettering. *(Courtesy of
V. R. Willemson.)*

GERMANY

A century ago Thomas Ewbank gave us the most comprehensive history of hydraulics and the development of early fire-extinguishing apparatus ever written. In this monumental work he records that in 1518 A.D. fire engines were used in Augsburg, Germany, and that in 1656 pump engines were used in Nuremburg. He also asserts that the Germans were proverbially far in advance of the rest of Europe in almost every department of the arts, and that the excellency of these people rested in their mechanical ability to produce inventions which were the admiration of the world. They were almost a century ahead of England in the development of equipment to extinguish fires.

Certain insurance histories refer to an insurance *Casse* in Hamburg prior to 1676, but no mention has been made of its ever issuing a fire mark. We are able to illustrate the trade sign of the *Hamburger Feuerkasse* of 1676, probably the oldest existing fire insurance company in the world. The concerns whose marks are illustrated here were all recorded in the years between the two world wars, many or most of

which probably have passed away since. The earliest of these underwriting groups were compulsory mutual organizations, while most of those formed in the past century were stock organizations representing free enterprise.

Germany is the only country other than Great Britain whose fire marks and trade signs very forcibly set forth a highly developed and ornate art. Their signs are extremely colorful and in most cases depict the crest or arms of a community or of the monarchy itself. The use of the marks closely follows or parallels the practice of Britain, with most of the newer and modern types employed for publicity purposes only. It can be noted that German companies are domiciled in far more diversified localities than those of any other country and consequently were influenced by the economic progress of each community. The use of fire marks in Germany has remained a custom much longer than in most other countries, a factor undoubtedly occasioned by the desire of the householder to display an artistic item on his property. The custom was abandoned during World War II.

1334

1335

1336

1337

1338

(1334)   HAMBURGER FEUERKASSE OFFENTLICH-RECHT-LICHE VERSICHERUNGS ANSTALT. HAMBURG, GERMANY. 1676-

This is the trade sign of the oldest known existent fire insurance company. *(Courtesy of company.)*

(1335)   STADTISCHE FEUERSOZIETAT VON BERLIN. BERLIN, GERMANY.   1718-

Iron. Rectangular. 6³⁄₁₆″ x 9⁵⁄₁₆″. Black background with white lettering and border. White, black and red crest.

(1336)   FEUERSOZIETAT DER PROVINZ BRANDENBURG. BERLIN, GERMANY.   1719-

Iron. 6¼″ x 9⅜″. White background with black lettering and border. Red, blue and yellow crest.

(1337)   STETTINER OFFENTLICHE FEUERVERSICHE-RUNGSANSTALT. STETTIN, GERMANY.   1722-

Iron. Rectangular, slightly convexed. 8⅝″ x 6⅝″. Red and blue background with white lettering and crest.

(1338)   WESTFALISCHE PROVINZIAL FEUERSOZIETAT GEMEINNUTZIGE OFFENTLICH RECHTLICHE VERSICHE-RUNGS ANSTALT. MUNSTER, GERMANY.   1722-

Iron. 6¼″ x 9½″. White background with black lettering. Crest vari-colored.

Feuersozietät

für die Provinz
Ostpreußen

1339

Provinzial-
Feuersozietät

1340

Landschaftliche Brandkasse

Hannover

1341

Landschaftliche Brandkasse
200 Jahre
1750   1950

HANNOVER

1342

Pommersche

Feuersozietät
Stettin

1343

Schleswig-Holsteinische

Landesbrandkasse.

1344

LÜBECKER
Feuer-Versicherungs Gesellschaft

1345

Hessische
Brandversicherungs-
Anstalt

Gebäude und
Mobiliar

1346

Land-Feuersozietät

Errichtet 1833

der Provinz Sachsen

1347

MECKLENBURGISCHE
Versicherung
NEUBRANDENBURG

1348

Nassauische

Brand-Versicherungs-
Anstalt

1349

Berlinische
Feuer-
Versicherungs-
Anstalt

1350

BERLINISCHE FEUER-VERSICHERUNGS-ANSTALT

GEGR. 1812

1351

Leipziger
feuer
-VERSICHERUNGS-ANSTALT

1352

Gothaer
Feuerversicherungsbank
a.G.

1353

VATERLÄNDISCHE
ELBERFELD

1354

Aachener

u.   M.

Feuer-Versich.-Ges.

1355

AACHEN & MUNICH

FIRE
Insurance Co.

1356

AACHEN
&
MUNICH
1825

1357

Aachener
u.
Münchener
VERSICHERUNG

1358

(1339) FEUERSOZIETAT FUR DIE PROVINZ OSTPREUS-
ZEN. KONIGSBERG, GERMANY. 1723-

Aluminum. Rectangular. 5½" x 7⁵⁄₁₆". Aluminum background
with raised black and gold crest and raised black lettering. Black
border.

(1340) OBERSCHLESISCHE PROVINZIAL FEUER-
SOZIETAT. RATIBOR, GERMANY. 1742-

Iron. Rectangular. 4¹¹⁄₁₆" x 7¹⁄₁₆". Blue and white background,
yellow lettering, white border. Crest blue, yellow and black.

(1341-1342) LANDSCHAFTLICHE BRANDKASSE HANN-
OVER OFFENTLICHE FEUERVERSICHERUNGSANSTALT.
HANNOVER, GERMANY. 1750-

1341. Iron. Slightly convexed. 6⅞" x 5⅛". Red background
with white lettering and border and white horse.

1342. Iron. Slightly convexed. 6⅞" x 5⅛". Red background
with white lettering and border and white horse. Anniversary mark.

(1343) POMMERSCHE FEUERSOZIETAT. STETTIN,
GERMANY. 1750-

Iron. Octagonal, slightly convexed. 6¼" x 7⅞". Light blue
background with white lettering, border and blue and white griffin.

(1344) SCHLESWIG HOLSTEINISCHE LANDESBRAND-
KASSE. KIEL, GERMANY. 1759-

Iron. Slightly convexed. 9¾" x 7". White background with
black letters and vari-colored crest.

(1345) LUBECKER BRANDKASSE OFFENTLICH-RECHT-
LICHE FEUERVERSICHERUNGSANSTALT. LUBECK,
GERMANY. 1765-

Rectangular. Raised border, crest and lettering. (Courtesy of Chartered Insurance Institute.)

(1346) HESSISCHE BRANDVERSICHERUNGS ANSTALT.
KASSEL, GERMANY. 1767-

Iron. Slightly convexed. 5½" x 8⅝". White background with
black lettering and border. Blue, red, yellow and black crest.
"Mobiliar" underlined in red.

(1347) LAND FEUERSOZIETAT DER PROVINZ SACHSEN.
MAGDEBURG, GERMANY. 1789-

Tin plate. 9⅞" x 7⅛". Black background with raised brass
borders and lettering. Center crest black, cream, green and brass,
raised, on white background.

(1348) MECKLENBURGISCHE HAGEL UND FEUER VER-
SICHERUNGS GESELLSCHAFT, A. G. NEWBRANDENBURG,
GERMANY. 1797-

Iron. Slightly convexed. 7¹⁄₁₆" x 4³⁄₁₆". Cream background
with black and red lettering and black border.

(1349) NASSAUISCHE BRAND VERSICHERUNGS
ANSTALT. WIESBADEN, GERMANY. 1806-

Iron. Convexed. 6⅛" x 9¼". White background with blue lettering and blue and yellow crest.

(1350-1351) BERLINISCHE FEUER VERSICHERUNGS
ANSTALT. BERLIN, GERMANY. 1812-

1350. Iron. Convexed. 9⅜" x 6¼". White background with
lettering and emblem in blue.

1351. Brass. Oval. 2¼" x 3½". White background with gold
border and lettering. Black, red and gold figures.

(1352) LEIPZIGER FEUER-VERSICHERUNGS-ANSTALT.
LEIPZIG, GERMANY. 1819-

Tin. Rectangular, convexed. 9⅝" x 6⅜". Cream background
with black lettering and red emblem.

(1353) GOTHAER FEUER VERSICHERUNGSBANK AUF
GEGENSEITIGKEIT. GOTHA, GERMANY. 1820-

Iron. Slightly convexed. 7¼" x 5⅛". Red background with
white lettering and border.

(1354) VATERLANDISCHE FEUER VERSICHERUNGS
AKTIEN GESELLSCHAFT. ELBERFELD, GERMANY.
1822-1871-1914.

Tin. Square. 5⅝" x 5⅝". Raised border, lettering and trademark.

(1355-1358) AACHENER UND MUNCHENER FEUER VER-
SICHERUNGS GESELLSCHAFT. AACHEN, GERMANY.
1825-

1355. Tin. Rectangular. 10¼" x 7¼". Raised border, lettering and crest. From building in Greece.

1356. Tin. Rectangular. 10¼" x 7¼". Raised border, lettering and crest.

1357. Tin. Oval. 9¹³⁄₁₆" x 5¾". Raised black lettering with
rolled border and yellow background.

1358. Iron. Convexed. 5⅞" x 4". Yellow background with
black lettering.

247

GEGR. 1828

Württembergische
FEUERVERSICHERUNG
AG.IN STUTTGART

1359

GEGR. 1828

Württembergische
FEUERVERSICHERUNG
AG. IN STUTTGART

1360

Bayerische
Versicherungsbank
A.G.
vorm. Versicherungsanstalten der
Bayer. Hypotheken-und Wechselbank
München

1361

Bayerische
Versicherungsbank
Allianz
und
Stuttgarter Verein
München

1362

Bayerische
Versicherungsbank
Allianz
und
Stuttgarter Verein
München

1363

Provinzial-
feuer-
Versicherungs-
Anstalt

1364

Provinzial-
Feuer-
Versicherungs-
Anstalt

1365

STÄDTE-
FEUERSOZIETÄT
DER
PROVINZ SACHSEN

1366

GEGR. 1839
C
COLONIA
KÖLN

1367

LA BADENSE
Compania de Seguros Maritimos
Fluviales y Terrestres
Fundada en 1840.

1368

AGRIPPINA VERSICHERUNGEN
SEIT 1844

1369

Versichert
Magdeburg.

1370

1844
M
Magdeburger

1371

Magdeburger

1372

1844
M
Magdeburger

1373

Compagnie d'Assurances
NATIONALE PR.
STETTIN.

1374

N National-
Versicherung

1375

N National-
Versicherung

1376

Schlesische
Feuerversicherung

1377

Versichert
Schlesische
Feuerversicherungs-Gesellschaft
gegr. 1848.

1378

Schlesische
Feuerversicherung

1379

248

(1359-1360) WURTTEMBERGISCHE FEUERVERSICHE-
RUNG AKTIENGESELLSCHAFT IN STUTTGART. STUTT-
GART, GERMANY. 1828-

1359. Iron. Rectangular, slightly convexed. 5½" x 7¾". Dark
blue background with orange lettering and blue, orange and white
emblem.

1360. Iron. Rectangular, slightly convexed. 5½" x 7¾". Dark
blue background with orange lettering and blue, orange and white
emblem.

(1361-1363) BAYERISCHE VERSICHERUNGSBANK
AKTIENGESELLSCHAFT. MUNCHEN, GERMANY. 1835-

1361. Tin. 9½" x 6⁷⁄₁₆". Cream background with raised blue
lettering. Crest blue, orange and white, raised. Border raised with
blue stripe.

1362. Iron. Convexed. 9⅜" x 6¼". White background with
wide blue border and blue lettering. Crests blue, orange and white.

1363. Iron. Convexed. 9⅜" x 6¼". White background with
blue border and blue lettering. Crests blue, yellow and white.
Border and lettering narrower than in mark No. 1362.

(1364-1365) PROVINZIAL FEUERVERSICHERUNGS
ANSTALT DER RHEINPROVINZ. DUSSELDORF, GERMANY.
1904-

1364. Iron. Convexed. 6¼" x 9⅜". White background with
black lettering and green border, crest is green, black and blue.

1365. Iron. Rectangular, convexed. 6" x 7⅞". White background with black lettering, green border and green and white
shield.

(1366) STADTE FEUERSOZIETAT DER PROVINZ
SACHSEN. MERSEBURG, GERMANY. 1838-

Iron. Convexed. 5½" x 8⅝". White background with black
lettering and grey, black, yellow and green crest. Black border.

(1367) "COLONIA" KOLNISCHE FEUER—UND KOL-
NISCHE UNFALL-VERSICHERUNGS—AKTIENGESELL-
SCHAFT. COLOGNE, GERMANY. 1839-

Iron. 5½" x 6⅝". White background with red and black lettering. Red border.

(1368) BADISCHE GEBAUDEVERSICHERUNGSANSTALT.
KARLSRUHE, GERMANY. 1840-

Rectangular. Black background with raised border. (*Courtesy of
Chartered Insurance Institute.*)

(1369) AGRIPPINA SEE—FLUSS—UND LANDTRANSPORT-
VERSICHERUNGS GESELLSCHAFT. COLOGNE, GERMANY.
1844-

Metal alloy. Oval. 3½" x 3¾". Cream background with blue,
red, and gold ornamentation. Gold lettering on blue band. Gold
borders. An auto mark.

(1370-1373) MAGDEBURGER FEUERVERSICHERUNGS—
GESELLSCHAFT. MAGDEBURG, GERMANY. 1844-

1370. Tin. Rectangular. 9¾" x 7⅜". Design and lettering
raised gold on black background. Raised border.

1371. Iron. Slightly convexed. 7¹⁄₁₆" x 4¾". Red background
with white lettering, crest and border.

1372. Iron. Slightly convexed. 7¹⁄₁₆" x 4¾". Red background
with white lettering, crest and border. Similar to mark No. 1371,
but does not contain date. (*Courtesy of V. R. Willemson.*)

1373. Iron. Slightly convexed. 7¹⁄₁₆" x 4¾". Red background
with white lettering, characters, crest and border.

(1374-1376) NATIONAL ALLGEMEINE VERSICHERUNGS
AKTIEN GESELLSCHAFT. STETTIN, GERMANY. 1845-

1374. Tin. Rectangular. 10¼" x 7¼". Raised eagle, lettering
and border. From building in Greece.

1375. Iron. Slightly convexed. 7¾" x 5¹⁄₁₆". Black background with pale yellow lettering, border and black and yellow
emblem.

1376. Iron. Rectangular, convexed. 7⅞" x 5¹⁄₁₆". Black background with yellow lettering, border and black and yellow emblem.

(1377-1379) SCHLESISCHE FEUERVERSICHERUNGS
GESELLSCHAFT. BRESLAU, GERMANY. 1848-

1377. Tin. 9¹⁵⁄₁₆" x 7⁵⁄₁₆". Design and lettering raised gold on
black background. Raised border.

1378. Tin. 9⅞" x 6⅞". Black background with raised lettering
in deep yellow. Raised black border with yellow stripe.

1379. Iron. 7" x 5½". Design, lettering and striping black on
deep yellow background.

1380

1381

1382

1383

1384

1385

1386

1387

1388

1389

1390

1391

1392

1393

1394

1395

1396

1397

1398

1399

1400

1401

1402

250

(1380) GLATZER FEUER SOZIETAT AKTIEN GESELLSCHAFT. GLATZ, GERMANY. 1849-

Iron. Rectangular. 7⅞" x 4¾". White background with orange lettering and figure. Orange and yellow crest. Yellow stripe below name.

(1381) DIE VERSICHERUNGS GESELLSCHAFT THURINGIA IN ERFURT. ERFURT, GERMANY. 1853-

Iron. Slightly convexed. 7" x 5$\frac{1}{16}$". Yellow background with lettering and emblem in black.

(1382-1383) VICTORIA ZU BERLIN ALLGEMEINE VERSICHERUNGS ACTIEN GESELLSCHAFT. BERLIN, GERMANY. 1853-

1382. Iron. Slightly convexed. 7⅛" x 4$\frac{5}{16}$". Yellow background with lettering and border in black.

1383. Iron. Square. 12½" x 12½". Maroon and off-white with emblem and interchanged lettering.

(1384-1386) HAMBURG-BREMER FEUER VERSICHERUNGS GESELLSCHAFT. HAMBURG, GERMANY. 1854-

1384. Tin. Rectangular. 9½" x 7". Black background with raised gold lettering and raised crest in gold, red and white. Raised border. Type used in English-speaking countries.

1385. Tin. Rectangular. 9½" x 7". Black background with raised gold lettering and characters and raised crest in gold, red and white. Raised border. Type used in China.

1386. Tin. Rectangular. 9½" x 6⅞". Black background with raised gold lettering and raised crest in gold, red and white. Raised border.

(1387) PROVIDENTIA, FRANKFURTER VERSICHERUNGS GESELLSCHAFT IN FRANKFURT A/MAIN. FRANKFURT, GERMANY. 1856-1926.

Tin. 7¼" x 3$\frac{11}{16}$". Raised border and lettering. From building in the South of Europe.

(1388-1393) NORD-DEUTSCHE VERSICHERUNGS GESELLSCHAFT. HAMBURG, GERMANY. 1857-

1388. Tin. Rectangular. 6¾" x 4¾". Black background with raised gold lettering and raised border.

1389. Tin. 9¾" x 7". Black background with raised gold lettering and raised border.

1390. Tin. 7⅛" x 4¾". Black background with raised gold lettering and raised red border with gold stripe.

1391. Tin. Rectangular. 10⅞" x 6¾". Black background with raised gold lettering and vari-colored crest. Raised wavy border in dark green.

1392. Iron. Rectangular, slightly convexed. 7" x 4¾". Red background with white lettering, slightly raised.

1393. Iron. Rectangular, slightly convexed. 7" x 4¾". Red background with white lettering, slightly raised. Much deeper color than No. 1392.

(1394) HAMBURG MAGDEBURGER FEUERVERSICHERUNGS GESELLSCHAFT.

Tin. Rectangular. Raised border, crest and lettering. *(Courtesy of Chartered Insurance Institute.)*

(1395) NORDSTERN ALLGEMEINE VERSICHERUNGS AKTIENGESELLSCHAFT. BERLIN-SCHONEBERG, GERMANY. 1866-

Iron. Convexed. 7¾" x 5¾". Blue and black background with yellow lettering and border. Yellow and black emblem.

(1396) PREUSSISCHE FEUER VERSICHERUNGS AKTIEN-GESSELSCHAFT. GERMANY.

Rectangular. Raised border, crest and lettering. *(Courtesy of Chartered Insurance Institute.)*

(1397-1399) TRANSATLANTISCHE FEUER VERSICHERUNGS AKTIEN GESELLSCHAFT. HAMBURG, GERMANY. 1872-1907.

1397. Tin. Rectangular. 9⅞" x 6¾". Raised border, design and lettering. From building in Greece.

1398. Tin. 9¾" x 6½". Raised border, design and lettering. From building in Parana, Brazil. Bears bullet holes supposedly resulting from one of numerous revolutions.

1399. Tin. Rectangular. 9½" x 6½". Raised border, design and lettering.

(1400) UNION ALLGEMEINE VERSICHERUNGS AKTIEN GESELLSCHAFT. BERLIN, GERMANY.

(Courtesy of Chartered Insurance Institute.)

(1401) UNION UND RHEIN VERSICHERUNGS AKTIEN GESELLSCHAFT. BERLIN, GERMANY. 1873-

Iron. 9⅜" x 6$\frac{3}{16}$". White background with black lettering and border. Blue globe with white lettering.

(1402) AACHEN LEIPZIGER VERSICHERUNGS AKTIEN GESELLSCHAFT IN AACHEN. AACHEN, GERMANY. 1876-

Iron. 5⅞" x 3$\frac{15}{16}$". Light red background with white border and lettering.

1403

1404

1405

1406

1407

1408

1409

1410

1411

1412

1413

1414

1415

1416

1417

1418

1419

1420

1421

1422

252

(1403-1404) MANNHEIMER VERSICHERUNGSGESELLSCHAFT. MANNHEIM, GERMANY. 1879-

1403. Tin. 6⅝" x 9¾". Raised crest of gold, red, gray and black on gold bordered yellow panel set on black background. Raised gold lettering. Raised yellow border.

1404. Tin. 3¾" x 5". Raised crest of gold, red, gray and black on gold bordered yellow panel set on black background. Raised gold lettering. Raised white border.

(1405) MUHLEN VERSICHERUNGS GESELLSCHAFT AUF GEGENSEITIGKEIT ZU OSNABRUCK. OSNABRUCK, GERMANY. 1880-

Tin. Rectangular. 9⅞" x 7³⁄₁₆". Raised gold lettering on black background. Raised border.

(1406-1409) FEUERVERSICHERUNGS GESELLSCHAFT RHEINLAND AKTIEN GESELLSCHAFT. NEUSS, GERMANY. 1880-

1406. Tin. Rectangular. 7¼" x 3⅜". Raised border and raised white lettering on red background.

1407. Tin. Rectangular. 10" x 6⅞". Yellow background. Raised red border with black stripe. Raised black and gold lettering and vari-colored crest on gold base.

1408. Iron. Slightly convexed. 8⅝" x 4¹¹⁄₁₆". White background with green borders and lettering.

1409. Iron. Convexed. 7¹³⁄₁₆" x 5⅞". White background with green lettering and border.

(1410) GLOBUS VERSICHERUNGS AKTIEN GESELLSCHAFT. HAMBURG, GERMANY. 1885-

Tin. 7⅛" x 4¾". Black background with raised yellow lettering and border.

(1411) ALLIANZ VERSICHERUNGS AKTIEN GESELLSCHAFT. BERLIN, GERMANY. 1890-1927.

Tin. 7⅛" x 9⅞". Raised design, lettering and border. From building in Greece.

(1412-1413) ALBINGIA VERSICHERUNGS AKTIENGESELLSCHAFT. HAMBURG, GERMANY. 1901-

1412. Tin. Rectangular. 9⅞" x 6¾". Blue background with raised gold lettering and center figure. Raised black border.

1413. Iron. Slightly convexed. 7¹⁄₁₆" x 4¹¹⁄₁₆". Red lettering on white and gray lettering on black. Gray borders.

(1414) DEUTSCHE BEAMTEN FEUERVERSICHERUNG AUF GEGENSEITIGKEIT. BERLIN CHARLOTTENBURG, GERMANY. 1906-

Iron. 7¾" x 4¾". White background with red crest and black lettering and border.

(1415-1416) INTAG PHOBUS VERSICHERUNGS AKTIENGESELLSCHAFT. BERLIN SCHONEBERG, GERMANY. 1908-1930.

1415. Brass. 11¾" x 7⅞". Black background with raised brass trademark and lettering. Brass border.

1416. Brass. Circular. 2¼" in diameter. Black background with polished brass center bearing red and black lettering. Brass lettering above. Brass stripe around edge.

(1417) VOLKSFURSORGE ALLGEMEINE VERSICHERUNGS-AKTIENGESELLSCHAFT. HAMBURG, GERMANY. 1912-

Tin. Rectangular. 7¹⁵⁄₁₆" x 5¹³⁄₁₆". Cream background with raised blue lettering and blue and black emblem raised.

(1418) ALLGEMEINE FEUERASSEKURANZ AKTIEN GESELLSCHAFT. HAMBURG, GERMANY. 1920-

Tin. Rectangular. 7⅛" x 5⅛". Cream background with raised black lettering. Raised black border with black stripe.

(1419) GILDE DEUTSCHE VERSICHERUNGS AKTIEN GESELLSCHAFT. DUSSELDORF, GERMANY. 1921-

Tin. Rectangular. 8⅜" x 5⅝". Black background with raised gold border and lettering.

(1420) AGRIPPINA ALLGEMEINE VERSICHERUNGS AKTIEN GESELLSCHAFT. COLOGNE, GERMANY. 1922-

(Courtesy of V. R. Willemson.)

(1421) DEUTSCHER BAUERNDIENST ALLGEMEINE VERSICHERUNGS-AKTIENGESELLSCHAFT LEBENSVERSICHERUNGS–GESELLSCHAFT A. G. BERLIN, CHARLOTTENBURG, GERMANY. 1922-

Iron. Shield shape, slightly convexed. 5" x 8". Yellow and black. Yellow border.

(1422) DEUTSCHE ALLGEMEINE VERSICHERUNGS AKTIEN GESELLSCHAFT. BERLIN, GERMANY. 1923-

Iron. Slightly convexed. 7¾" x 5⅞". White background with red center circle and black ribbon. Black design and lettering.

1423

1424

1425

1426

1428

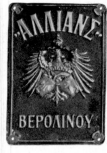

1427

(1423-1424) HAMBURG MUNCHENER LLOYD VERSICHE-RUNGS AKTIEN GESELLSCHAFT. HAMBURG, GERMANY. 1923-1925.

1423. Brass. Rectangular. 7½″ x 10½″. Black background with raised lettering, border and gold center figure. From building in Greece.

1424. Tin. Rectangular. 7½″ x 10¼″. Raised lettering, border and center figure. From building in Greece.

(1425-1427) ALLIANZ UND STUTTGARTER VEREIN VER-SICHERUNGS AKTIEN GESELLSCHAFT. BERLIN, GER-MANY. 1927-

1425. Iron. 6⅜″ x 9½″. Slightly raised lettering, design and raised border. From building in Greece.

1426. Iron. Convexed. 6¼″ x 9½″. Blue background with white enamel lettering and border.

1427. Tin. 6¾″ x 9⅞″. Raised gold lettering, gold and vari-colored crest, and green border on black background.

(1428) NEUE FRANKFURTER ALLGEMEINE VERSICHE-RUNGS AKTIEN GESELLSCHAFT. FRANKFURT AM RHEIN, GERMANY. 1929-

Iron. Convexed. 9½″ x 6¼″. Blue with white lettering, em-blem and border.

GIBRALTAR

To most people the Rock of Gibraltar exists only as a great promontory, commanding the entrance to the Mediterranean in behalf of the British crown. It is, of course, definitely a fortress, but commerce and trade do exist to such an extent that foreign fire insurance companies, as well as a single local institution, have for many years used fire marks.

Tourists for almost a century have marvelled at the formations of the Hill Caves of Gibraltar. St. Michael's Cave, for instance, has an entrance eleven hundred feet above the sea with a slope of earth giving admission to a hall two hundred feet long and seventy feet high. Massive stalactite pillars support the ceiling of this room which is only a reception area to a series of other similar caves which reach to a distance of three hundred feet below the surface. It is one of the world's wonders which competes with the splendor of Mammoth Cave of Kentucky in America.

1429

(1429) ROCK FIRE ASSURANCE COMPANY, LIMITED. GIBRALTAR. 1841-

Oval with center containing the image of the Rock of Gibraltar. Company name on outer band. *(Courtesy of Chartered Insurance Institute.)*

GREECE

The inhabitants of this country, both ancient and modern, have always called their country Hellas, but the Romans, who reduced the former highly cultured nation of the Hellenes to the status of a province at the time of Christ, called the section Greece. The city states of ancient Greece, especially Athens, have left us an imperishable record of art and architecture, and their thought and culture has indelibly influenced European civilization. After the conquest by the Romans, Greece formed part of the Eastern Empire until this in turn fell in 1453 A.D., when the Greeks passed under the hegemony of the Turks. Greece did not become an independent nation again until 1827, and after undergoing numerous military and political contingencies in our time succumbed to the Nazi war machine until the liberation in 1944.

In a nation proud of its great heritage, insurance company names were frequently derived from the legends and literature of Hellas, and the fire marks they issued were deeply influenced by the early Greek arts. The marks of only two Greek companies established prior to 1917 are shown; the remainder of the companies were formed subsequent to that year when new insurance laws were enacted by the government permitting venture capital to enter the fire insurance field.

In 1935 and the ensuing three years, Michel H. Gattegno of Thessaloniki and Alexander J. Zoidas of Athens secured some four hundred very old and rare fire marks of almost two hundred insurance companies from old buildings in the Mediterranean area. These represented concerns founded in Europe and Asia, and they now form a valuable part of the exhibits of numerous signevierists in the United States and Canada. All of these marks are represented in the various chapters of this work. To the untiring efforts of these two Hellenic representatives, who exhibited such patience and native stamina in their extensive travels and search, must go our gratitude and much of the credit for the preservation of important items of fire insurance history. Very few marks remain since the recent war.

1430

1431

1432

1433

1434

1435

1436

1437

1438

1439

1440

1441

1442

1443

1444

1445

1446

(1430) ETHNIKI ANONYMOSHELLINIKI HETERIA GHENIKON ASPHALION. ATHENS, GREECE. 1891-

Tin. Rectangular. 11¼" x 6¾". Raised fret border and lettering in white on blue background.

(1431-1432) ANATOLI ANONYMOS HELLINIKI ASPHALIS-TIKI HETERIA. ATHENS, GREECE. 1906-

1431. Tin. Rectangular. 6⅞" x 9⅝". Slightly raised black lettering, border and figure on yellow background.

1432. Tin. Rectangular. 6⅞" x 9⅝". Slightly raised brown lettering, border and figure on orange background.

(1433) ATHINAIKI ANONYMOS ASPHALISTIKI HETERIA. PIRAEUS, GREECE. 1917-

Tin. Rectangular. 6⅝" x 9¾". White and gold lettering, gold, grey and white emblem and white border on red background.

(1434) GHENIKI ASPHALIE TIS HELLADOS ANONYMOS HETERIA. ATHENS, GREECE. 1917-

Tin. Rectangular. 11" x 7⅞". Raised white lettering and fret border, and gold emblem on blue background.

(1435) ANONYMOS HETERIA ASPHALION I PRONIA. ATHENS, GREECE. 1917-1927.

Tin. Rectangular. 6⅝" x 9⅝". Raised black lettering and crest in red and white on red background. Raised border had been white. From building in Greece.

(1436-1438) ANONYMOS HETERIA ASPHALION I PRO-
PONTIS. PIRAEUS, GREECE. 1917-

1436. Tin. Oval. 10¾" x 7⅜". Raised black and white trademark, raised and flat black lettering and raised black border on
white background. From building in Greece.

1437. Tin. Oval. 10¾" x 7⅜". Raised vari-colored trademark, raised black and red lettering on yellow background. Rolled
border with blue and black striping. From building in Greece.

1438. Tin. Oval. 10¾" x 7⅜". Raised vari-colored trademark, raised black and red lettering on cream background. Rolled
border with blue and black striping.

(1439-1440) KALI PISTIS ANONYMOS ETAIREIA GENIKON
ASPHALISION. PIRAEUS, GREECE. 1918-1928.

1439. Tin. 9¹³⁄₁₆" x 6⅝". Raised lettering, design and border.
From building in Greece.

1440. Tin. Rectangular. 9¹³⁄₁₆" x 6⅝". Raised border and
lettering in cream, raised trademark in blue and cream on blue
background. From building in Greece.

(1441) PANELLINIOS ASPHALISTIKI HETERIA. PIRAEUS,
GREECE. 1918-

Tin. Rectangular. 9¾" x 6⁹⁄₁₆". Raised blue lettering on white
background. Blue ornamental border. Raised white outer border.

(1442) TITAN ETAIRIA GENIKON ASFALEION. ATHENS,
GREECE. 1918-1928.

Tin. Circular, convexed. 9" in diameter. Raised lettering, figure and borders. From building in Greece.

(1443) KYKLADIKI ANONYMOS ELLENIKI ASPHALISTIKI
HETERIA. ATHENS, GREECE. 1919-

Tin. 6⅝" x 9¾". Raised black border and anchor, raised red
lettering, red flames on cream background.

(1444) ETHNIKI ZOE ANONYMOS HELLENIKI ETAIREIA.
ATHENS, GREECE. 1920-1928.

Tin. 9¾" x 6¾". Raised cream lettering and raised border with
cream fret. Blue background.

(1445) ELLENIKI ANONYMOS HETERIA GHENIKON
ASPHALION. ATHENS, GREECE. 1927-

Tin. 8½" x 8⅝". Raised figure and lettering in blue and cream
on blue background. Raised borders.

(1446) ASTIR ANONYMOS ASPHALISTIKI HETERIA
PYROS, ZOES KE ATY. ATHENS, GREECE. 1931-

Tin. 6¾" x 9¾". Raised border, circle and lettering in blue,
yellow star and background.

HOLLAND

The Netherlands, the country which is so rich in
folklore, centered around the Zuider Zee. It is a land
(much of it below the level of the sea) populated by
an industrious people largely of Germanic origin with
some Celtic and Alpine admixture. These ingenious
people, in solving the need to pump the water from
low spots, perfected the windmill which soon became
a symbol of Holland. These lazy, winged mills were
not confined to pumping water, however, but also
were used to grind meal and later to perform other
power duties.

The superintendents of fire apparatus in the city
of Amsterdam in 1672 were John and Nicholas Van
der Heide (or Van der Heyden) who were responsible for the most extraordinary advances made in
fire-fighting methods for many centuries. Until this
time large engines could not be used to extinguish
fires in the interiors of dwellings; it was only after

the flames burst through the windows or roof that
they came into play. It was a common occurrence to
have engines, placed too close to a burning building,
succumb to the flames or be crushed by a falling wall.
The Van der Heides first used their new appurtenances in 1672. These consisted of hose or leather
tubes to convey water from the engines to the fires
inside of buildings, thus permitting the pumpers to
remain at a safe distance from the structure itself.
The tubes were in fifty-foot lengths, with brass screws
fitted to the ends, so that a number of them could be
fitted together quickly.

Up to this time it was necessary to pour water into
the engine's feedbox via bucket brigades. When the
clever Van der Heides connected a length of hose
to the bottom of the engine and ran it to a pond or
other water source, however, they then provided a
form of suction hose. As it was then necessary to

A syringe or "screw" engine used on the continent in the middle of the 16th century.

change the construction of the lower parts of the pumps to form a suction, the inventors preferred making entirely new machines. They eventually obtained an exclusive privilege to construct such engines for a period of twenty-five years. These improvements, made in 1675, just nine years after the great fire in London, indicate the extent of the progress of fire fighting in the Netherlands in contrast to that of other countries. As a result, the system of applying hose lines became popular and by 1720 canvas hose was woven without seams in Leipzig and other places in Germany.

Gleanings from certain old Dutch works make it evident that fire insurance schemes or plans existed there as early as they did elsewhere, and quite possibly antedated others. A review of the dates of organization of the fire insurance companies which issued fire marks in Holland reveals that all came into being well before the end of the nineteenth century. We also find that most of the marks were made of lead, a practice indulged in only by the earliest concerns. Just what function the mark served in Holland is not clear, for the earliest fire brigades were municipal affairs (in Amsterdam alone some sixty of Van der Heides engines were maintained by the community in 1695), yet the marks were systematically posted upon insured premises. The advertising type of mark continued into this century.

1447

1448

1449

1450

1451

1452

1453

1454

1455

1456

(1447) HAAGSCHE ASSURANTIE COMPAGNIE VOOR BRAND ENZ. VAN 1805. THE HAGUE, HOLLAND. 1805-

Iron. 7¾" x 9⅜". Lettering, stork and border in gold on black background.

(1448) NOORDHOLLANDSCHE BRANDWAARBORG-MAATSCHAPPIJ. TE OUDKARSPEL, HOLLAND. 1816-

Glass. Rectangular. 11¾" x 7¾". Gold letters on black background.

(1449) MIJ. VAN ONDERLINGEN WAARBORG TEGEN BRANDSCHADE AAN GEBOUWEN EN ROERENDE GOEDEREN HOLLAND. MIDDELBURG, PROVINCE OF ZEELAND, HOLLAND. 1829-

Lead. Rectangular. 5⅝" x 8⅛". Crest raised in yellow and green with red lion. Black background. Letters raised at bottom.

(1450-1452) N. V. NEDERLANSCHE MAATSCHAPPIJ VAN BRANDVERZERKRING. TIEL, HOLLAND. 1883-

1450. Lead. Oval. 4" x 2½". Border and lettering raised.

1451. Lead. Oval. 7" x 9⅜". Gold crest and lettering raised on black background.

1452. Tin. Oval. 7⅛" x 9¼". Gold border, lettering and crest raised on black background.

(1453-1454) N. V. MAATSCHAPPIJ VAN BRANDVERZEKERING VOOR HET KONINGRIJK DER NEDERLANDEN TE 'S-HERTOGENBOSCH. HERTOGENBOSCH, HOLLAND. 1838-

1453. Lead. Oval. 8" x 9¼". Black border and lettering and red, gold and black crest, all raised. Background white.

1454. Lead. Oval. 8" x 9¼". Black border, lettering and date red, gold and black crest, all raised. Background cream.

(1455) N. V. 'S-HERTOGENBOSCH BRANDWAARBORG MIJ. VAN 1841. HERTOGENBOSCH, HOLLAND. 1841-

Lead. Raised crest and lettering. (Courtesy of V. R. Willemson.)

(1456) HOLLANDSCHE-NEDERLANDSCHE (HOLLANDSCHE ASSURANTIE SOCIETEIT VAN 1841—NEDERLANDSCHE BRAND EN ZEE ASSUR. MIJ VAN 1842) AMSTERDAM. AMSTERDAM, HOLLAND. 1841-

Iron. 9¾" x 4". Black lettering, light gray background, dark gray panels.

1458

1457

1461

1459

1460

1463

1462

1464

1465

(1457-1460) N. V. ASSURANTIE—MAATSCHAPPIJ "DE NEDERLANDEN" VAN 1845. THE HAGUE, HOLLAND. 1845-

1457. Tin. Rectangular. 8¾" x 6⅜". Border, lettering and crest in raised gold on black background.

1458. Tin. Rectangular. 10¹⁄₁₆" x 7¹⁄₁₆". Border, lettering and crest in raised gold on black background. From building in Martinique.

1459. Tin. Rectangular. 10" x 7⅛". Raised letters and crest gold on black background. Chinese characters in red. Border raised.

1460. Tin. Rectangular. 10¼" x 7¼". Gold letters on black.

(1461) N. V. NEDERLANDSCHE LLOYD. AMSTERDAM, HOLLAND. 1853-

Iron. Rectangular. 8¼" x 2⅞". Black crest and lettering on white background.

(1462) N. V. BRANDVERZEKERING—MAATSCHAPPIJ, HOLLAND VAN 1859. DORDRECHT, HOLLAND. 1859-

Tin. Oval. 4⅜" x 3⅛". Raised border, crest and lettering blue. Cream colored background.

(1463) UTRECHTSCHE ALGEMEENE BRANDVERZEKERING MAATSCHAPPIJ. UTRECHT, HOLLAND. 1867-

Lead. Oval. 10" x 8½". Border, gold lettering and design raised. Crest is gold, white and red. Background black.

(1464-1465) N. V. DE NEDERLANDSCHE BRAND-ASSURANTIE—MIJ "DE SALAMANDER VAN 1888." DORDRECHT, HOLLAND. 1888- (Established at Amsterdam.)

1464. Tin. Rectangular. 8⅛" x 6⅜". Border, design and lettering raised. From building in Istanbul, Turkey.

1465. Tin. 8" x 6¼". Red center oval with raised gold letters and salamander on green background. Raised gold Chinese characters. Border raised.

HUNGARY

Most fire marks recorded here were acquired after World War I when Hungary had freed itself from the former Austrian empire. Because Hungary has been intermittently torn with strife the specimens of fire marks of the early insurance companies are rare, although they were used in the traditional manner. Far more frequent, however, are the modern types of advertising marks used between the years of the two great wars to indicate the extent of the protection offered by the various insurance concerns.

1467

1466

1468

1469

1470

1472

1471

(1466) ELSO MAGYAR ALTALANOS BIZTOSITO TARSA-SAG. BUDAPEST, HUNGARY. 1857-

Aluminum. Rectangular. 7" x 5". Black letters, green and red borders, green, red, gold and white crest on white background.

(1467) FONCIERE ALTALANOS BIZTOSITO INTEZET. BUDAPEST, HUNGARY. 1864-

Tin. Rectangular. 9¾" x 6⅝". Blue letters and vari-colored crest raised on cream background. Yellow border raised.

(1468-1469) MAGYAR FRANCIA BIZTOSITO RESZVENY-TARSASAG. BUDAPEST, HUNGARY. 1879-

1468. Tin. Rectangular. 4¾" x 4¹⁄₁₆". Vari-colored crest, white and yellow letters and yellow border raised. Dark blue background.

1469. Iron. Rectangular. 5⅞" x 4¾". Yellow border, white lettering on dark blue background.

(1470) HAZAI ALTALANOS BIZTOSITO RESZVENYTARSA-SAG. BUDAPEST, HUNGARY. 1895-

Tin. Rectangular. 7⁵⁄₁₆" x 4⅞". Raised black and white border. Raised red, black and white letters on green background.

(1471-1473) GAZDAK BIZTOSITO SZOVETKEZETE. BUDA-PEST, HUNGARY. 1900-

1471. Tin. Rectangular. 6⅞" x 4⅞". Raised red and silver border with raised silvered letters on dark green background. "Gazdak" trimmed with red.

1472. Aluminum. Rectangular. 5½" x 3⁵⁄₁₆". Raised black letters and border. Background gold.

.1474

1475

1476

1473

1477

1478

1479

1480

1481

1482

1473. Aluminum. 5½" x 3¹⁵⁄₁₆". Raised black letters and border. Background white.

Aluminum. Rectangular. 6⁹⁄₁₆" x 4¹¹⁄₁₆". Raised blue letters and border on silver-white background.

(1474) MAGYAR HOLLANDI BIZTOSITO RESZVENYTAR-SASAG. BUDAPEST, HUNGARY. 1916-

Iron. Rectangular. 7⅛" x 4¾". Lettering in red and blue on white background.

(1478) KATHOLIKUS NEPSZOVETSEG BIZTOSITASI IRODAJA UT. BUDAPEST, HUNGARY. 1920-

Tin. Rectangular. 6¹¹⁄₁₆" x 4¹¹⁄₁₆". Raised blue border, letters and crest on silver-white background.

(1475) KISBIRTOKOSOK BIZTOSITO INTEZETE RESZVE-NYTARSASAG. BUDAPEST, HUNGARY. 1918-

Tin. Rectangular. 6¹³⁄₁₆" x 4⅞". Outer border white with inner border raised black. Raised black letters on red, white and green background.

(1479-1480) KOZEPEUROPAI ES MINERVA ALTALANOS BIZTOSITO RESZVENYTARSASAG. BUDAPEST, HUNGARY. 1920-

1479. Tin. Rectangular. 4⅞" x 3½". Raised red oval, raised cream letters on dark blue background. Raised red border.

1480. Tin. Rectangular. 7" x 4⅞". Red oval and raised cream letters outlined in black on dark blue background. Raised red border.

(1476) PENZINTEZETEK ORSZAGOS BIZTOSITO RESZ-VENYTARSASAG. BUDAPEST, HUNGARY. 1918-

Tin. Rectangular. 6⁵⁄₁₆" x 4⁹⁄₁₆". Raised black letters and border on white background.

(1481-1482) PROVIDENTIA BIZTOSITO R. T. BUDAPEST, HUNGARY. 1924-

1481. Iron. Rectangular. 4¾" x 3⅛". White border and lettering on light green background.

1482. Iron. Rectangular. 5⅞" x 5⅛". White border and lettering on light green background.

(1477) ELSO KERESZTENY BIZTOSITO INTEZET RESZ-VENYTARSASAG. BUDAPEST, HUNGARY. 1920-

INDIA

India, known to the West since the days of Alexander the Great, had passed through nearly two thousand years of changing empires and kingdoms when the great Mogul empire was founded in 1526. This empire reached its peak of power and influence in the seventeenth and eighteenth centuries. With the erection of the East India Company's first factory in India in 1612, the British began to expand their influence. With the defeat of Mohammedan and other forces by Lord Clive in the decade ending in 1760, the foundation of the British Empire in India was laid.

During our present century the empire was filled with unrest and revolt. As a result India was granted independence in 1947. Over 90 per cent of this nation's effort is agricultural, still medieval in form, but its industries are in most cases patterned after the British system.

Fire insurance is conducted by the companies of Great Britain or in cooperation with them by local concerns. Fire marks have never been in common use, and the two specimens here illustrated have not been used in the traditional sense but rather as an advertising medium. The mark of the New India was probably also used as an agency sign.

1483

1484

(1483)   NEW INDIA ASSURANCE COMPANY, LIMITED. BOMBAY, INDIA.   1919-

Tin. 8⅞" x 7".   Vari-colored lettering and trademark on light green background. Border black and green.

(1484)   THE BOMBAY FIRE & MARINE INSURANCE COMPANY, LTD. FORT, BOMBAY, INDIA.   ? - ?

Tin. Circular. Trademark in center. Company name on outer circle. *(Courtesy of Chartered Insurance Institute.)*

INDO-CHINA

Located in the southeast corner of Asia and composed of an area of five states, Indo-China has been under French influence for many years, one state as a colonial possession and the remainder as protectorates. As in all countries of the East, agriculture dominates the economy. As a result little fire insurance development has taken place except in the establishment of one company whose fire marks are illustrated. There are instances where foreign insurance concerns used marks in Indo-China.

1485

1486

1487

(1485-1487)   COMPAGNIE FRANCO AMERICAINE D'ASSURANCES SOCIETE ANONYME FRANCAISE D'ASSURANCES ET DE REASSURANCES. SAIGON, INDO CHINA. 1930-

1485. Alloy. Circular. 2¹¹⁄₁₆" in diameter. Raised lettering and borders in natural nickel. Dark green center, with surrounding band blue.

1486. Alloy. Rectangular. 7¹³⁄₁₆" x 4¹¹⁄₁₆". Raised border, lettering and Chinese characters in natural nickel on dark red background.

1487. Square tin. Border, lettering and characters painted. *(Courtesy of American Reserve Insurance Company.)*

ITALY

The history of the Roman Empire is, of course, also the history of Italy, that much diminished area of the greatest political power which ever dominated the earth. A sketch of Italian history after the fall of the empire would involve a study of many states, some independent, some under foreign domination. Italy as we know it today was unified in the middle of the nineteenth century. In 1861 a parliamentary form of government was established under the leadership of the house of Savoy. The Savoy dynasty came to an end after World War II.

In the old Roman Empire, commerce had been established with practically every part of the then known world, and the trade and business characteristics of the people have continued down through the centuries. So, too, have they maintained a line of successive measures in connection with fire. The buildings of ancient Rome were unusually high with the upper floors made of wood and were situated on lanes and narrow streets which made fire fighting extremely difficult. They did have engines—on the whole, primitive and inefficient—for throwing water, and sponges or mops were affixed to the ends of long poles which together with grapples and other means of going from one wall to another permitted firemen to fight the flames as best they could.

Then came the great conflagration—Rome burned while, according to legend, Nero fiddled. When the city was rebuilt precautions to prevent fires were inaugurated, and the height of buildings was limited to seventy feet. Every citizen was required to keep in his house "a machine for extinguishing fire." It has not been determined what this apparatus was, but in the writings of Ulpian, the noted lawyer who was also the secretary to Emperor Alexander Severus, we find that he enumerates "fixtures, among them SIPHONES employed to extinguish fires." Undoubtedly many of our more modern devices are patterned upon basic designs created in the civilization of the ancient world.

Hand in hand with the progress made in firefighting methods in the more modern Italy has gone the development of fire insurance. The methods once employed in Britain in reference to that industry and its use of fire marks and fire fighting, have been on a comparable basis with Italy.

1488

1489

1490

1491

1492

1493

1494

1495

1496

1497

1498

1499

1500

1501

1502

1503

1504

(1488)   MILANO COMPAGNIA DI ASSICURAZIONE. MILAN, ITALY.   1825-

Tin. Rectangular. 10¼″ x 8¼″.   Raised gold letters and border and design on black background.

(1489-1490)   SOCIETA REALE MUTUA DI ASSICURA-ZIONE. TURIN, ITALY.   1822-

1489.   Tin. Rectangular. 10¼″ x 8¼″.   Gold, red, white and black crest raised in center. Names in raised gold letters on black background. Border raised.

1490.   Tin. Rectangular. 10⅝″ x 8″.   Gold, red, white and black crest raised in center and name in raised gold letters on black background. Border raised.

(1491-1504)   ASSICURAZIONI GENERALI SOCIETA ANONIMA. TRIESTE, ITALY.   1831-

1491.   Tin. Rectangular. 10¼″ x 7⅞″.   Raised border, raised gold letters and winged lion with tail down on red background.

1492.   Tin. 10¼″ x 8″.   Raised border. Raised gold letters and winged lion with tail up on red background.

1493.   Zinc. Rectangular. 11″ x 7¹³⁄₁₆″.   Raised white characters and company name on red background. Outer border raised. From building in Palestine.

1494. Iron. Rectangular. 11½″ x 8½″. Raised border, company name and date. From building in Greece.

1495. Tin. 10¾″ x 8⅛″. Raised border and company name and date. From building in Greece.

1496. Tin. Rectangular. 9¾″ x 7″. Raised border, date and Greek lettering.

1497. Zinc. Rectangular. 12⅜″ x 9¹⁄₁₆″. Raised border, date and Greek lettering. Lettering had been gold. From building in Greece.

1498. Tin. Rectangular. 10⁹⁄₁₆″ x 8¹⁄₁₆″. Raised border, date and Greek lettering. From building in Greece.

1499. Tin. Rectangular. 10½″ x 8″. Raised gold lettering on black background. Border raised.

1500. Tin. Rectangular. 10⅝″ x 7⅞″. Date and Greek lettering gold on black background. Border raised. Used in Greece.

1501. Tin. Rectangular. 10⅞″ x 7⅞″. Raised gold border and lettering on black background.

1502. Tin. Rectangular. 9⅞″ x 7¾″. Raised border, raised gold letters and winged lion with tail down on red background.

1503. Tin. Rectangular. 10¹⁵⁄₁₆″ x 7¹³⁄₁₆″. Raised gold lettering and border. Black background. From building in Palestine.

1504. Tin. Rectangular. 6⅞″ x 5¹³⁄₁₆″. Black German lettering on cream colored center, slightly raised. Black background. Border raised.

1505

1506

1507

1508

1509

1510

1511

1512

1513

1514

1515

1516

1517

1518

1519

1520

1521

1522

1523

1524

1525

1526

1527

1528

(1505) COMPAGNIA ANONIMA D'ASSICURAZIONE DI TORINO. TURIN, ITALY. 1833-

Tin. Rectangular. Raised border, lettering and bull. *(Courtesy of V. R. Willemson.)*

(1506-1518) RIUNIONE ADRIATICA DI SICURTA. TRIESTE, ITALY. 1838-

1506. Tin. Octagonal. 10$\frac{7}{8}$″ x 8$\frac{1}{4}$″. Raised gold border, center figure and lettering on red background.

1507. Zinc. Rectangular. 11$\frac{3}{8}$″ x 8$\frac{1}{4}$″. Raised border and lettering. From building in Greece.

1508. Tin. Rectangular. 11$\frac{3}{8}$″ x 8$\frac{1}{4}$″. Raised border and lettering. From building in Greece.

1509. Tin. Rectangular. 11$\frac{3}{8}$″ x 8$\frac{1}{4}$″. Raised border and lettering. From building in Greece.

1510. Zinc. Rectangular. 11$\frac{1}{2}$″ x 8$\frac{5}{16}$″. Raised border, Greek lettering and date. From building in Greece.

1511. Iron. Rectangular. 11$\frac{3}{4}$″ x 8$\frac{1}{2}$″. Border and raised white lettering on blue. From building in Greece.

1512. Tin. Rectangular. 9$\frac{13}{16}$″ x 6$\frac{5}{8}$″. Raised white letters and border on dark blue background.

1513. Tin. Rectangular. 9$\frac{9}{16}$″ x 6$\frac{13}{16}$″. Border and lettering and characters in raised gold on black background.

1514. Tin. Rectangular. 9$\frac{1}{2}$″ x 6$\frac{7}{8}$″. Raised border, Greek lettering and date cream color on blue background.

1515. Tin. Rectangular. 9$\frac{3}{8}$″ x 6$\frac{1}{4}$″. Raised gold border and raised and flat gold lettering on black background.

1516. Tin. Rectangular. 8$\frac{1}{4}$″ x 5$\frac{3}{8}$″. Raised border and lettering cream color on dark blue background.

1517. Tin. Rectangular. 8$\frac{1}{8}$″ x 5$\frac{1}{2}$″. Raised border and raised and flat lettering white on blue background.

1518. Tin. Rectangular. Type mark used for Polish. *(Courtesy of V. R. Willemson.)*

(1519) ITALIA. ITALY. ? - ?

Tin. Rectangular. Raised border and lettering. *(Courtesy of Chartered Insurance Institute.)*

(1520-1523) LA FONDIARIA, COMPAGNIA ITALIANA DI ASSICURAZIONI CONTRO L'INCENDIO. FLORENCE, ITALY. 1879-

1520. Zinc. Rectangular. 11$\frac{1}{4}$″ x 7″. Raised border and lettering.

1521. Zinc. Rectangular. 10$\frac{7}{8}$″ x 6$\frac{1}{4}$″. Raised border and lettering buff on black background.

1522. Tin. 11″ x 6$\frac{3}{4}$″. Raised border and raised buff letters on very dark blue background. From building in Greece.

1523. Tin. Rectangular. 9$\frac{7}{8}$″ x 6$\frac{11}{16}$″. Raised border and raised white letters on blue background.

(1524) SOCIETA ANONIMA ITALIANA PER L'ASSICURAZIONE CONTRO L'INCENDIO. MILAN, ITALY. 1889-

Tin. Rectangular. 9$\frac{3}{4}$″ x 7″. Raised border and lettering cream color on blue background.

(1525-1526) SOCIETA CATTOLICA DI ASSICURAZIONE. VERONA, ITALY. 1896-

1525. Tin. Rectangular. 10$\frac{1}{4}$″ x 7$\frac{7}{8}$″. Raised white border and company name with center figure raised blue and white on blue background.

1526. Tin. Rectangular. 9$\frac{13}{16}$″ x 6$\frac{7}{8}$″. Raised border, company name and emblem cream color on blue background.

(1527) SAVOIA SOCIETA ANONIMA ITALIANA D'ASSICURAZIONI. GENOA, ITALY. 1896-

Tin. Rectangular. 10″ x 6$\frac{3}{4}$″. Gold border and slightly raised gold lettering on peacock blue background.

(1528) LA PROVIDENZA. MILAN, ITALY. ? - ?

Tin. Rectangular. Raised border and lettering. *(Courtesy of Chartered Insurance Institute.)*

1529

1530

1531

1532

1533

1534

1535

1536

1537

1538

1539

1540

1541

1542

1543

1544

(1529)   L'ITALICA SOCIETA ANONIMA DI ASSICURAZIONI E RIASSICURAZIONI. MILAN, ITALY.   1904-

Tin. Rectangular. 9″ x 6½″. Raised border and center figure and raised and flat lettering on blue background.

(1530)   L'EQUITA. GENOA, ITALY.   ? - ?

Tin. Rectangular. Raised border and lettering. *(Courtesy of Chartered Insurance Institute.)*

(1531)   L'EMILIANA ASSICURAZIONI BOLOGNA. ITALY. ? - ?

Tin. Rectangular. Border and lettering raised. *(Courtesy of Chartered Insurance Institute.)*

(1532)   LA VITTORIA COMPANIA ANONIMA DI ASSICURAZIONI GENERALI. MILAN, ITALY.   1912-

Tin. 9¾″ x 5¾″. Raised figure, letters and border in gold on deep blue background.

(1533)   CASSA NAVALE E D'ASSICURAZIONI SOCIETA ANONIMA. GENOA, ITALY.   1914-

Tin. Rectangular. 9⅞″ x 6⅝″. Raised design black, grey and red with raised letters and border.

(1534)   ALLEANZA SECURITAS ESPERIA SOCIETA ANONIMA DI ASSICURAZIONI. ROME, ITALY.   1915-

Tin. Rectangular. 9¹⁵⁄₁₆″ x 6¹⁵⁄₁₆″. Raised cream colored letters and raised black shadows. Blue background. Modern.

(1535) LA PREVIDENTE COMPAGNIA ITALIANA DI ASSICURAZIONI. MILAN, ITALY. 1917-

Tin. Rectangular. 19⅝″ x 13⅝″. Raised gold letters and red border on black blackground.

(1536) LA PACE SOCIETA ANONIMA ASSICURAZIONI E RIASSICURAZIONI. MILAN, ITALY. 1919-

Tin. Rectangular. 9¾″ x 7⅝″. Raised border and letters on dark blue background.

(1537) ISTITUTO ITALIANO DI PREVIDENZA S. A. MILAN, ITALY. 1920-

Tin. Rectangular. Raised border and lettering. (Courtesy of Chartered Insurance Institute.)

(1538-1539) ITALIAN EXCESS INSURANCE COMPANY (SOCIETA ANONIMA DI ASSICURAZIONI E RIASSICURA-ZIONI). MILAN, ITALY. 1921-

1538. Tin. 9¾″ x 6⅝″. Raised lettering and border in gold on red ground. From building in Greece.

1539. Tin. 9¾″ x 6″. Raised gold lettering and border on red background.

(1540) ISTITUTO DI SICURTA GENERALI & GLOBO. TURIN, ITALY. 1922-

Tin. Rectangular. Raised border and lettering. (Courtesy of V. R. Willemson.)

(1541) LE ASSICURAZIONI D'ITALIA SOCIETA ANONIMA PER AZIONI. ROME, ITALY. 1923-

Tin. 9⅜″ x 6⅝″. Raised gold and blue border and raised gold lettering on deep blue background.

(1542) IL DUOMO SOCIETA ANONIMA DI ASSICURA-ZIONI E RIASSICURAZIONI. MILAN, ITALY. 1923-

Tin. Rectangular. 9¾″ x 6⅝″. Cream colored lettering, silver castle on midnight blue.

(1543) ASSICURAZIONI ALTA ITALIA SOCIETA ANO-NIMA. TURIN, ITALY. 1924-1932.

Tin. Rectangular. 9⅞″ x 6¹¹⁄₁₆″. Dark brown border, raised cream colored lettering on raised tan center.

(1544) FIUME SOCIETA ANONIMA DI ASSICURAZIONI E REASSICURAZIONI. FIUME, ITALY. 1924-

Tin. Rectangular. 6¾″ x 4¾″. Raised white letters on red background. Border raised.

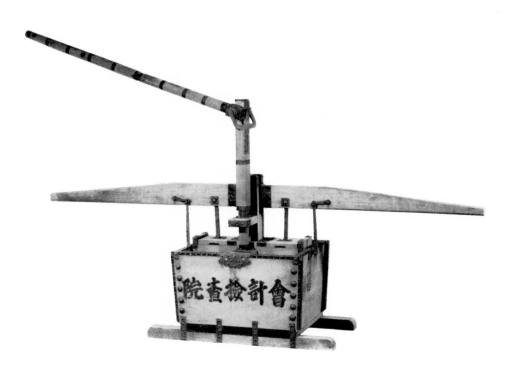

An early hand-pumper used in Tokyo by the Japanese fire brigades.
Courtesy of Peabody Museum of Salem.

The early history of Japan is interfused with mythology, one legend relating the creation of their country by the sun goddess, Amaterasu Omikami, from whom the emperors are supposedly descended. The goddess' grandson, Jimmu Tenno, became the first emperor and ascended the throne about 660 B.C. The first contact made with the outside world was with Korea and China. Kublai Khan made two unsuccessful invasion attempts and then abandoned the idea of capturing Japan when in 1281 A.D. a typhoon ("Divine wind") is said to have sunk some thirteen hundred of his craft with a loss of about one hundred and seventy thousand men.

When a Portuguese ship sailed off course in 1542, Japan experienced its first contact with the West. There followed an influx of traders and missionaries until 1638, when the Portuguese supported a local Japanese revolution which resulted in banning all foreigners from entry to Japan for one hundred and fifteen years. Not until the famous voyage of Commodore Perry in 1853 when he brought the American fleet into Tokyo Bay and a message from President Fillmore did the West regain trading relations with this land except for a concession which the Dutch had held in Nagasaki. Under the impetus of this new contact Japan rapidly underwent a period of transition from the medieval to the modern.

Fire-fighting methods on these islands have always remained somewhat archaic, but local fire insurance concerns have been established there for over seventy-five years. The older companies as well as the foreign underwriters have all issued fire marks. Many of the domestic issues contain the family designations of the principals of those organizations. The use of the mark is no longer customary in Japan. It did, however, continue until the recent war.

1545

1546

1547

1549

1548

1550

1551

1552

(1545) TOKIO MARINE & FIRE INSURANCE CO. LTD. TOKYO, JAPAN. 1897-

Alloy Metal. 3¾" x 2½". Red background, blue center with red and white letters. An auto mark.

(1546) MEIJI FIRE INSURANCE COMPANY, LIMITED. TOKYO, JAPAN. 1891-

Tin. 6⅝" x 7". Blue background with red band containing white Japanese characters. Raised gold border and lettering. Red star.

(1547-1548) KOBE KAIJO KASAI HOKEN KABUSHIKI
KAISHA. KOBE, JAPAN. 1907-

1547. Tin. Circular. 7⅜″ in diameter. Raised gold and red
dragons. Raised gold characters and slightly raised red anchor and
circle at top. Black background.

1548. Tin. Circular. 3⅜″ in diameter. Anchor and bands blue
on white ground.

(1549) TOYO FIRE INSURANCE COMPANY, LIMITED.
TOKYO, JAPAN. 1908-

Iron. Circular. 4½″ in diameter. Upper section blue with red
and white characters. White border. Lower section yellow with
dark blue characters and border.

(1550) TAISHO MARINE AND FIRE INSURANCE COM-
PANY, LIMITED. TOKYO, JAPAN. 1918-

Tin. Shield shape. 6¾″ x 7¾″. White floral ornamentation,
blue and white mountain peak at top and raised white characters
on red band across center. Raised letters at bottom on black background. Natural tin border.

(1551) MANCHURIAN COMPANY, LTD.
TOKYO, JAPAN. 1919-

Iron. Square, slightly convexed. 6″ x 6″. White shield on red
background. Characters and lettering red.

(1552) DARIEN FIRE & MARINE INSURANCE CO. LTD.
DARIEN, JAPAN. 1922-

Tin. Circular. 6⅞″ in diameter. Lavender background with
natural tin border. Red and white insignia at top. Raised gold characters in center. Flat gold characters on red scroll.

LATVIA

Latvia, another Baltic state, has been under the
domination of Russia since the time of Peter the
Great. After the Russian Revolution, Latvia was set
up as an independent republic. Riga, the capital of
the republic in 1918, became the headquarters of all
Latvian fire insurance companies. Two of these were
formed when the country was under Russian control;
the remaining three came into being during the modern republican era. All issued fire marks, those signs
of more recent vintage remaining as a stark reminder
of that republic's domination by Russia since 1940.
Today, fire insurance is monopolistic.

1553

1554   1555

(1553) PIRMA RIGAS APDROSINASANAS SABIEDRIBA.
RIGA, LATVIA. 1765-

Tin. Oval. 8″ x 5″. Raised black letters and border on green
ground.

(1554-1555) KURZEME APDROSINASANAS AKCIJU
SABIEDRIBA. RIGA, LATVIA. 1861-

1554. Tin. Rectangular. 3¹⁵⁄₁₆″ x 2⅜″. Yellow and black borders and yellow and black lettering on green background.

1555. Iron. Rectangular. 7¹³⁄₁₆″ x 4⅝″. Black center panel
with white name and border; remaining letters black on green
background.

1556

1557

1558

(1556)   LATVIJAS LLOIDS APDROSINASANAS UN TRANSPORTA AKEIJU SABIEDRIBA. RIGA, LATVIA.   1920-

Tin.   6⅞″ x 4⁵⁄₁₆″.   Raised black letters on red background. Raised white border.

(1557)   APDROSINASANAS AKCIJU SABIEDRIBA RIGAS UNIONS. RIGA, LATVIA.   1920-

Tin.   Hexagonal.   6¾″ x 8¾″.   Raised black letters and border.

Raised company seal and flat lettering black and white. Yellow and orange background.

(1558)   APDROSINASANAS UN TRANSPORTA AKCIJU SABIEDRIBA LATVIJA. RIGA, LATVIA.   1922-

Tin.   Circular, slightly convexed.   6⅜″ in diameter.   Rolled ornamental outer border, raised sun and lettering. White, blue and green center with surrounding red band.

LITHUANIA

The farthest south of the three Baltic states, Lithuania is inhabited by a people of proud heritage and strong nationalism. Some three thousand years before Christ their Neolithic forebears engaged in extensive agriculture and even one thousand years before Christ they had perfected the crude arts of weaving in wool and linen and had domesticated animals. Having been under a variety of governments, they finally gained independence as a republic at the close of World War I. A new commercial development included the organization of at least three new fire insurance concerns, and in justifiable pride these proponents of the free enterprise system placed a modern fire mark above the door of each insured building. Only twenty-two years after gaining their independence, the Lithuanians once again had to submit to Russian annexation. As a result of this domination the country's present commercial importance is limited to its role as an outlet for Russian goods. Here, too, fire insurance is a state monopoly.

1559

1560

1561

1562

1563

(1559-1560) APDRAUDIMO DRAUGJA LIETUVA. KAUNAS, LITHUANIA. 1921-

1559. Tin. Rectangular. 8³⁄₁₆″ x 6¼″. Raised maroon border and black lettering with yellow, green and red background. Vari-colored emblem.

1560. Tin. Rectangular. 4⅞″ x 3¼″. Raised maroon border and black lettering with yellow, green and red background. Vari-colored emblem.

(1561-1562) VALSTYBES DRAUDIMO ISTAIGOJ. KOVNO, LITHUANIA. 1921-

1561. Tin. Oval. 9″ x 5¼″. Black and red lettering—crest in red, black and white, and red and black border, all raised. White background.

1562. Tin. Oval. 3⅞″ x 2⁵⁄₁₆″. Black and red lettering, crest in red, black and white, and red and black border, all raised. White background.

(1563) LIETUVOS LLOYDAS AKCINE APDRAUDIMO BENDROVE. KAUNAS, LITHUANIA. 1922-

Tin. Circular. 3⅝″ in diameter. Raised and flat blue lettering, slightly raised blue and white shield. Raised border with blue stripe.

LUXEMBOURG

The House of Luxembourg took over the rule of this small nation in 1060 A.D. Control then passed to Spain and Austria until in 1815, through the Congress of Vienna, Luxembourg was established as a Grand Duchy under the King of the Netherlands. The treaty of London in 1839 gave the western part of the country to Belgium, while the balance remained as a Grand Duchy. This little buffer state, located between France, Germany, and Belgium, is very active in industry and commerce. As a result of this activity some of the citizens in 1922 established their own fire insurance company, utilizing a mark similar to those used in the surrounding nations. Luxembourg has extraordinary scenery and caters particularly to the tourists. Its limited population of less than a third of a million people produces an enormous amount of pig iron and steel. In a trade agreement with both Belgium and Holland, this small nation, in a strategic geographic location, has retained her balance in the economy of western Europe.

1564

(1564) LE FOYER COMPAGNIE LUXEMBOURGEOISE D'ASSURANCES SOCIETE ANONYME. LUXEMBOURG. 1922-

Iron. Square, convexed. 12⅝″ x 12⅝″. Blue center, yellow band at top and bottom. Black and white lettering. White background.

MADEIRA

Prince Henry, the Navigator, exercised the guiding hand when the Portuguese decided to colonize their new discovery of the previously uninhabited island of Madeira in 1420 A.D. Pioneers soon deforested the land and planted a considerable amount of sugar cane and grapes. Madeiran sugar eventually became a very profitable crop, followed closely in importance by the world renowned Madeira wine. Until a century ago the Madeirans had great difficulty in growing their grapes because of plant disease, but soon their own scientists produced a chemical to check the disease and subsequently the plants thrived. Madeira is a strong-bodied wine of excellent bouquet and fine quality. With only two major products the citizens of this island have been able to balance their economy which includes two fire insurance companies, both of which issue a mark of assurance. These definitely reflect the Portuguese influence in design.

1565   1566

(1565) ALLIANCA MADEIRENSE COMPANHIA DE SE-GUROS SOCIEDADE ANONIMA DE RESPONSABILIDADE LIMITADA. FUNCHAL, MADEIRA. 1890-

Tin. Shield shape. 7⅞" x 9⅝". Raised vari-colored crest and gold letters on black background. Gold border.

(1566) COMPANHIA DE SEGUROS GARANTIA FUNCHA-LENSE. FUNCHAL, MADEIRA. 1906-

Tin. 7¼" x 9½". Raised gold figure on red background; raised gold lettering on black. Raised borders.

MAURITIUS

Some five hundred miles east of Madagascar, there juts out of the Indian Ocean the volcanic island of Mauritius. The French settled here in 1715 only to have their land seized by the British in 1810. They then gained the island officially as a part of the Treaty of Paris in 1814. The land is densely settled by a people who gain their livelihood almost exclusively from the production of sugar. To serve the local population is a fire insurance company which continues to issue a fire mark. Undoubtedly it participates also in the protection afforded to the merchants who have so substantially invested in the trading and production of sugar. Evidently foreign fire insurance companies did not use fire marks here.

1567

(1567) MAURITIUS FIRE INSURANCE COMPANY. MAURITIUS. 1855-

Odd shape. Emblem, company name and ornamentation raised.
(Courtesy of Chartered Insurance Institute.)

MEXICO

Another good neighbor of the United States, Mexico has commonly been known as the land of the wealthy Aztec nation which was conquered by the Spaniards and ruled by them for three hundred years. Mexico gained its independence through the Treaty of Cordoba in 1821, but the years intervening, until 1934, were spotted with foreign and domestic strife. The nation did have an era of comparative quiet between 1877 and 1911. During this period its economy and industrial progress showed considerable advance. In 1934 a new government seized oil properties and inaugurated a plan of extensive labor reforms and distribution of land to the peasants. Heretofore foreign fire insurance companies had protected Mexican properties, and many had issued marks to their policyholders. But on August 31, 1935, a new insurance law went into effect, placing such prohibitive restrictions upon foreign fire insurance concerns that they were obliged to withdraw from the country. There followed the organization of many new local companies in Mexico which now operate under a restricted monopoly and a system of self-containment. The need having passed, these new concerns do not issue fire marks.

1568

1569

1570

(1568)   COMPANIA GENERAL ANGLO MEXICANA DE SEGUROS S. A. MEXICO CITY, MEXICO.   1900-

Aluminum.   Square.   2¾" x 2¾".   Polished aluminum lettering and panel border. Black background.

(1569)   UNION DE SEGUROS, S. A. MEXICO CITY, MEXICO.   1924-

Brass.   3⅛" x 2¾".   Slightly raised brass lettering and border. Black background.

(1570)   ASEGURADO EN LA AZTECA COMPANIA MEXICANA DE SEGUROS. S. A. MEXICO, D. F.   1933-

Tin.   Oval.   10⅜" x 14¾".   Raised yellow lettering and border. Red background.

NEW SOUTH WALES

When Captain Cook discovered New South Wales in 1770 he, of course, had no idea that some day the state would contain nearly one half of the population of the Australian Commonwealth. After the war with the American colonies, New South Wales became the outlet for the overflowing jails of England and what is now Sydney formed the nucleus of a new penal colony. Along with these developments colonization expanded, and in 1855 a new constitution which gave the settlers freedom and self-government was passed. Queensland, a part of New South Wales, contributed to the rapid expansion in the mining of coal, silver, lead, and zinc as well as in agriculture, and the entire country thrived. In order to supplement the British fire insurance companies, it was desirable to form local concerns, five of which issued fire marks. The system was typically British, and the support of fire brigades by insured concerns was similar to those of the motherland. These marks are exceedingly rare today.

1571

1572

1573

1574

1575

1576

(1571)   SYDNEY FIRE INSURANCE COMPANY. MEL-BOURNE, NEW SOUTH WALES, AUSTRALIA.   1851-1880.

Copper.   Oval.   10¼″ x 7″.   Raised borders, design and lettering.

(1572)   PACIFIC FIRE AND MARINE INSURANCE COM-PANY. SYDNEY, NEW SOUTH WALES, AUSTRALIA. 1862-1893.

Copper.   Circular, convexed.   9⅝″ in diameter.   Raised lettering, continent of Australia and meridians gold on black. Surrounding border raised.

(1573-1574)   THE UNITED INSURANCE COMPANY, LIM-ITED. SYDNEY, NEW SOUTH WALES, AUSTRALIA.   1862-

1573.   Tin.   10″ x 11¼″.   Painted shield containing figures of the emu and kangaroo with "United" below.

1574.   Tin.   Oval.   10¼″ x 7½″.   Raised borders and lettering.

(1575)   MERCANTILE MUTUAL INSURANCE COMPANY, LIMITED. SYDNEY, NEW SOUTH WALES, AUSTRALIA. 1878-

Copper.   Oval.   8⅛″ x 5¹³⁄₁₆″.   Raised gold lettering and inner border with black background. Outer border raised.

(1576)   QUEENSLAND INSURANCE COMPANY, LIMITED. SYDNEY, NEW SOUTH WALES, AUSTRALIA.   1886-

Tin.   Circular.   8¼″ in diameter.   Raised lettering, characters and crest, gold and black.

NEW ZEALAND

The British Dominion of New Zealand is situated some twelve hundred miles east of Australia. It became economically important when a large demand was made upon it for grains, wool, sheep, and cattle during the Australian gold rushes in the 1850's. Then came the New Zealand bonanza hunts of the 1860's. Along with this sharp increase in commerce and trade there was naturally an added need for more fire insurance facilities. The need was filled by the five New Zealand fire insurance companies which were founded between 1859 and 1877. The entire system of insurance, fire fighting, and fire marks was modelled on that of Britain itself, as was the case in most other British colonies.

1577

1578

1579

1580

1581

1582

1583

1584

1585

1586

1587

(1577-1582)   NEW ZEALAND INSURANCE COMPANY, LIMITED. AUCKLAND, NEW ZEALAND.   1859-

1577.   Tin.   Oval.   10¾" x 6⅝".   Raised gold lettering with red background. Raised border had been gold. Two tabs for affixing to building.

1578.   Tin.   7" x 9¼".   Vari-colored raised design of two kiwi birds, a mamaku tree and two flax bushes. Raised gold lettering. Raised border. Four tabs for affixing to building.

1579.   Iron.   9" x 4½".   White lettering and border with blue background.

1580.   Tin.   Circular.   8⅛" in diameter.   Lettering with Chinese characters in gold.

1581.   Tin.   Circular.   8½" in diameter.   Raised gold characters and lettering. Inner circle and outer border red. Band black. Type used in China.

1582.   Iron.   Diamond shape, slightly convexed.   5⅞" x 5⅞". Lettering, characters and border white with blue background.

(1583-1586)   THE SOUTH BRITISH INSURANCE COMPANY, LIMITED. AUCKLAND, NEW ZEALAND.   1872-

1583.   Copper.   7½" x 8¼".   Raised figure, lettering and slightly raised border. Four tabs for affixing to building.

1584.   Tin.   7⅝" x 8½".   Raised gold design, lettering and characters and raised borders. Had four tabs for affixing to building.

1585.   Tin.   Rectangular.   8" x 5".   Raised lettering and characters white on red. Border and vari-colored center emblem raised.

1586.   Iron.   10½" x 6".   Lettering in black on white background.

(1587-1588)   NATIONAL INSURANCE COMPANY OF NEW ZEALAND, LTD. DUNEDIN, NEW ZEALAND.   1873-

1587.   Tin.   Shield shape.   8" x 8¼".   Gold lettering, red emblem and border all raised. Green background.

1591

1588   1589   1590

1588. Tin. Shield shape. 7⅞" x 7⅞". Gold lettering on diagonal blue band. Blue border. Background had been white.

(1589-1590) STANDARD INSURANCE COMPANY, LIMITED. DUNEDIN, NEW ZEALAND. 1874-

1589. Iron. Oval. 8¼" x 10⁵⁄₁₆". Vari-colored banner on red background. Lettering on black band.

1590. Tin. 7¾" x 10". Raised crest on convexed center oval. Border, lettering and stars raised. Four tabs for affixing to building.

(1591) THE UNION FIRE & MARINE OF NEW ZEALAND. ? - ?

Rectangular. Displays crest, company name, and clasped hands. *(Courtesy of Chartered Insurance Institute.)*

NORWAY

Norway, a strong, independent nation up to the Middle Ages, was so weakened by civil wars and by the Black Death that it came under the domination of Denmark and Sweden and was bound with them in various unions until 1905. In the early Middle Ages it was the source of great Viking fleets which sailed the seas for plunder, exploration, and conquest. At one time or another Norwegians held the Shetlands, the Faroes, and the Orkney Islands, the northern parts of Scotland, and some of the Western Isles, Iceland, and parts of Ireland. In 1388 Norway entered a union with Denmark which lasted until after the Napoleonic Wars, at which time it was ceded to Sweden in the Treaty of Kiel (1814). Norway, how-

ever, managed to retain its customs, government, and separate military forces until, in 1905, it became an independent constitutional monarchy. This land of the Norsemen thrived on a commerce consisting principally of wood products, fish, and their by-products. Many fire insurance companies furnished security to the citizens, but fire marks were never commonly used. Those marks illustrated were adopted entirely for publicity purposes. The sons of the Vikings have long since established Norway as an essentially maritime nation with twenty-one thousand registered fishing craft, a most formidable merchant fleet. Norway's insurance is geared principally to meet its maritime needs.

1592   1593   1594   1595   1596

(1592-1594) CHRISTIANIA ALMINDELIGE FORSIKRINGS AKTIESELSKAP. OSLO, NORWAY. 1847-

1592. Tin. Oval. 4" x 5⅛". Gold finish. Raised lettering, border and figures.

1593. Tin. Rectangular. 9″ x 11¾″. Raised red shield with raised white lettering. Gold figure at top. Red, black and white emblem below. Raised white border.

1594. Tin. Rectangular, convexed. 3⅛″ x 4¼″. White lettering and red border. Black background. Red, white and black emblem. "Storebrand" raised.

(1595) NORSKE KJOBMAEND FORSIKRINGSAKTIESEL-SKAP ASSURANCEKASSEN. OSLO, NORWAY. 1917-

Iron. Rectangular, convexed. 3⅛″ x 6⅞″. White lettering and yellow, red and white flame on black background.

(1596) NORSE MERKANTILE FORSIKRINGS AKTIESEL-SKAP. OSLO, NORWAY. 1918-

Tin. Rectangular. 3⅛″ x 6⅞″. Red and black lettering and center figure. Cream background.

PALESTINE

Invasion and conquest were the predominant factors in the progress of this "Land of Canaan." The kingdoms of Judah and Israel—the Palestine of today—were at various times ruled by Assyrians, Babylonians, Egyptians, Persians, Macedonians, Romans, and Byzantines. They passed on to the Arabs, Frankish Crusaders, Turks, and finally to the British who recognized the two opposing groups, the Zionists and the Arabs. Hostilities developed between these two groups but in 1949 an armistice agreement, freezing their respective positions, was concluded between Israel and Egypt.

During the present century Palestine, or Israel, has progressed materially in expanding both agriculture and industry. In consequence housing and merchandising have also been extended. The inevitable parallel of insurance organization accompanied these business successes, and the newcomers during the past quarter century illustrate how fire insurance has kept up with the pace. Not only these companies, but also most foreign fire insurance concerns which have operated in Palestine, have issued their customary marks. These marks clearly illustrate the modern tendencies in their art.

1597

1598

1599

1600

1601

(1597) HASSNEH INSURANCE COMPANY OF PALESTINE LTD. TEL AVIV, PALESTINE. 1924-

Tin. Rectangular. 6″ x 7⅞″. Yellow, cream and black lettering, vari-colored center figure. Red background. Polished tin border with yellow stripe.

(1598) THE PALESTINE GENERAL INSURANCE COMPANY, LIMITED. TEL AVIV, PALESTINE. 1932-

Tin. 6⅞″ x 9⅝″. Yellow lettering and center design on blue background. Cream colored border.

(1599) THE PALESTINE LLOYD INSURANCE COMPANY, LIMITED. TEL AVIV, PALESTINE. 1933-

Tin. Circular. 8⅝″ in diameter. Green lettering, silver and green center figure. Cream background. Three green borders raised.

(1600) MIGDAL INSURANCE COMPANY, LIMITED. JERUSALEM, PALESTINE. 1934-

Tin. Rectangular. 6⅞″ x 9¾″. Silver and white lettering with black outlines and grey minaret. White background, silver border.

(1601) ZION THE PALESTINE NATIONAL INSURANCE COMPANY LIMITED. TEL AVIV, PALESTINE. 1935-

Tin. Rectangular. 6⅞″ x 9⅝″. Raised red lettering and flat white lettering—red side borders. Black background. Grey, black and cream emblem.

PANAMA

Following the visits of Columbus and Balboa in the sixteenth century, Panama developed into a transfer point in the shipping of goods and treasures from Spain to Central and South America. When Colombia revolted against Spain in 1821, Panama joined her. The latter country then spent the next eighty-two years endeavoring to disassociate herself. With back-ing from the United States, the country proclaimed its independence in 1903. The economic wealth of this small nation comes from the Panama Canal and the export of bananas. Its people are able to support one fire insurance company among their business ventures, although some foreign underwriters also maintain agencies there.

1602

(1602) COMPANIA INTERNACIONAL DE SEGUROS S. A. PANAMA, REPUBLIC OF PANAMA. 1910-

Tin. Rectangular. 13⅞" x 6³⁄₁₆". "Compania-Internacional" in raised lettering and remainder of name painted in black. Yellow background. Black border.

PHILIPPINE ISLANDS

Two hundred miles south of Formosa lies that group of islands known as the Philippines, discovered in 1521 by Ferdinand Magellan. Spain took possession a few years later, but at the conclusion of the Spanish-American War in 1899 the islands were ceded to the United States. Complete independence was granted in 1946, the result of a liberation planned for by Congressional Act in 1934. The country is rich in agriculture, and its general exports and commerce are rapidly expanding. Local insurance came into being after the United States took possession of the islands, but only one of the fire insurance companies issued a mark of assurance. In its earlier history foreign companies employed the use of these marks, but all of them disappeared during the period of insurrection.

1603

(1603) FILIPINAS COMPANIA DE SEGUROS. MANILA, PHILIPPINE ISLANDS. 1913-

Iron. Circular, slightly convexed. 5¹⁄₁₆" in diameter. Red background. White and red lettering. Woman's portrait in natural colors; white dress.

POLAND

After being involved in numerous wars Poland was finally partitioned among Russia, Prussia, and Austria between 1772 and 1795. The Poles then spent the next century in a determined struggle for independence which was finally gained at the close of World War I. As an independent republic Poland, inspired by her newly gained freedom, refused to yield to Hitler and he attacked in 1939. The people of Poland have always been industrious. Although they have been primarily an agricultural nation, they have—up until

their recent domination by the Soviet Union—exported considerable coal, textiles, clothing, iron, and steel.

Considering its size Poland has had its full share of fire insurance institutions. Although most of them were formed during its short era of independence, there are in signeviery some five companies which predated World War I. Foreign companies were of British, German, and Italian origin, and they followed the same practices as those of their homeland.

1604

1605

1606

1607

1608

1609

1610

(1604) ZAKLAD UBEZPIECZEN WZAJEMNYCH W POZNANIU. POZNAN, POLAND. 1784-

Iron. Rectangular, slightly convexed. 7¼" x 4¼". Lettering and crest white on red background.

(1605) POWSZECHNY ZAKLAD UBEZPIECZEN WZAJEMNYCH. WARSAW, POLAND. 1803-

Iron. Rectangular, slightly convexed. 6" x 3⅞". Slightly raised lettering and crest in white on red background.

(1606-1607) KRAKOWSKIE TOWARZYSTWO UBEZPIECZEN FLORJANKA SPOLKA AKCYJNA W KRAKOWIE. KRAKOW, POLAND. 1860-

1606. Tin. Rectangular. 6⅞" x 7⅞". Raised gold lettering and center figure on red background. Raised border.

1607. Iron. Rectangular, convexed. 5⅛" x 3½". Slightly raised black lettering on white background.

(1608-1609) WARSZAWSKIE TOWARZYSTWO UBEZPIECZEN SPOLKA AKCYJNA. WARSAW, POLAND. 1870-

1608. Iron. Rectangular, convexed. 6¾" x 4¾". Raised white lettering on red background.

1609. Tin. Rectangular. 4½" x 2¾". White lettering outlined in black on red background. Gold border. Probably an auto mark.

(1610) DNISTER TOWARYSTWO WZAJEMNYCH UBEZPIECZEN. LWOW, POLAND. 1892-

Tin. Rectangular. 4¾" x 6⅞". Raised vari-colored crest and raised gold lettering on red background. Raised gold border.

1611

1612

(1611) TOWARZYSTWO UBEZPIECZEN PORT SPOLKA AKCYJNA. WARSAW, POLAND. 1919-

Tin. 5″ x 7″. Raised and flat red lettering and raised red border on yellow background.

(1612) SILESIA TOWARZYSTWO UBEZPIECZEN SPOLKA AKCYJNA. BIELSKO, POLAND. 1922-

Iron. 7″ x 5″. Red lettering and border with white background.

PORTUGAL

As a result of her great voyages of discovery Portugal controlled the world's largest colonial empire until the union with Spain in 1580 when all her colonial possessions were lost. These possessions were subsequently regained after Portugal won her separation from Spain in 1640. The most important colony still remaining to Portugal is Angola, though smaller colonies remain in India and China. Portugal had a liberal revolution early in the nineteenth century which limited the powers of the monarchy, and another in 1910 which overthrew the monarchy and established the republican constitution of 1911. Another revolution in 1926 set up a military dictatorship.

This new government has brought about a new form of economic stability and now Portugal's exports of cork, wine, olive oil, textiles, and fish have once more placed her in a position of security.

Fire insurance companies were formed in Portugal one hundred and fifty years ago and like the concerns of other European countries they, too, issued fire marks to identify insured properties. First these were made of lead, then of copper, and the modern plate usually contained colorful lithography and stamping. The older fire marks seem to have disappeared completely although insurance company archives attest to their use.

1613

1614

1615

1616

1617

1618

1619

1620

1621

1622

1623

1624

1625

1626

1627

1628

(1613) BONANCA COMPANHIA DE SEGUROS. LISBON, PORTUGAL. 1808-

Tin. Oval. 7¼″ x 8⅜″. Raised gold lettering and anchor, raised beaded black border and red ribbons. Metallic blue background.

(1614) COMPANHIA DE SEGUROS FIDELIDADE. LISBON, PORTUGAL. 1835-

Tin. Octagonal. 8⅝″ x 5¾″. Raised lettering and dog in gold on blue background. Slightly raised border.

(1615-1616) COMPANHIA DE SEGUROS DOURO SOCIEDADE ANONIMA DE RESPONSABILIDADE LIMITADA. PORTO, PORTUGAL. 1846-

1615. Tin. Rectangular. 9¾″ x 7⅜″. Raised gold lettering and border with blue background.

1616. Brass. 2⅜″ x 3⅛″. Gold lettering and border and red and gold design on black background. Type used for autos.

(1617) GARANTIA, CIA DE SEGUROS. OPORTO, PORTUGAL. 1853-

Tin. Octagonal. Raised border and lettering. *(Courtesy of Chartered Insurance Institute.)*

(1618) COMPANHIA DE SEGUROS INDEMNISA DORA. PORTO, PORTUGAL. 1871-

Tin. Oval. Center figure, lettering and border raised. *(Courtesy of Chartered Insurance Institute.)*

(1619) COMPANHIA DE SEGUROS TRANQUILIDADE PORTUENSE. PORTO, PORTUGAL. 1871-

Tin. Oval. 6¾″ x 8⅛″. Raised ivory center figure with raised gold lettering and border. Black background.

(1620) CONFIANCA PORTUENSE SEGUROS CONTRA FOGO. PORTUGAL. ? - ?

Tin. Oval. Raised center figure, lettering and beaded border. *(Courtesy of Chartered Insurance Institute.)*

(1621) COMPANHIA DE SEGUROS TAGUS SOCIEDADE ANONIMA DE RESPONSIBILIDADE LIMITADA. LISBON, PORTUGAL. 1877-

Tin. Rectangular. 10¼″ x 7⅛″. Black center with raised gold lettering and border. Red background with raised gold lettering. Slightly raised black outer border.

(1622) COMPANHIA DE SEGUROS PORTUGAL. LISBON, PORTUGAL. 1884-

Tin. Shield shape. 6¾″ x 9⅛″. Raised gold border and lettering. Vari-colored raised crest. Black background.

(1623-1624) ULTRAMARINA SOCIEDADE ANONIMA DE RESPONSIBILIDADE LIMITADA. LISBON, PORTUGAL. 1901-

1623. Tin. Rectangular. 10 3/16″ x 7 7/16″. Raised vari-colored center design bordered in gold. Raised gold lettering on black background. Red outer border raised.

1624. Bronze. Shield shape. 2⅜″ x 3 5/16″. Ornamentation and lettering in relief.

(1625) ARGUS COMPANHIA DE SEGUROS. PORTO, PORTUGAL. 1907-

Tin. Triangular. 11⅞″ x 10¾″. "Argus" in raised gold on black, surrounded by orange band with raised gold lettering. Inner border and corner triangles raised gold. Outer border raised black.

(1626-1627) COMMERCIO E INDUSTRIA COMPANHIA DE SEGUROS. LISBON, PORTUGAL. 1907-

1626. Tin. 7¼″ x 10″. Raised silver lettering and gold border on red background. Center design in silver, black and white with raised gold border.

1627. Brass. 2¾″ x 3⅜″. Design in relief in gold center circle with gold lettering on surrounding blue band. Gold crown at top raised with red base.

(1628) PROSPERIDADE. PORTO, PORTUGAL. ? - ?

Tin. Octagonal. Raised border, center design and lettering. *(Courtesy of Chartered Insurance Institute.)*

1629

1630

1631

1632

1633

(1629)   SAGRES CIA DE SEGUROS LUZO-BRAZILEIRA. LISBON, PORTUGAL.   ? - ?

Tin.   Oval.   Raised border, crest and lettering. *(Courtesy of Chartered Insurance Institute.)*

(1630)   ALENTEJO, CIA DE SEGUROS. ELVAS, PORTUGAL. 1918-

Tin.   Rectangular.   Raised crest, border and lettering. *(Courtesy of Chartered Insurance Institute.)*

(1631)   COMPANHIA DE SEGUROS ATLAS SOCIEDADE ANONIMA DE RESPONSABILIDADE LIMITADA. LISBON, PORTUGAL.   1918-

Tin.   Rectangular.   6¾″ x 9¾″.   Gold and black figure of Atlas with globe on red. Black lettering on white. Light blue background. Raised gold border.

(1632)   A SEGURADORA CIA DE SEGUROS E RESEGUROS. PORTO, PORTUGAL.   1918-

(Courtesy of Chartered Insurance Institute.)

(1633)   EUROPEA COMPANHIA DE SEGUROS SOCIEDADE ANONIMA DE RESPONSABILIDADE LIMITADA. LISBON, PORTUGAL.   1922-

Tin.   7″ x 9⅝″.   Red, yellow, grey and blue. Lettering red and yellow.

PORTUGUESE WEST AFRICA

Along the west coast of Africa for almost one thousand miles stretches a new land whose production potentialities have only recently been realized. Portuguese West Africa, or Angola as it is now known, was explored by the Portuguese. After many negotiations covering a thirty-year period which ended in 1905, its boundaries were finally established. The country has a wide variety of resources including large asphalt lakes, diamond mines, copper, iron, manganese, and uranium, while the adjacent waters provide the finest fishing in the African world. This new colony has already provided a fire insurance company which has fulfilled colonial tradition by adopting its own mark of distinction.

1634

(1634)   COMPANHIA DE SEGUROS LUANDA. LUANDA, PORTUGUESE WEST AFRICA.   ? - ?

Brass.   Small odd shape.   2⅜″ x 3″.   Inside—gold circle with lion and blue "Angola" in relief. Gold castle at top. Surrounding blue band with gold letters. Auto mark.

REUNION

A very important possession of France is the island of Reunion which rises from the waters of the Indian Ocean some four hundred and fifty miles east of Madagascar. Vertically this island can be separated into five areas. The first or maritime level is the one upon which the towns and villages are built. Second, at a height of twenty-six hundred to four thousand feet lie the sugar plantations, a veritable land of green which surrounds the island and is dotted with country homes. Up another flight is a land of forests. The fourth division is the plateau level, while high above on the fifth level range the lofty peaks of the mountains. Sugar and rum provide the island's economic stability. St. Denis is the capital of this island and there the home office of La Creole, the sole representative of the fire insurance industry, is quartered. Its mark bears evidence that even in this remote island security prevails.

1635

(1635) SOCIETE ANONYME D'ASSURANCE CONTRE L'INCENDIE LA CREOLE. ST. DENIS, REUNION. 1865-

Iron. Rectangular. 9⅞" x 5⅞". Gold painted lettering on black background.

RUMANIA

The name of Dacia, found in the names of fire insurance companies of this country, represented the Roman province from which Rumania was formed. Under the Turks since the Ottoman conquest of southeastern Europe, Rumania was formed as an independent nation by the union of Moldavia and Walachia in 1861. It became a kingdom in 1881. From the spoils of the Second Balkan War of 1913, plus the grants at the close of World War I, Rumania became the largest Baltic state. Since World War II, it has been reduced in size and is now a part of the Soviet bloc. The country has never advanced in commerce to the stage where they have become a real factor in the world economy, but they did form their own fire insurance companies. Their fire marks are mostly of a modern type and were used for publicity rather than for traditional purposes. Apparently fire insurance is now a state monopoly.

1636

1637

(1636-1637) TRANSSYLVANIA BANCA GENERALA DE ASIGURARE S. P. A. SIBIU, RUMANIA. 1868-

1636. Tin. 8⅛" x 4⅝". Slightly raised black and white lettering on orange background. Slightly raised border.

1637. Tin. Oval. 3¼" x 2¼". Yellow and red lettering on black background. Slightly raised border.

1638

1639

1640

1641

1642

1643

1644

1645

1646

1647

1648

(1638-1639)   DACIA ROMANIA SOCIETATE GENERALA DE ASIGURARE IN BUCURESTI. BUCHAREST, RUMANIA. 1871-

1638.   Tin.   Oval.   12½″ x 9″.   Raised gold lettering and vari-colored crest on black background. Rolled border.

1639.   Tin.   Oval.   9⅞″ x 7⅛″.   Raised gold lettering and vari-colored crest on black background. Rolled border.

(1640-1641)   GENERALA SOCIETATE ROMANA DE ASIGU-RARI GENERALE S. A. BUCHAREST, RUMANIA.   1897-

1640.   Tin.   13″ x 8¾″.   Red center oval with raised gold and black date. Black background with raised gold lettering and border.

1641.   Tin.   5½″ x 3⅞″.   Red center oval with raised gold and black date. Black background with raised gold lettering and border.

(1642)   PRIMA ARDELEANA SOCIETATE ANONIMA DE ASIGURARI GENERALE. CLUJ, RUMANIA. 1911-

Tin.   Oval.   7⅝″ x 5½″.   Raised gold lettering on black background. Rolled red and gold outer border. Red inner border.

(1643)   FRANCO ROMANA SOCIETATE ANONIMA DE ASIGURARI GENERALE. BUCHAREST, RUMANIA.   1920-

Tin.   Rectangular.   6⁹⁄₁₆″ x 4¹³⁄₁₆″.   Raised red lettering on white oval. Blue background. Raised white border.

(1644-1647)   AGRONOMUL SOCIETATE DE ASIGURARI GENERALE SOCIETATE ANONIMA. BUCHAREST, RUMANIA.   1921-

1644.   Tin.   Rectangular.   7⁵⁄₁₆″ x 5″.   Raised cream border and lettering on dark blue background.

1645.   Iron.   Rectangular, convexed.   7½″ x 5″.   Slightly raised white lettering on blue background.

1646.   Tin.   Rectangular.   7⅜″ x 5″.   Raised cream border and lettering on dark blue background.

1647.   Tin.   Rectangular.   7⅜″ x 5″.   Raised cream border and lettering on dark blue background.

(1648)   STEAUA ROMANIEI SOCIETATE ROMANA DI ASIGURARI IN BUCURESTI. BUCHAREST, RUMANIA.   1921-

Iron.   10¼″ x 6¼″.   Blue and white lettering and border on white background.

RUSSIA

The history of Russia extends back to the legendary figure of Rurik, the Viking who founded the first Russian dynasty at Novgorod. In 1240 A.D. Mongol hordes devastated Kiev and split the territory, already the world's largest country in area, into many small dukedoms. Ivan III, reigning duke, finally cast off the yoke of the Mongol rule, but the foundation of the Russian state is credited to Ivan IV (the Terrible), who reigned from 1533 to 1584. The great change from medievalism to westernization came under the rule of Peter the Great a century later. Russia abolished serfdom in 1861, but its citizens remained oppressed by weighty restrictions. Following their defeat at the hands of Japan in 1905, there were a series of uprisings, strikes, and disorders and finally the devastation of World War I which led up to the famous revolution of 1917 the Bolshevik phase of which was guided by Lenin and Trotsky. Through a succession of acts, internal strife, foreign interventions, and wars, there emerged the present Union of Soviet Socialist Republics.

The economic potentialities of these states are known to most. Their almost limitless resources in minerals, agriculture, and industry constitute potentialities which in this decade have frightened so many peoples into submission to the will of dictatorship. Commerce in Russia had been successful for well over a century. Fire insurance, established in the old capital of St. Petersburg, was not only recognized locally but operated successfully in foreign countries as well. Their fire marks, used as originally intended, have been found in far distant places, including America. With the revolution, all this became history, for in 1921 *Gosstrakh* was initiated as the Monopolistic State Insurance Department of the U.S.S.R. It is worthy of note, however, that this bureau retained the tradition of placing a fire mark upon insured properties. These signs of collectivist participation leave no doubt as to the loyal adherence of the householder. The two fire marks of *Gosstrakh* illustrated here were issued early in its period of organization.

1649

1650

1651   1652   1653

(1649) FIRST RUSSIAN INSURANCE SOCIETY. ST. PETERSBURG, RUSSIA. 1827-1921.

Tin. 4½" x 3¼". Raised gold date on black center oval with raised red border. Raised black lettering on gray band. Outer border of red and black raised.

(1650-1652) SALAMANDER FIRE INSURANCE COMPANY. ST. PETERSBURG, RUSSIA. 1846-1921.

1650. Copper. Oval. 12⅜" x 14⅜". Gold salamander, black lettering and gold border in center, all raised. Raised gold lettering on surrounding black band. Outer border raised gold.

1651. Tin. Oval. 4⅝" x 3¾". Raised gold lettering and borders on black background.

1652. Copper. Oval. 4⅝" x 3⅞". Raised design, lettering and borders had been gold.

(1653) ROSSIA INSURANCE COMPANY OF ST. PETERSBURG. ST. PETERSBURG, RUSSIA. 1881-1918.

Tin. Circular. 9⅝" in diameter. Raised star, lettering and border.

1654

1655

(1654-1655) GOSSTRAKH (STATE INSURANCE DEPART-MENT U. S. S. R.). MOSCOW, RUSSIA. 1921-

1654. Tin. Rectangular. 10″ x 7⅛″. Red and yellow raised lettering and borders on black background. Blue-gray panel with yellow border and red and yellow characters.

1655. Brass. Rectangular. 3⅞″ x 2″. Brass lettering and borders on black background.

SOUTH AFRICA

In 1652 the Dutch had colonized a portion of what is now known as the Union of South Africa only to lose the land to the British during the Napoleonic Wars. The great influx of British and their domination so disturbed the Boers that ten thousand of them conducted the famous "Great Trek" northward to the High Veld in 1836. British colonization expanded vastly at this period, and in 1849 and 1855 local fire insurance companies were formed along with the continental system of fire brigades and the use of marks of assurance became a custom. This prac-tice was short-lived. Further progress was made when diamonds were discovered in the Orange River in 1867 and gold in the Transvaal in 1886. Following these discoveries came the bitter Boer War in 1899. After three years of guerilla warfare and seven years under British rule the colonies of Transvaal, Orange Free State, Cape Colony, and Natal were united by act of imperial parliament to form The Union of South Africa. Since then South Africa has become the biggest single producer of gold, so playing a vital part in the continuance of the world's monetary systems.

1656

1657

1658

(1656) NATAL FIRE OFFICE. SOUTH AFRICA. 1849-

Circular. Raised center figure, border and lettering. Had tabs on side for fastening to building. *(Courtesy of Chartered Insurance Institute.)*

(1657) COMMERCIAL MARINE & FIRE ASSURANCE. CAPE TOWN, SOUTH AFRICA. 1855-

Circular. Raised borders and lettering. *(Courtesy of Chartered Insurance Institute.)*

(1658) SOUTH AFRICAN NATIONAL TRUST AND ASSUR-ANCE CO. LTD. CAPE TOWN, SOUTH AFRICA. 1918-

Circular with panel below. Raised crest, border and lettering. *(Courtesy of V. R. Willemson.)*

SOUTH AUSTRALIA

The first settlers came to South Australia in the 1830's and formed the nucleus of the British province established in 1836. A charter was granted to the South Australia Company to develop the land, but its expenditures were so costly that it was suspended by the rulers of Britain. South Australia became a Crown Colony in 1841. In that same year the wheel of a dray, going over a hill in Adelaide, brought to view a specimen of silver-lead ore. This started a succession of discoveries of copper, manganese, nickel, and bismuth. The subsequent advances in the mining industry were so great that the country's credit was soon reestablished, enabling the colony to form its own constitution and self-government in 1856. In this thriving industrial community, commerce, too, had expanded so that in 1865 the South Australians were able to set up the Equitable Fire Insurance Company at Adelaide. It goes without saying that the system of fire brigades and the use of the marks were patterned after the practice in Britain.

1659

(1659) EQUITABLE FIRE INSURANCE COMPANY. ADE-LAIDE, SOUTH AUSTRALIA, AUSTRALIA. 1865-1890.

Tin. 10¾″ x 8½″. Raised design, lettering and borders. Background had been blue.

SPAIN

Spain, with its tremendous colonial possessions, was at one time Europe's most wealthy and powerful nation. In the Treaty of Utrecht in 1713, however, Spain lost Gibraltar and all its holdings in southern Italy and the Netherlands. At the same time that she resisted Napoleon, her American colonies gained their independence through revolt. The *coup de grâce* was dealt at the conclusion of the Spanish-American War when Spain lost the Philippines, Cuba, and Puerto Rico. That reduced Spain to a minor role in world affairs. Her entire economy has followed the rise and fall of her political fortunes and so, too, has the fire insurance business. Fire marks of the old Spanish companies have been removed from buildings in the colonial possessions, while the plates of the more recently established institutions can be seen only in Spain and her few existing colonies, a true barometer of the rise and fall of nations.

1660

1661

(1660-1663) LA UNION Y EL FENIX ESPANOL COMPANIA DE SEGUROS REUNIDOS. MADRID, SPAIN. 1864-

1660. Tin. Rectangular. 9¾″ x 6¾″. Red center oval with raised gold phoenix and raised border. Raised gold lettering on black background. Raised border.

1661. Tin. Rectangular. 9¾″ x 6¾″. Raised phoenix, borders and lettering. From building in Greece.

LA UNION Y EL FENIX ESPAÑOL

1662

LA UNION Y EL FENIX ESPAÑOL

1663

LA CATALANA
SEGUROS CONTRA INCENDIOS A PRIMA FIJA

1664

LA PREVISION ESPAÑOLA
FUNDADA
EN
1883
SEGUROS CONTRA INCENDIOS

1665

LA PREVISION ESPAÑOLA
SEGUROS CONTRA INCENDIOS

1666

LA IBERICA
CONTRA-SEGUROS

1667

ASEGURADO EN
PLUS ULTRA

1668

A COMMERCIAL
COMPANHIA DE SEGUROS

1669

SEGUROS
AURORA
BILBAO

1670

LA GUARDA

1671

EL DIA
INCENDIE

1672

EL DIA
SEGUROS

1673

MUTUA
CATALANA
DE ACCIDENTES
E INCENDIOS

1674

LA CONSTANCIA
SEGUROS
INCENDIOS

1675

LA MUNDIAL
SEGUROS
INCENDIOS

1676

MUTUA GENERAL
DE SEGUROS
INCENDIOS

1677

LA
PATRIA
HISPANA
S. A. DE
SEGUROS

1678

AVIZ
1918

1679

UNIÓN LEVANTINA
ASEGURADO
DE
INCENDIOS

1680

A Ω
COVADONGA

1681

290

1662. Tin. Rectangular. 11¾" x 8". Red center oval with raised gold phoenix and border. Raised gold lettering on black background. Raised border.

1663. Tin. Rectangular. 4" x 2¾". Red center oval with raised gold phoenix and border. Gold lettering on black background.

(1664) LA CATALANA SOCIEDAD DE SEGUROS CONTRA INCENDIOS. BARCELONA, SPAIN. 1865-

Tin. Rectangular. 8⅞" x 10⅝". Raised gold lettering and stars with raised red and gold shield on black background. Raised border.

(1665-1666) LA PREVISION ESPANOLA COMPANIA DE SEGUROS CONTRA INCENDIOS. SEVILLE, SPAIN. 1883-

1665. Tin. Rectangular. 9⅞" x 8". Raised gold lettering and border on pale blue background.

1666. Tin. Rectangular. Raised flag, border and lettering. *(Courtesy of V. R. Willemson.)*

(1667) LA IBERICA CONTRA SEGUROS. SPAIN. ? - ?

Tin. Square. Raised center figure, border and lettering. *(Courtesy of Chartered Insurance Institute.)*

(1668) PLUS ULTRA COMPANIA ANONIMA DE SEGUROS GENERALES. MADRID, SPAIN. 1887-

Tin. 10⅜" x 8⅝". Blue and white raised crest and lettering.

(1669) LA COMMERCIAL COMPANHIA DE SEGUROS. SPAIN. 1891-

Tin. Oval. Raised crest, border and lettering. *(Courtesy of Chartered Insurance Institute.)*

(1670) AURORA COMPANIA ANONIMA DE SEGUROS. BILBAO, SPAIN. 1900-

Tin. 9¾" x 6⅝". Raised white lettering and gold borders. Blue background.

(1671) LA POLAR SOCIEDAD ANONIMA DE SEGUROS. BILBAO, SPAIN. 1900-

Tin. Circular, slightly convexed. 7¼" in diameter. Raised five pointed star in center circle with raised Arabic characters above and lettering below. Flat border.

(1672-1673) COMPANIA ANONIMA DE SEGUROS EL DIA. CARTAGENA, SPAIN. 1901-1924.

1672. Tin. Oval. 8" x 9¾". Raised design, border and lettering. From building in Istanbul, Turkey.

1673. Tin. Oval. 8" x 9¾". Raised design, borders and lettering. From building in Greece.

(1674) MUTUA CATALANA DE ACCIDENTES E INCENDIOS. BARCELONA, SPAIN. 1905-

Tin. Rectangular. 11¾" x 7⅞". Raised tan lettering, polished brass border and vari-colored medallions with blue metallic background.

(1675) LA CONSTANCIA COMPANIA ANONIMA DE SEGUROS. BARCELONA, SPAIN. 1906-

Tin. Rectangular. Raised figure, border and lettering. *(Courtesy of Chartered Insurance Institute.)*

(1676) LA MUNDIAL SOCIEDAD ANONIMA DE SEGUROS. MADRID, SPAIN. 1906-

Tin. Rectangular. 9¾" x 8³⁄₁₆". Raised gold border and gold striping with raised cream lettering on blue background. "La Mundial" outlined in gold.

(1677) MUTUA GENERAL DE SEGUROS. BARCELONA, SPAIN. 1907-

Tin. Rectangular. 10¼" x 8¼". Raised red lettering and gold and black medallion and raised gold border with black background.

(1678) LA PATRIA HISPANA SOCIEDAD ANONIMA DE SEGUROS. MADRID, SPAIN. 1916-

Tin. Rectangular. 7⅝" x 9⅜". Raised shield in blue with raised white letters and blue lettering on white band. Blue striping. White background. Outer border raised.

(1679) AVIZ. SPAIN. 1918-

Tin. Rectangular. Raised border, crest and lettering. *(Courtesy of Chartered Insurance Institute.)*

(1680) UNION LEVANTINA SOCIEDAD ANONIMA DE SEGUROS. VALENCIA, SPAIN. 1918-

Tin. 10⅝" x 8⅝". Raised cream lettering with gold, blue, red and cream crest on black background. Raised gold border with black striping.

(1681) COVADONGA SOCIEDAD ANONIMA DE SEGUROS. MADRID, SPAIN. 1924-

Tin. 8¾" x 9". Raised gold cross and black lettering with cream crescent on blue shield with raised gold border. Lower panel gray with raised gold lettering and border. Lettering and borders outlined in black. Raised scrolls in black and gold.

1682

1683

1684

1685

1686

1687

1688

1689

1690

1691

(1682) OMNIA SOCIEDAD ANONIMA COMPANIA DE SEGUROS DEL AUTOMOVIL CLUB DE ESPANA. MADRID, SPAIN. 1926-

Tin. 10″ x 7¾″. Raised black lettering and gold border with red background.

(1683) LA EQUITATIVA (FUNDACION ROSILLO) COMPANIA ANONIMA DE SEGUROS RIESGOS DIVERSOS. MADRID, SPAIN. 1928-

Tin. Rectangular. 8¼″ x 10⅛″. Raised gold design, lettering and borders. Gray background.

(1684-1685) GENERAL ESPANOLA DE SEGUROS SOCIEDAD ANONIMA. MADRID, SPAIN. 1928-

1684. Tin. 7⅝″ x 12″. Dark blue, cream background. Lettering raised.

1685. 2⅜″ x 3½″. Black and silver. Blue and silver crest. Red lettering.

(1686) COMPANIA VASCONGADA DE SEGUROS Y REASEGUROS. SAN SEBASTIAN, SPAIN. 1930-

Tin. Oval. 9¾″ x 8″. Raised gold and white letters and gold border with deep blue background.

(1687-1688) COMPANIA ESPANOLA DE SEGUROS IMPERIO S. A. MADRID, SPAIN. 1938-1945.

1687. Odd shaped tin. Raised crest and lettering. (Courtesy of V. R. Willemson.)

1688. Metal alloy. 3⅞″ x 2⅞″. Red, white and gold with black and gold lettering. An auto mark.

(1689-1690) MARE NOSTRUM SOCIEDAD ANONIMA DE SEGUROS Y REASEGUROS. PALMA DE MALLORCA, BALEARIC ISLANDS, SPAIN. 1942-

1689. Tin. Rectangular. Raised border, crest and lettering. (Courtesy of V. R. Willemson.)

1690. Metal alloy, enameled. 3¼″ x 2⅜″. Gold lettering. Blue, red, gold and white crest. Maroon background. An auto mark.

(1691) EL LEON. SPAIN. ? - ?

Tin. Rectangular. Oval with lion and globe at top. "The Lion" below. (Courtesy of Chartered Insurance Institute.)

The British Crown Colony known as the Straits Settlements was comprised of Singapore, Penang, Malacca, and Christmas Island. Founded in 1819, it later became a separate Crown, and now, as the Malayan Confederation, it is only a defensive protectorate of Britain. Practically all of its fire insurance companies have been founded under English influence. The use of fire marks has been limited to the adoption of the marks as talismen by the native population. They no longer serve even as a desirable form of advertisement to the respective companies which originally issued them.

1692

1693

1694

1695

1696

1697

1698

(1692)   THE STRAITS FIRE INSURANCE COMPANY, LIMITED. SINGAPORE, STRAITS SETTLEMENTS.   1886-1894.

Copper. 9" x 10½". Raised gold design on red center, raised gold lettering on black. Borders raised.

(1693)   EASTERN UNITED ASSURANCE CORPORATION, LIMITED. SINGAPORE, STRAITS SETTLEMENTS.   1913-

Tin. Circular. 8" in diameter. Raised silver lettering and borders. Characters and "Singapore" black on yellow. Design silver and yellow on black.

(1694)   SINCERE INSURANCE & INVESTMENT COMPANY, LIMITED. SINGAPORE, STRAITS SETTLEMENTS.   1915-

Tin. Circular. 4⅞" in diameter. White letters and border and blue background.

(1695)   THE OVERSEAS ASSURANCE CORPORATION LIMITED. SINGAPORE, STRAITS SETTLEMENTS.   1920-

Tin. Octagonal. 6" x 6". Raised gold lettering and borders. Chinese characters in black. Gray, black and cream background. Outer border black.

(1696-1697)   THE ASIA INSURANCE COMPANY, LIMITED. SINGAPORE, STRAITS SETTLEMENTS.   1930-

1696. Tin. Oval. 8¾" x 5½". Cream lettering raised on navy blue background. Cream borders, inner border raised.

1697. Alloy. Oval. 2⅞" x 1⅞". Raised nickeled lettering and borders on blue background.

(1698)   SINGAPORE INSURANCE COMPANY, LTD. SINGAPORE, STRAITS SETTLEMENTS.   ? - ?

Copper. Shield shape. 10¼" x 11¼". Design, lettering and borders raised. Lion red, crescents silver, stars gold. Lettering gold. Borders red. Background black.

SWEDEN

Like its neighbor Norway, Sweden has retained many of its ancient Nordic traditions. Almost purely Teutonic in origin, the Swedish people became dominant in the Baltic in the sixteenth century, controlling Finland, Karelia, Estonia, Latvia, and other countries of the eastern Baltic until their disastrous war with Peter the Great at the beginning of the eighteenth century when all these territories were lost. Sweden has given the world two great military leaders, Gustavus Adolphus, one of the Protestant leaders in the Thirty-Years' War, and Charles XII who led the Swedes in their war against Peter the Great and a coalition consisting of Russia, Denmark, Poland, and Saxony. The Swedish-Norwegian Union, dissolved in 1905, is a modern example of the peaceful settlement of differences between nations.

As a nation which maintained a strict neutrality in both world wars, Sweden's economy was considerably enhanced. It is often considered one of the world's most progressive states. Because of its social welfare program and the attendant cooperative movement which extends to the fire insurance business, stock insurance corporations are in the minority. They do, however, represent the sturdiest of the Swedish underwriters. So far as can be ascertained, only the very old companies used fire marks, and the three specimens of these are illustrated in this chapter.

1699

1700

1701

(1699) STOCKHOLMS STADS BRANDFORSAKRINGS-KONTOR. STOCKHOLM, SWEDEN. 1746-

Lead. 9" x 9¾". Designs in relief. Entire mark gold.

(1700) STADERNAS ALLMANNA BRANDSTODSBOLAG. STOCKHOLM, SWEDEN. 1828-

Bronze. 8" x 8¼". Raised lettering and border of center circle dull gold with black background. Surrounding ornamentation dull gold with black.

(1701) BRAND-OCH-OLYCKSFALLFORSAKRINGS A. B. SKANDINAVIEN. STOCKHOLM, SWEDEN. 1886-

Iron. Rectangular. White background with black lettering. (Courtesy of V. R. Willemson.)

SWITZERLAND

The Treaty of Westphalia recognized the independence of the regions comprising Switzerland in 1648. In 1815 she became an independent neutral state in perpetuity, the nation's borders being established as they exist today. Subsequently, the Cantons of Switzerland bound together in mutual defense and have been so effective that no country has yet dared to disturb the Swiss neutrality. Scenery, unsurpassed anywhere in the world, brings to Switzerland a vast tourist trade which bolsters an economy almost self-sufficient. Industry is limited principally to manufacture for export of small, expensive, and meticulously made commodities such as watches, clocks, jewelry, and other similar metal products. For more than a century this "land of the Helvetians" has provided its own fire insurance companies, some of them extending operations into distant countries. Most have used fire marks, and in Switzerland they have had the old traditional association with the fire brigades.

1702

1703

1704

1705

1706

1707

1708

1709

1710

1711

1712

1713

(1702-1705) SOCIETE SUISSE POUR L'ASSURANCE DU MOBILIER. BERNE, SWITZERLAND. 1826-

1702. Tin. Rectangular. 9¾" x 6¾". Raised gold lettering and phoenix with shield of Switzerland on black background. Raised border.

1703. Tin. Rectangular. 9⅞" x 7¼". Red, black and cream design, black lettering, raised red border, cream background.

1704. Tin. Rectangular. 10" x 7". Raised gold phoenix with red and white shield and gold initials on black background. Raised border.

1705. Tin. Rectangular. 9⅞" x 7¼". Red, black and cream design, black lettering, raised red border, cream background.

(1706-1715) HELVETIA SWEIZERISCHE FEUERVERSI-CHERUNGS GESELLSCHAFT. ST. GALLEN, SWITZERLAND. 1861-

1706. Tin. Rectangular. 8⅜" x 11⅛". Raised lettering, design and border. From building in the south of Europe.

1707. Tin. Rectangular. 7⅛" x 10". Raised gold lettering and figure holding shield of red, silver and gold. Black background. Raised border. From building in Greece.

1708. Tin. Rectangular. 8⅜" x 11⅛". Raised lettering, design and border. From building in Greece.

1709. Tin. Rectangular. 8¼" x 5⅝". Raised crest in red, white and gold. Raised gold lettering. Black background. Raised border.

1710. Tin. Rectangular. 7⅛" x 10". Raised gold lettering and figure holding shield of red, silver and gold. Black background. Raised border.

1711. Tin. Rectangular. 8¼" x 5⅝". Raised crest in red, white and gold. Raised gold lettering. Black background. Raised border.

1712. Tin. Rectangular. 7⅛" x 10". Raised gold lettering and figure holding shield of red, silver and gold. Black background. Raised border.

1713. Tin. Oval. 9½" x 7⅛". Raised red, white and gold crest, gold characters and border. Black background.

HELVETIA
חברה שוייצרית
לאחריות אש
הלוציה

1714

VERSICHERT
HELVETIA

1715

1716

VERSICHERT
BASEL

1717

VASSURE
BALOISE

1718

Assuré
a la
BALOISE

1719

Versichert
BASEL

1720

BASLER
FEUER

1721

„הבזיל'אית"
חברה לאחריות
נגד אש

1722

LA BALOISE
COMPAÑIA DE SEGUROS
contra
INCENDIOS

1723

BALOISE
FIRE
INSURANCE
COMPANY.

1724

LA BASILESE
1863
INCENDI

1725

EMMENTHALISCHE
MOBILIAR
VERSICHERUNG.

1726

Versichert
Eidgenössische
Zürich

1727

NEUENBURGER
VERSICHERUNGEN

1728

NEUCHATELOISE
ASSURANCES

1729

NEUCHATELOISE
ASSICURAZIONI

1730

Schweizerische
National-Versicherungs-Gesellschaft
in Basel
Feuerversicherung

1731

ASSURÉ À LA
COMPAGNIE D'ASSURANCES
NATIONALE SUISSE
À BÂLE

1732

SCHWEIZERISCHE NATIONAL
VERSICHERUNGS GESELLSCHAFT
IN BASEL
FEUERVERSICHERUNG

1733

UNION GENEVE
UNION GENEVE
ASSURANCES

1734

UNION GENEVE

1735

296

1714. Tin. Rectangular. 8⅝″ x 6½″. Gold and red characters and lettering with black background. Gold striping.

1715. Tin. Rectangular. 7⅛″ x 10″. Raised gold lettering and figure holding shield of red, silver and gold. Black background. Raised border.

(1716-1725) BASLER VERSICHERUNGS GESELLSCHAFT GEGEN FEUERSCHADEN. BASEL, SWITZERLAND. 1863-

1716. Tin. Circular. 8¾″ in diameter. Gold, silver and red crest raised on black center. Lettering and scrolls raised gold. Borders red.

1717. Tin. Rectangular. 7⁵⁄₁₆″ x 10¹⁄₁₆″. Crest, lettering and borders raised. From building in Greece.

1718. Tin. Rectangular. 7¼″ x 10″. Crest, lettering and borders raised. From building in Greece.

1719. Tin. Rectangular. 8⁵⁄₁₆″ x 5⅝″. Lettering and border raised. From building in Greece.

1720. Tin. Rectangular. 8¼″ x 5¾″. Raised border and lettering in gold with black background.

1721. Iron. Convexed. 7¾″ x 9½″. Black lettering and borders on white background. Vari-colored crest.

1722. Tin. Rectangular. 6⅝″ x 9⁹⁄₁₆″. Black lettering and borders on off-white background. Vari-colored crest. From building in Palestine.

1723. Tin. 9⅝″ x 7⅜″. Raised black lettering and border with yellow background. Type formerly used in Mexico.

1724. Tin. Rectangular. 7½″ x 10¼″. Raised lettering and border. Dark blue background.

1725. Tin. Rectangular. Raised border and lettering. (*Courtesy of V. R. Willemson.*)

(1726) EMMENTHALISCHE MOBILIAR VERSICHERUNGS AKTIEN GESELLSCHAFT. ZAEZIWIL, SWITZERLAND. 1874-

Tin. Rectangular. 9⅜″ x 6⅝″. Raised gold lettering on black background. Raised border.

(1727) EIDGENOSSISCHE VERSICHERUNGS AKTIEN GESELLSCHAFT. ZURICH, SWITZERLAND. 1881-

Aluminum. Rectangular. 6⅝″ x 8⅞″. Raised center crest in black, silver, gold and red, with raised gold lettering and black background. Gold striping.

(1728-1730) LA NEUCHATELOISE COMPAGNIE SUISSE D'ASSURANCES GENERALES. NEUCHATEL, SWITZERLAND. 1869-

1728. Tin. Rectangular. 6⅞″ x 9¾″. Vari-colored crest and raised gold lettering. Red background. Raised black border.

1729. Tin. Rectangular. 6⅞″ x 9¾″. Vari-colored crest and raised gold lettering. Red background. Raised black border.

1730. Tin. Rectangular. 6⅞″ x 9¾″. Vari-colored crest and raised gold lettering. Red background. Raised black border.

(1731-1733) SCHWEIZERISCHE NATIONAL VERSICHE-RUNGS GESELLSCHAFT IN BASEL. BASEL, SWITZERLAND. 1883-

1731. Iron. Slightly convexed. 5⅞″ x 4″. Black lettering and border. Red circle containing white cross. White background.

1732. Tin. Rectangular. 7⅛″ x 4⅞″. Raised white lettering and border. Red, white and black crest raised. Blue background.

1733. Tin. Rectangular. 8″ x 5½″. Gold lettering and red and gold border. Crest in red, gold, black and white. Black background.

(1734-1735) UNION GENEVE COMPAGNIE D'ASSURANCES. GENEVA, SWITZERLAND. 1926-

1734. Tin. Rectangular. 9¹³⁄₁₆″ x 6¹¹⁄₁₆″. Black and gold lettering and raised gold border. Bright red background. Raised diamond bears name and crest in black and gold. From building in Palestine.

1735. Tin. Rectangular. 9⅞″ x 6¹¹⁄₁₆″. Black and gold lettering and raised gold border. Bright red background. Raised diamond bears name and crest in black and gold. From building in Greece.

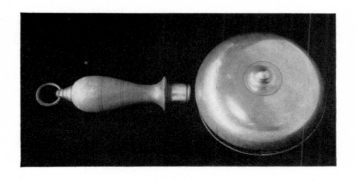

TASMANIA

Abel Tasman, a Dutch navigator, discovered an island lying off the southeast coast of Australia in 1642. Henceforth the isle was known as Tasmania. Becoming a British penal colony in 1804, having also been designated as "Van Diemen's Land," it was made independent in 1825. A few years later business had advanced to such a point that it was prudent for its citizens to form the Tasmanian Fire Insurance Company. This organization was closely followed by three additional concerns within a six-year period. All contributed to the maintenance of fire brigades and to the use of fire marks, all of which are illustrated here. These marks have become a rarity and only a few specimens remain.

1736

1737

1738

1739

1740

(1736-1737)   TASMANIAN FIRE INSURANCE COMPANY. HOBART, TASMANIA, AUSTRALIA.   1835-About 1850.

1736.   Copper.   7″ x 9¼″.   Design, lettering and borders raised.

1737.   Copper.   Oval.   7″ x 9¼″.   Design, lettering and borders raised.

(1738)   TAMAR FIRE AND MARINE INSURANCE COMPANY. HOBART, TASMANIA, AUSTRALIA.   1836-About 1855.

Copper.   8″ x 9¼″.   Raised gold sun on convexed blue background. Red borders and panel containing raised gold lettering. Borders raised.

(1739)   DERWENT AND TAMAR ASSURANCE COMPANY, LIMITED. HOBART, TASMANIA, AUSTRALIA.   1838-

Copper.   8¼″ x 9½″.   Raised gold phoenix on convexed red background. Border and panel below blue with raised gold lettering. Raised gold borders.

(1740)   CORNWALL FIRE INSURANCE COMPANY. LAUNCESTON, TASMANIA, AUSTRALIA.   1841 - ?.

Copper.   8¾″ x 11″.   Raised design, lettering and borders.

A Turkish fire brigade manning a hand-pumper, circa 1870.

TURKEY

It was a small tribe of Turks who originally formed the great Ottoman Empire in the thirteenth century. The entire Near East and the Balkans came under their control as did Constantinople in 1453. Then started the retrogression. First came the Turkish defeat at Vienna in 1683, then defeat by the Russians in 1878, losses to the Italians in 1911, and losses in the Balkans in 1913. Shortly before the latter, in 1909, the liberal young Turks led a successful revolution, unseating the Sultan and securing the establishment of a constitutional regime.

Modern Turkey has shown unusual progress in agriculture and trade. Most of its fire insurance companies were inaugurated subsequent to the revolution. Only the fire marks of the Ottomans survive to give evidence of the industry during the reign of the Sultan. Yet, the marks of numerous foreign concerns can still be found in Istanbul.

1741

1742

1743

(1741-1743) SOCIETE GENERALE D'ASSURANCES OTTOMANE. ISTANBUL, TURKEY. 1906-1918.

1741. Copper. Circular with panel below. 7½" x 9⅛". Raised gold crescent and star on red circle. Raised characters and company name in gold on black. Raised gold outer border.

1742. Tin. Circular with panel below. 7½" x 9". Raised crescent and star, borders, characters and lettering.

1743. Tin. 8⅞" x 11". Raised gold crescent and star on red circle with raised gold border. Raised characters and company name in gold on black. Raised gold outer border.

1744

1745

1746

(1744) UNION NATIONALE SOCIETE TURQUE D'ASSUR-ANCES. ISTANBUL, TURKEY. 1918-

Tin. Rectangular. 9¾" x 6⅝". Raised gold lettering and characters on green slightly convexed oval with raised border. Red, gold, black and white crest raised. Background red. Raised outer border maroon with gold striping.

(1745) L'ORIENT SOCIETE ANONYME D'ASSURANCES. ISTANBUL, TURKEY. 1923-

Tin. 9½" x 6⅞". Raised lettering and trademark, characters and border cream and black on red background.

(1746) ANATOLIE SOCIETE ANONYME TURQUE D'ASSURANCES. ISTANBUL, TURKEY. 1925-

Tin. Rectangular. 9¾" x 6½". Raised gold lettering on blue oval, black background. Raised red border.

URUGUAY

The Republic of Uruguay, one of the most democratic of South American republics, was formed in 1830. Except for wars with Argentina and Paraguay and local internal incidents leading up to the present century, the country has enjoyed a peaceful life.

Agriculture provides almost exclusively for the nation's economy. Until recently, only two local fire insurance companies were listed, only one of which has issued a mark of its trade. It is presumed that this was adopted for publicity purposes.

1747

(1747) BANCO DE SEGUROS DEL ESTADO. MONTEVIDEO, URUGUAY. 1912-

Iron. Circular, convexed. 8⁹⁄₁₆" in diameter. Pale blue crest on white. Darker blue band with border and lettering in yellow.

VENEZUELA

Simon Bolivar was active in the revolution of 1821 in which Venezuela gained its independence. His liberal influence apparently died with him, however, for repeated internal disorders rent this country until 1948. Its economy has suffered and to supplement

this the country has established such restrictive laws that no foreign fire insurance company is enabled to do business there. The only companies to issue fire marks are the *La Previsiora* and the *Nacional,* two local concerns.

1748

1749

(1748) COMPANIA NACIONAL ANONIMA DE SEGUROS
LA PREVISORA. CARACAS, VENEZUELA. 1913-

Tin. Rectangular. 10⅞" x 8¼". Raised gold lettering on black
background. Raised border. Green and cream design on slightly
raised oval with gold border.

(1749) LA NACIONAL. CARACAS, VENEZUELA. ? - ?

(Courtesy of V. R. Willemson.)

VICTORIA

While Victoria was recognized as a separate colony
in the Australian states in 1851, it took two years for
it to gain a new constitution and fifty years for it to
become part of the Commonwealth of Australia. Victoria is the smallest state on the mainland. Its economy is limited to agricultural products, but it does
have a record of some very old and substantial fire
insurance companies formed between 1838 and 1878
respectively. These concerns worked in close harmony with the fire brigades which naturally followed
their distinctive fire marks, all of them having become
rarities to the signevierist.

1750

1751

1752

(1750) VAN DIEMEN'S LAND INSURANCE COMPANY.
MELBOURNE, VICTORIA, AUSTRALIA. 1838-1849.

Copper. 9½" x 11". Figure of kangaroo, lettering and borders
raised.

(1751) THE MELBOURNE FIRE INSURANCE COMPANY.
MELBOURNE, VICTORIA, AUSTRALIA. 1839-1843.

Copper. Shield shape. 8" x 9". Raised gold lettering on black.
Border raised.

(1752-1757) VICTORIA INSURANCE COMPANY, LIMITED.
MELBOURNE, VICTORIA, AUSTRALIA. 1849-

1752. Zinc. Shield shape. 12" x 10½". Raised bird, lettering,
ribbon and border.

1753

1754

1755

1756

1757

1758

1759

1760

1761

1762

1763

1764

1765

1753. Zinc. Shield shape. 9″ x 8½″. Raised bird, lettering, ribbon and border.

1754. Zinc. Shield shape. 8¾″ x 8″. Raised bird, lettering, ribbon and border.

1755. Copper. Shield shape. 12″ x 10½″. Raised gold lettering on blue ribbon—raised gold bird on red background. Raised border.

1756. Copper. Shield shape. 9″ x 8½″. Raised gold lettering on blue ribbon, raised gold bird on red background. Raised border.

1757. Copper. Oval. 7″ x 9¼″. Raised bird, lettering and borders.

(1758) AUSTRALASIAN FIRE AND LIFE INSURANCE COMPANY. MELBOURNE, VICTORIA, AUSTRALIA. 1857-1872.

Tin. Circular. 9″ in diameter. Convexed center containing 5 raised stars of Southern Cross. Raised lettering and borders.

(1759) PROVIDENT INSTITUTE INSURANCE. MELBOURNE, VICTORIA, AUSTRALIA. 1859-About 1865.

Copper. 10″ x 7⅜″. Raised gold sunburst and lettering. Raised borders.

(1760) AUSTRALIAN ALLIANCE ASSURANCE COMPANY. MELBOURNE, VICTORIA, AUSTRALIA. 1862-

Circular. Raised center figure, lettering on garter border. (*Courtesy of Chartered Insurance Institute.*)

(1761-1765) THE COLONIAL MUTUAL FIRE INSURANCE COMPANY, LTD. MELBOURNE, VICTORIA, AUSTRALIA. 1878-

1761. Tin. Oval, slightly convexed. 8¾" x 6". Raised lettering and border.

1762. Tin. 9" x 10". Raised lettering, torch at top, and borders.

1763. Tin. 9" x 10". Raised lettering, torch at top, and borders.

1764. Zinc. 9" x 10⅛". Raised lettering, torch at top, and borders.

1765. Tin. 9" x 10". Raised lettering, torch at top, and borders. (Shapes of Nos. 1762, 1763, 1764 and 1765 each differ slightly.)

WESTERN AUSTRALIA

This is another member of the Australian Commonwealth which is also a great agricultural area. Mines abound and much of the state's economy is centered around these mineral deposits. The Western Australian Insurance Company, the one concern whose fire mark has been found, used as its sign of assurance the imprint of a swan, representative of the principal river of the area, the Swan River.

1766

(1766) THE WESTERN AUSTRALIAN INSURANCE COMPANY, LIMITED. PERTH, WESTERN AUSTRALIA. 1912-

Tin. 13¾" x 6". Raised lettering and swan (originally had blue background—white swan). From building in Greece.

YUGOSLAVIA

Following World War I the southern Slavonic peoples east of the Adriatic were formed into the "Kingdom of the Serbs, Croats, and Slovenes" which in 1918 was renamed the "Kingdom of Yugoslavia." Their period of independence ended when the Nazis occupied the country in 1941. At the end of World War II, Yugoslavia emerged as a Russian satellite. At this writing, it remains a communistic nation independent of Russia. A review of the fire insurance companies which issued marks reveals that they were established in the cities of what is now Yugoslavia long before the present area was set aside. Most of these provided indemnity in the agrarian sections and will undoubtedly remain as a symbol of a temporary freedom of enterprise enjoyed for less than a quarter century.

1767

(1767) BEOGRADSKA ZADRUGA BANK AKCIONARSKO DRUSTVO. BELGRADE, YUGOSLAVIA (BEOGRAD). 1882-

Iron. Slightly convexed. 7⅞" x 4¹¹⁄₁₆". White lettering, blue border on bright red background.

CROATIA

USTANOV. 1884.

1768

CROATIA

UTEMELJ. 1884.

1769

Osigurala "CROATIA" u ZAGREBU

1770

ZAVAROVALA

VZAJEMNA

1771

VZAJEMNA ZAVAROVALNICA V LJUBLJANI

1772

SRBIJA PRVO SRPSKO DRUŠTVO ZA OSIGURANJE u BEOGRADU

1775

ОСИГУРАВА УЗАЈАМНО

1773

ЗАВАРУЈЕ VZAJEMNA

1774

СРБИЈА ПРВО СРПСКО ДРУШТВО ЗА ОСИГУРАЊЕ У БЕОГРАДУ

1776

OSIGURALA SRBIJA BEOGRAD

1777

Osigurala JUGOSLAVIJA

1778

ОСИГУРАЛА ЈУГОСЛАВИЈА

1779

JUGOSLAVIJA 1913

1780

ШУМАДИЈА ПРВО СРПСКО ДРУШТВО ЗА ОСИГУРАЊЕ и РЕОСИГУРАЊЕ У БЕОГРАДУ

1781

ШУМАДИЈА А. Д. ЗА ОСИГУРАЊЕ и РЕОСИГУРАЊЕ У БЕОГРАДУ

1782

ŠUMADIJA A. D. ZA OSIGURANJE i REOSIGURANJE U BEOGRADU

1783

Osigurava DUNAV

1784

304

1785

1787

1786

(1768-1770) CROATIA OSIGURAVAJUCA ZADRUGA U ZAGREBU. ZAGREB, YUGOSLAVIA. 1884-

1768. Tin. 6¾″ x 9¹³⁄₁₆″. Vari-colored picture on raised panel. Blue background with raised white lettering and border.

1769. Iron. Convexed. 6¾″ x 9¾″. Vari-colored picture, blue background with white lettering and border.

1770. Iron. Square. Background and lettering porcelain enamel. *(Courtesy of V. R. Willemson.)*

(1771-1774) VZAJEMNA ZAVAROVALNICA V LJUBLJANI. LJUBLJANA, YUGOSLAVIA. 1900-

1771. Tin. Rectangular. 6⁵⁄₁₆″ x 9¹¹⁄₁₆″. Raised cream lettering and vari-colored center figure on black background. Raised silver border.

1772. Tin. Rectangular. 7¼″ x 5¹⁄₁₆″. Raised pale gold lettering and border on very dark blue background.

1773. Tin. Rectangular, slightly convexed. 7″ x 3¹³⁄₁₆″. Raised cream lettering on dark blue. Raised border with cream striping.

1774. Tin. Rectangular. 7¹⁄₁₆″ x 3³⁄₁₆″. Raised cream lettering on dark blue. Raised border with cream striping.

(1775-1777) SRBIJA PRVO SRPSKO OSIGURAVAJUCE DRUSTVO. BELGRADE, YUGOSLAVIA. 1905-

1775. Iron. Convexed. 3¹⁄₁₆″ x 11¾″. Vari-colored picture, red background with white lettering and border.

1776. Iron. Convexed. 12½″ x 5¾″. Vari-colored picture, blue background with white lettering and border. Red lettering on white band.

1777. Iron. Rectangular, convexed. 7¹⁄₁₆″ x 3¹³⁄₁₆″. White border and lettering on blue. Red lettering on white band.

(1778-1780) JUGOSLAVIJA OPSTE OSIGURAVAJUCE DRUSTVO. BELGRADE, YUGOSLAVIA. 1913-

1778. Iron. Rectangular, convexed. 7¼″ x 10⁵⁄₁₆″. Vari-colored design, and white lettering and border on green background.

1779. Iron. Rectangular, convexed. 7¼″ x 10⁵⁄₁₆″. Vari-colored design and cream lettering on darker green background. Light green border.

1780. Tin. Rectangular. 9⁷⁄₁₆″ x 3⅝″. Raised white lettering and border. Red background.

(1781-1783) SUMADIJA AKCIONARSKO DRUSTVO ZA OSIGURANJE I REOSIGURANJE. BELGRADE, YUGO-SLAVIA. 1913-

1781. Tin. Rectangular. 12⅝″ x 5⅞″. Vari-colored picture, dark blue background, raised white lettering and blue and white border. Raised red lettering on white band.

1782. Iron. Rectangular, convexed. 7¹³⁄₁₆″ x 5¹³⁄₁₆″. White lettering and border on blue background. Red lettering on white panel.

1783. Iron. Rectangular, convexed. 7¹³⁄₁₆″ x 5¹³⁄₁₆″. White lettering and border on blue background. Red lettering on white panel.

(1784-1785) DUNAV, OSIGURAVAJUCE DIONICARSKO DRUSTVO U ZAGREBU. ZAGREB, YUGOSLAVIA. 1920-

1784. Iron. Slightly convexed. 7¹⁄₁₆″ x 2¾″. White border and lettering on green background.

1785. Iron. Slightly convexed. 7¹⁄₁₆″ x 2¾″. White border and lettering on green background.

(1786) ROSIJA FONSIER DRUSTVO ZA OSIGURANJE I REOSIGURANJE. BELGRADE, YUGOSLAVIA. 1921-

Iron. Rectangular, slightly convexed. 8⅞″ x 3¾″. White border and lettering on blue background.

(1787) SAVA OPCE OSIGURAVAJUCE DIONICARSKO DRUSTVO U ZAGREBU. ZAGREB, YUGOSLAVIA. 1921-

Iron. Convexed. 8⁹⁄₁₆″ x 5″. Cream colored lettering and border on blue background.

1788

1789

1790

1791

1793

1794

1792

1795

1796

(1788-1791)   SLAVIJA JUGOSLOVANSKA ZAVAROVALNA
BANKA. LJUBLJANA, YUGOSLAVIA.   1922-

1788. Tin. Rectangular.   7" x 5 1/16".   Raised cream border and
letters on blue background.

1789. Tin. Rectangular, convexed. 6 7/8" x 4 1/16". Raised cream
lettering on dark blue background. Raised border with cream
striping.

1790. Tin. Rectangular, convexed.   6 7/8" x 4".   Raised cream
lettering on dark blue background. Raised border with cream
striping.

1791. Tin. Rectangular, slightly convexed. 6 15/16" x 4 1/16".
Raised cream lettering on dark blue background. Raised border
with cream striping.

(1792-1796)   VARDAR, HERCEG-BOSNA, TRIGLAV UJEDIN-
JENO OSIGURAVAJUCE DRUSTVO. ZAGREB, YUGOSLAVIA.
1922-

1792. Tin. Rectangular. 7 3/8" x 4 5/8". Raised lettering and
border. "Osigurava" blue; "Herceg-Bosna" red and blue. Border
blue. Background cream color.

1793. Tin. Rectangular. 7" x 5 1/8". Raised blue and white
border and white lettering on blue background.

1794. Iron. Rectangular, convexed. 8 1/4" x 3 9/16". White lettering and border on blue background.

1795. Iron. Rectangular, convexed. 8 1/4" x 3 1/2". White lettering and border on blue background.

1796. Iron. Rectangular, convexed. 8 1/4" x 3 1/2". White lettering and border on blue background.

306

BIBLIOGRAPHY

AGRICULTURAL INSURANCE CO. *Seventy-Five Years.*
Watertown, 1928

ALLEN, PHILIP MEREDITH. *The First Hundred.* Philadelphia, 1943

ALLEN, W. B. *A History of Kentucky*

AMERICAN FIRE INSURANCE COMPANY, THE. EST. 1810.
Philadelphia, 1891

AMERICAN RESERVE INSURANCE COMPANY. *Fire Marks.*
New York, 1938

ANDREWS, WILLIAM LORING. *The Continental Insurance Company
of New York 1853-1905.* New York, 1906

ASHLEY, WILLIAM JAMES. *Economic History.* London, 1913-1914

BALTIMORE AMERICAN. *A History of Baltimore, Its Men and
Institutions.* Baltimore, 1902

BANK OF MANHATTAN. *The Manhattan Library.* New York, 1935

BARRETT, WALTER. *The Old Merchants of New York City*
(3 Vols.). New York, 1862

BEARD, CHARLES A. AND MARY R. *A Basic History of the United
States.* New York, 1944

BONNER, WILLIAM T. *New York the World's Metropolis 1623-1923.*
New York, 1924

BONSTIN, ELMER W. *Romance of the Insurance Business As
Disclosed Through Ancient Fire Marks.* San Francisco, 1936

BOYD, JOHN. *Annals of Winchester, Conn.* Hartford, 1871

CALLAHAN, JAMES MORTON. *History of West Virginia.* 1913

CHAMBER OF COMMERCE. *Chambersburg, Its Record and Its
Prospect.* Chambersburg, 1945

CHARLESTON MUSEUM QUARTERLY, THE. *150th Anniversary
Number.* Charleston, S. C., 1923

CHARTERED INSURANCE INSTITUTE. *Museum Catalog.* London, 1937

CHITTY, A. *Fire Insurance Offices and Fire Marks in Australasia.*
Melbourne, 1925

CHRISTIAN, W. A., DD. *Richmond, Her Past and Present.*
Richmond, 1912

CITY OF YORK CASTLE MUSEUM. *History of Fire Fighting.*
York, 1940

COFFIN, JOSEPH. *Coin Collecting.* New York, 1938

CONRAD, E. *An Act to Incorporate the Mutual Insurance Company
of the City of New York.* New York, 1823

CROSS, LYON. *A Shorter History of England and Great Britain.*
New York, 1922

CUNNINGHAM, WILLIAM. *The Growth of English Industry and
Commerce.* Cambridge, 1882

DREW, BERNARD. *The London Assurance Fire Marks.* London, 1950

DULANY'S. *History of Maryland.* Baltimore, 1901

DUNN, JACOB PIATT. *Greater Indianapolis.* Chicago, 1910

DUNSHEE, KENNETH HOLCOMB. *Enjine! Enjine!* New York, 1939

Eagle's History of Poughkeepsie. Poughkeepsie, 1836

EASTERN UNDERWRITER, THE. *The North River Insurance Company.*
New York, April 21, 1950

EDWARDS, GREENOUGH & DEVED. *Edwards' Annual Directory of
Lafayette, Indiana.* 1867

EDWARDS, GREENOUGH & DEVED. *The Edwards' Freeport Directory.*
Freeport, 1867

FLEMING, GEORGE THORNTON. *History of Pittsburgh and Environs.*
1922

FOLSOM, JOSEPH F. *The Municipalities of Essex County, N. J.
1666-1924.* New York, 1925

FORD, HENRY A. AND KATE B. *History of Cincinnati, Ohio.*
Cleveland, 1881

FOTHERGILL, GEORGE A. *British Fire Marks from 1680.*
Edinburgh, 1911

FRANKLIN, B. *The Charters of the Province of Pensilvania and City
of Philadelphia.* Philadelphia, 1742

FULLER, GEORGE N. *Historic Michigan*

GEORGE, W. S. & Co. *Lansing, the Capital of Michigan.*
Lansing, 1873

GILLESPIE AND WALSH. *Fire Insurance House Marks of the
United States.* Philadelphia, 1915

GILLINGHAM, HARROLD. *Fire Marks of American Fire Insurance
Companies.* Philadelphia, 1914

GLENDINING & Co. *Sale Catalogs of Fire Marks.* London, 1935,
1936, 1937, 1939

GLENS FALLS INSURANCE COMPANY. *A Report on One Hundred
Years.* Glens Falls, 1949

GOLD, PLEASANT DANIEL. *History of Duval County, Florida.*
Jacksonville, 1928

GRAY, JEROME B. *One Hundred Years.* Philadelphia, 1929

GREEN, J. R. *A Short History of the English People* (4 Vols.).
London, 1892

GRIFFITH, A. E. *History of The Southern Mutual Insurance
Company.* Athens, 1923

GRISWOLD, J. *The Chronicle — Fire Insurance Companies and
Their Emblems.* New York, Dec. 24, 1891

HAINES, FREDERICK H. *Chapters of Insurance History.* London, 1926

HANOVER FIRE INSURANCE COMPANY, THE. NEW YORK.
Seventy-Five Years of Progress. New York, 1927

HARTFORD AGENT, THE

HARTFORD COUNTY MUTUAL

HINE, C. C. *Insurance Blue Book — 1876-1877.* New York, 1877

HOME INSURANCE COMPANY, THE. *Addresses Delivered At
Banquet — Fiftieth Anniversary.* New York, 1903

HOME INSURANCE COMPANY, THE. *Amended Charter of the Home
Insurance Co.* New York, 1860

HOME INSURANCE COMPANY, THE. *Milestones.* New York, 1928

HOME INSURANCE COMPANY, THE. *The Home Insurance Company
— 1853-1903.* New York, 1903

Howe, Henry. *Historical Collections of Ohio.* Cincinnati, 1888

Hudson, J. L. Co. *Sixty Years.* Detroit, 1941

Huguenot Society of South Carolina. *Transactions of the Huguenot Society of South Carolina, No. 56.* Charleston, 1951

Hunt, W. and Poole, R. L. *The Political History of England.* London, 1905-1911

Insurance Company of North America. *American Fire Marks.* Philadelphia, 1933

James, Marquis. *Biography of a Business. 1792-1942. Insurance Company of North America.* Indianapolis, 1942

Ketcham, Edward A. *Essentials of the Fire Insurance Business.* 1922

Killikelly, Sarah H. *The History of Pittsburgh.* Albany, 1906

King, William T. *History of the American Steam Fire Engine.* The Pinkham Press, 1896

Latrobe, John H. B. *Picture of Baltimore.* 1832

Lawrence, William L. *Articles on Atomic Energy.* New York *Times*

Legg, L. G. Wickham. *Dictionary of National Biography.* London, 1931-1940

Low, J. Herbert. *English History.* New York, 1928

Martin, Charles J. *Address to the Board of Directors.* New York, 1878

Martin, Charles J. *History of the Home Insurance Company.* New York, 1883

McCants, E. C. *History Stories and Legends of South Carolina.* Dallas, 1927

McConnell and Liggett. *Wheeling's First 250 Years.* Wheeling, 1942

Meginness, John F. *History of Lycoming County, Pa.* Chicago, 1892

Mordecai, Samuel. *Virginia, Especially Richmond in By-Gone Days.* Richmond, 1860

Morton, William. *The Knickerbocker Fire Insurance Company.* New York, 1887

Murdock, Harold. *1872 — the Great Boston Fire.* Boston, 1909

Nolan, James B. *Southeastern Pennsylvania*

North River Insurance Company. New York, 1877

O'Connor, Harvey. *The Astors.* New York, 1941

Phenix Insurance Company. *A Brief Sketch of the History of the Phenix Insurance Company, Brooklyn, N. Y.* New York, 1878

Philadelphia Contributionship. *Fire Marks — Their Origin and Use.* Philadelphia, 1914

Platt, Edmond. *The Eagle's History of Poughkeepsie.* Poughkeepsie, 1905

Poughkeepsie Eagle, The. Poughkeepsie, 1889

Proctor, John Clagett. *Into Another Century.* 1937

Ranck, Geo. W. *History of Lexington.* Cincinnati, 1872

Relton, Francis Boyer. *An Account of the Fire Insurance Companies in Great Britain and Ireland.* London, 1893

Roe, George Mortimer. *Cincinnati — the Queen City of the West.* Cincinnati, 1895

Roelker & Collins. *One Hundred Fifty Years of Providence Washington Insurance Company.* Providence, 1949

Royal Exchange Assurance Magazine. London, July, 1911

Sachs, Edwin O. *A Record of the International Fire Exhibition.* London, 1903

Scharf. *History of Baltimore City*

Scharf, Col. J. Thomas. *The Chronicles of Baltimore.* Baltimore, 1874

Scharf, J. Thomas. *History of Western Maryland.* Philadelphia, 1882

Scharf, J. Thomas. *History of Saint Louis City and County.* Philadelphia, 1883

Schulman and Holzer. *The Coin Collectors' Almanac.* New York, 1946

Sherman, C. *Centennial Meeting of the Philadelphia Contributionship.* Philadelphia, 1852

Short History of The Oldest American Fire Insurance Company. Philadelphia

Singer Company. *Who Is Who in Insurance.* New York, 1908

Spectator, The. *Property Insurance Review.* New York, March 11, 1937

Springfield Fire and Marine Insurance Company. *A Half-Century of History.* Springfield, 1901

Stokes, I. N. Phelps. *The Iconography of Manhattan Island.* New York, 1926

Street, G. S. *The London Assurance 1720-1920.* London, 1920

Swigart, W. Emmert. *Old Fire Marks.* Norristown, 1946

Thorp, Prescott Holden. *How to Build A Stamp Collection.* New York, 1935

Todd, Frank Morton. *A Romance of Insurance.* San Francisco, 1929

Tyler, Sydney. *San Francisco's Great Disaster.* Philadelphia, 1906

Victorian Historical Magazine, The. Melbourne, Oct. 1921, Dec. 1921

Vogel, F. B. *Famous Fire Insurance Companies Insurance Register.* Feb. 1909

Walch, Charles E. *The Story of the Derwent & Tamar Assurance Company, Limited.* Hobart, 1914

Walford. *Insurance Cyclopaedia,* Vol. 3. London, 1874

Ward, A. W., Prothero, G. W., Leathes, Stanley. *Cambridge Modern History.* Cambridge, 1934

Warner, Peter R. *History of the North River Insurance Co.* New York, 1865

Weekly Underwriter. New York, May 26, 1934, May 28, 1949

White, Henry A. *The Making of South Carolina.* New York, 1906

Williams, Bertram. *Fire Marks and Insurance Office Fire Brigades.* London, 1927

Williams, Bertram. *Insurance Office Signs.* London, 1929

Williams, Bertram. *Specimens of British Fire Marks.* London, 1927

Williams, Thomas J. C. *History of Washington County, Maryland.* Baltimore, 1906

Wilson, H. *Trow's New York City Directory.* New York, 1853

Winsor, Justin. *Memorial History of Boston,* 3 Vols. Boston, 1880

Winsor, Justin. *The Memorial History of Boston.* Boston, 1881

Woodward, P. Henry. *Insurance in Connecticut.* Boston, 1897

Yeoman, Hewitt and Green. *Handbook of United States Coins.* Racine, 1942

INDEX

The consecutively numbered descriptions of the fire marks are arranged chronologically by countries or areas. They designate the corporate or adopted name of the organization and are followed by dates. The first is that date on which the organization assumed the exact name used; the second numeral indicates when it ceased doing business or when the name was altered, merged, consolidated or passed into the hands of another institution. Where no second figure is shown, the dash denotes that the organization is still active insofar as the author has been able to determine. In some instances, the fire marks themselves will indicate the date of organization used by an earlier unit of the specific company referred to, and in a few instances interrogation marks connote that the date of cessation or actual time of establishment was not available.

Aachener & Munchener, 247
Aachen Leipziger, 251
Abbott, Norris G., Jr., IX
Abeille Contre La Grele, 243
Abeille Incendie, France, 241
Aberdeen, Scotland, 177
Abolitionist, **57**
Account of The Fire Insurance Companies in Great Britain and Ireland, An, 308
Acme, Des Moines, 112
Acoriana, Azores, 210
Adams Agency, Warren, 85
Adams, Cincinnati, 99
Adams, Pres. John Quincy, 51
Addresses Delivered at Banquet—Fiftieth Anniversary, Home, 307
Address to The Board of Directors, Home, N. Y., 308
Adelaide, 289
Aefthryth, 171
Aetna, Hartford, 45, 49
Aetna, Wheeling, 101
Afrique Française, 205
Agrarian Era, 146
Agricultural, Canada, 221
Agricultural, Watertown, 74, 81, 307
Agrippina, Allgemeine, Germany, 253
Agrippina, See-Fluss, Germany, 249
Agronomul, Rumania, 286
Aigle, Incendie, France, 239
Alaska Purchase, 91
Alberschardt, Harry F., IX
Albert, England, 181, 189
Albert of Saxe-Coburg-Gotha, 180
Albingia, Germany, 253
Albion Fire, 163
Alentejo, Portugal, 284
Alexander the Great, 263
Alexandria, Egypt, 233
Alfalfa, 22
Alfred, King, 165
Alianza, Cuba, 227
Alleanza Securitas, 268, 269
Allemannia, Pittsburgh, 103
Allen, Philip Meredith, 307
Allen, W. B., 307
Allgemeine Feuerassekuranz, 253
Allianca da Bahia, 215
Allianca Madeirense, 274

Alliance, England, 171, 173
Alliance Co-op, Topeka, 114, 115
Alliance Regionale, France, 244
Allianz, Germany, 253
Allianz & Stuttgarter, 254
Allison, Robert, 114
Alpine, 257
Alsacienne, France, 243
Alta Italia, 269
Amazon, Cincinnati, 107
Amazonia, Brazil, 216
Amended Charter of The Home Insurance Co., 307
America, Argentina, 207
American Axe, XIII
American Asiatic Undr., 225
American Bald Eagle, 30, 72
American Central, St. Louis, 104
American, Chicago, 87
American Fire Marks, Ins. Co. N. A., 308
American Fed. of Labor, 110
American Fire, Pa., 39, 40, 41, 307
American Foreign, N. Y., 117, 119
American Fur Co., 50
American History, XIII
American International Undr., 117, 119
American, Newark, 64, 69
American Reserve Insurance Company, 307
American Weekly Mercury, 23
Americana, Brazil, 216
Amicable Contributors, 127
Amsterdam Brigades, 258
An Act to Incorporate The Mutual Insurance Company of The City of New York, 307
Anatoli, Greece, 256
Anatolie, Turkey, 300
Anchor, 165, 191, 193, 215, 271, 283
Anchor, England, 185
Anchor Fire Office, 165
Ancienne Mutuelle de la Seine, 237
Anderson, Charles, X
Anderson, Cornelius V., 74
Andes, Cincinnati, 104
Andrews, William Loring, 307
Anglo Danubian Lloyd, 210
Anglo Elementar, Austria, 209
Anglo Mexicana, 275
Angola, 282

Angola, Money, 2
Annals of Winchester, Conn., 307
Anne, Queen, 127, 134
Anniversary Number, 150th, Charleston Museum, 307
Annual Reports, 62
An Ping, China, 225
Aqua Salus, 147, 149
Arabic Characters, 173
Arabs, 279
Arachne, 169
Arctic Fire, N. Y., 81
Argentina, 300
Argentina Cia. de Seguros, 207
Argus, Portugal, 283
Arnhold Brothers, 225
Arrows, 165
Art, 159, 255, 272
Articles on Atomic Energy, 308
As You Pass By, 15
Aseguradora Argentina, 207
Aseguradora, Portugal, 284
Ashland Co., Ohio, 77
Ashley, William James, 307
Ashly, Lord, 180
Asia, Singapore, 293
Assekuranzverein der Zuckerindustrie, 231
Assicurazioni Generali, 265
Assiento Treaty, 134
Associated Firemen's, Balti., 64, 69
Associated Firemen's, Pittsburgh, 64, 71
Assyrians, 279
Astir, Greece, 257
Assicurazioni d'Italia, 269
Astor, John Jacob, 50
Astor, William B., 50
Astors, The, 308
Athenaeum, England, 185
Athene, Goddess, 169, 175, 185
Atkinson, Joel, 47
Atlantic Cable, 91
Atlantis, 165
Atlas, England, 165
Atlas, Java, 233
Atlas, Portugal, 284
Augsburg, Germany, 245
Aurora, Cincinnati, 107
Aurora, Spain, 291

Australasian Fire, 302
Australian Alliance, 303
Australian Commonwealth, 275
Automatic Reaper, 62
Auto Plate, 207, 249, 270, 281, 284, 292
Aviz, Spain, 291
Aylsham New Assn., 166
Azteca, Mexico, 275
Aztec Nation, 275

Babylonians, 279
Badische, Germany, 249
Bain, G. W., 14
Balboa, 280
Baldwin, Audrey Adams, IX
Ball, Henry, 141
Baltimore American, 307
Baltimore & Ohio R. R., 56, 73
Baltimore Conflagration, 117
Baltimore Equitable, 12, 31, 37, 55
Bamton, Richard, 143
Bancker, Charles N., 52, 53
Banco Nacional, Costa Rica, 226
Banco Seguros, Uruguay, 300
Bank of Cincinnati, 65
Bank of Ireland, 175
Bank of North America, 30
Bank of the U. S., 53, 55
Bank Run, 43
Bankruptcy Act, 62
Barbon, Dr. Nicholas, 126
Barebones Parliament, 125
Barebones, Praise-God, 125, 126
Barebones, Unless Christ, 125
Barker's Iron Foundry, 51
Barnes, Alfred S., 74
Barney, Humphrey & Butler, 74
Barnum, P. T., 63
Barrett, Walter, 307
Basic History of The United States, A, 307
Basler, Switzerland, 297
Batavia, 231
Batavische Zee en Brandassurantie, 232
Bath City, England, 146, 149
Bath Fire Office, 146, 147, 149
Bath Sun, 149, 151
Bauman, Odelia, IX
Bayerische Versicherungsbank, 249
Beacon, England, 169
Beard, Charles A. and Mary R., 307
Beaulieu, Director K., 220
Beck Engraving Co., Inc., X
Beehive, 241
Beeker, John, 27
Beenham, England, 145
Belgique, 213
Bell, Alexander G., 106
Bell Telephone Co., 106
Benz, Carl, 110
Beogradska, 303
Berkshire, Gloucestershire & Provident, 173
Berlin, Philip, 56
Berlinische, 247
Betts, Lukyn, 141
Biddle, Clement C., 52, 53
Billericay, England, 143
Bilsbro, Simon, 143
Biography of a Business, 1792-1942, Insurance Company of North America, 308
Birmingham, England, 159, 163
Bishop's Mitre, 183

Black Death, 278
Black Prince, 139
Blass, Ethyl, IX
Bliss, George, 74
Bloomington Fire, 103
Bob, Peter, 27
Boers, 288
Bolivar, Simon, 226, 300
Bolshevik, 287
Bombay Fire Ins., 263
Bonaccord, 183
Bonanca, 283
Bonanza Hunts, 276
Bond, Samuel, 74
Boneshaker Bicycle, 91
Bonner, William T., 307
Bonstin, Elmer W., 307
Borneo, 231
Boston Conflagration, 105, 106
"Bottle and Glass," 52
Boulton and Watts, 5
Bowen & McNamee, 74
Bowne, John L., 51
Boyd, John, 307
Brace, Thomas K., 45
Bradford, Andrew, 23
Bradford, William, 23
Bradshaw, Howard, IX
Brady Township, 106, 109
Brand, Virgil, 13
Bray, Charles, IX
Brazil Seguradora Edificadora, 216
Brief Sketch of The History of The Phenix Insurance Company, Brooklyn, N. Y., A, 308
Briggs, Samuel S., 56
Bristol Crown, 134, 139
Bristol Fire Office, 146, 149
Bristol Union, 166
Bristol Universal, 146, 149
Britannia, 141, 163, 165, 179, 189, 191, 197
Britannia Fire, 189
British America, 221
British Commercial, 166
British Crown, 199
British Dominions, 195
British Fire Ins. Co., 199
British Fire Marks from 1680, 307
British Fire Office, 157, 158
British General, 197
British Guiana & Trinidad Mutual, 217
British Guiana Mutual, 217
British & Irish United, 159, 163
British Traders, 223
Brodie, Oswald, 143
Broomfield, V. J., IX
Broughton, Governor Thomas, 20
Brown Brothers, X
Brown, Frederick, 52, 53
Brown, George, 143
Brown, Henry I., 14
Brown, John, 31
Bubble Act, 135
Buckeye Bell Factory, 56
Buckle, J. H., IX
Buffalo German, 101
Buffer State, 273
Bulau, A. E., XIII
Bulau, Martha, IX
Bulgaria, 237
Bulgaria Premiere, 219

Bull, Governor, 21
Bureau des Incendies, 235
Burgenlandische, Eisenstadt, 210
Burton, E. Milby, IX
Butler, Hamilton, 87
Butterfield & Swire, 225
Byron Family, 173
Byzantines, 279

Cabral, Pedro Alvarez, 210, 214
Caduceus, 166
Cadwallader, John, 52
Cahill, Holger, X, XIII
Cairo, Egypt, 197
Caledonian, 163
Calhoun, Alexander, 56
Calhoun, John C., 39, 43
Calico Printers, 38
Callahan, James Morton, 307
Calvados, France, 237
Calvert, Felix, 126
Cambridge Borough, 173
Cambridge Modern History, 308
Cantons of Switzerland, 294
Cape Colony, 288
Capital, Des Moines, 112
Car and General, 197
Carey, Henry C., 52, 53, 72
Caribbean, 227
Carnegie, Andrew, 106
Caroline, Queen, 167
Carson, Virginia, IX
Carthaginians, 205, 210
Cassa Navale, 268
Castle Hill, 177
Catalana, Spain, 291
Cats, John, 27
Celebes, 231
Celtic, 257
Centennial Meeting of The Philadelphia Contributionship, 308
Central, England, 195
Chamber of Commerce, Chambersburg, 307
Chambersburg Bank, 56
Chambersburg Fire, 56, 59, 122
Chambersburg, Its Record and Its Prospect, 307
Chambly Mutuelle, 244
Chapters of Insurance History, 307
Charles I, King, 125
Charles II, French King, 126, 141
Charles XII, 294
Charles, Robert, 23
Charleston Conflagration, 21
Charleston Fire Ins. Co., 43, 47
Charleston Museum, 31
Charleston Museum Quarterly, The, 307
Charleston, S. C., 19, 21
Charrua Indians, 206
Chartered Insurance Institute, IX, 14, 307
Charter Oak, Hartford, 73, 85, 117, 119
Charters of The Province of Pensilvania and City of Philadelphia, 307
Chatham, England, 143
Chauncey, Elihu, 52
Chetwynd, Lord, 136
Chicago Conflagration, 105
Chicago World's Fair, 113
Child Labor, 168
China Fire, 223

China Insurance Co., 225
China Union, 223
Chippenham, England, 146
Chitty, Alfred, 15, 307
Christian, W. A., D.D., 307
Christiania, 278, 279
Christmas Island, 293
Chronicle, 56
Chronicles of Baltimore, The, 308
Chronicle, The—Fire Insurance Companies
    and Their Emblems, 307
Church of England, 181, 183
Church, Ruby, IX
Ciancio, Silvio, X
Cie, Belge, 213
Cincinnati, O., 56, 64, 65
Cincinnati—The Queen City of the West,
    308
Cinquefoil, 179
Citizens, Columbia, 114, 115
Citizens', Wheeling, 85
City Fire, Hartford, 83
City Ins. Co., Cincinnati, 65, 67
City Mutual, St. Louis, 93
City, New Haven, 64, 71
City of London Fire, 191
City of York Castle Museum, History of
    Fire Fighting, 307
Claflin, Mellen & Co., 74
"Clark's Inn," 52
Clasped Hands, 127, 155, 157, 217
Clay Fire, Newport, 85
Clay, Henry, 43
Clermont Co. Mutual, 85
Cleveland, Grover, 110
Clive, Lord, 263
Clyde River, 163, 167
"Coach and Horses, The," 52
Coalfields, 158
Coal Mine—Britain, 180
Coates, Moses, 56
Cockerell, H. A. L., IX
Coffin, Joseph, 307
Coin as Medium of Exchange, 2
Coin Collecting, 307
Coin Collectors' Almanac, The, 308
Coin Manufacture, 5
Collecting Coins, 1, 8, 9
    See also Numismatics, Numismatist
Collectors in America, 11
    See also Numismatist
Collectors in Britain, 10, 11
Collins, Benjamin Franklin, X
Collins, Harry, X
Collins, Percy, 14
Colombia, 280
Colombiana, Bogota, 226
Colonia, Germany, 249
Colonial Mutual, Australia, 303
Columbia, Dayton, 110, 111
Columbiana Co., Ohio, 56, 61
Columbus, 227, 280
Combinatie Sluyters, 233
Comercial, Cuba, 227
Comet Steamboat, 167
Commercial Advertiser, 38
Commercial do Para, 215
Commercial, Dublin, 158
Commerciale de France, 243
Commercial, So. Africa, 288
Commercial, Spain, 291

Commercial Union, 127, 185, 187
Commercio e Industria, 283
Compagnie de Bruxelles, 211
Compagnie Général, France, 235
Company of London Insurers, 128
Compulsory Schools, 180
Concorde, France, 243
Concordia, Reichenberg, 229
Conestoga Wagons, 51, 52
Confederate States, 90
Confianca Portuense, 283
Confiance, France, 241
Confucius, 221
Connecticut Fire, 64, 71
Conrad, E., 307
Consortium, France, 244
Constancia, Spain, 291
Constantinople, 141, 239, 299
    See also Istanbul
Continental Bank, 75
Continental Insurance Company of New
    York, 1853-1905, The, 307
Continental, New York, 74, 79
Conway, John J., Jr., IX
Coogan, Jackie, 14
Cook, Capt., 275
Cooper, C. A., IX
Cooper, Dayton, 101
Cormorant, 151
Corner, George W., IX
Cornhill, England, 197
Cornwall, Australia, 298
Cornwallis Surrender, 25
Cotton, Egypt, 233
Cotton Mfg., 143
Council Bluffs Ins. Co., 111
Counterfeiting Methods, 9, 10
County Fire Office, 159, 163, 165, 201, 202
Covadonga, Spain, 291
Coxey, Jacob, 113
Crecy, 139
Creole, Reunion, 285
Croatia, Zagreb, 305
Croats, 303
Crockatt, James, 21
Croft, Capt. Edward, 21
Cromwell, Oliver, 125
Crop Failures, 159
Cross, Lyon, 307
Cuba, 289
Cumberland Valley R. R. Co., 56
Cunningham, William, 307

Dacia, 285
Dacia Romania, 286
Daft Electric Motor, 110
Daimler, Gottlieb, 110
Danby, Wm., 151
Darien Fire, 271
Davies, C. T., 14
Davis, Jefferson, 90
Davison, Earl B., IX
Dawson, A. Bashall, IX, 14
Dayton Ins. Co., 77
Dearden, Robert R., Jr., 14
De Birmingham, 177
Declaration of Independence, VII, 25, 29
Defiance, Ohio, 183
Deo Juvante, 139
Depression, 159
Derwent and Tamar, 298

Des Moines Fire, 107, 109
de Solis, Juan Dias, 206
Detroit Auto. Co., 114
Detroit Fire & Marine, 101
Deutsche Allgemeine, 253
Deutsche Beamten, 253
Deutscher Bauerndienst, 253
Dewey, Timothy, 50, 51
Dictionary of National Biography, 308
Diligent, 44
Diomedes, 175
Disraeli, Benjamin, 180
District, England, 177
Dividend Mutual Insurance Co., 63
Dividends, 51
Dnister, Poland, 281
Dog, 283
Dole, Sanford B., 113
Dom Pedro II, 214
Donau, Austria, 209
Douro, Portugal, 283
Doyle, Richard, X
Dragons, 175
Drew, Bernard, 307
Dublin City Hall, 155
Dublin Ins. Co., 146, 149
Dulany's, 307
Dunav, Zagreb, 305
Dundee, Scotland, 151
Dunham, C. H., IX
Dunn, Jacob Piatt, 307
Dunshee, Kenneth Holcomb, 15, 307
Du Pont, M. C. & C. I., 73
Dutchess Co. Fire, 43, 47
Duval, New York, 120, 121
Dwelling House, Boston, 106, 109

Eagle, 165
Eagle, Cincinnati, 65, 71
Eagle Engine Co. 13, N. Y., 14
Eagle, England, 165
Eagle Fire, Boston, 81
Eagle Mutual, Boston, 114, 115
Eagle's History of Poughkeepsie, 307, 308
    See also Platt
Eagles, Mo., 114, 115
Eagle Star & British Dominions, 200
Early Fire Brigades, 3
Early Fire Fighting, 22
Eastern Ins. Office, 225
Eastern Trading Co., 225
Eastern Underwriter, The, 307
Eastern United, Singapore, 293
East India, Batavia and Java Sea, 232
East India Co., 263
East Indians, 231
Eckel, Joseph, 13
Eclair, France, 243
Economic Fire, England, 191
Economic History, 307
Economic Ins. Co., England, 199
Economic of Kent, 173
Edison Elec. Light Co., 106
Edison, Thomas A., 106, 113
Edward III, 139, 171
Edward VII, 196
Edwards, Greenough & Deved, 307
Edwards' Annual Directory of Lafayette,
    Indiana, 307
Edwards' Freeport Directory, The, 307
Eeks-Maja, Estonia, 234

Eesti, Estonia, 234
Eesti Lloyd, 234
Eestimaa Eka, 234
Egypt, 233
Egyptians, 279
Eidenossische, Zurich, 297
El-Dia, Spain, 291
Eldred, J. & Co., 173
Electoral System—British, 168
Electric Telegraph, 62
El Iris, Cuba, 227
Elizabeth I, Queen, 153, 155
Elleniki, Greece, 257
El Plata, Argentina, 207
Elso Kereszteny, 262
Elso Magyar, Hungary, 261
Emiliana, Italy, 268
Emmenthalische Mobiliar, 297
Emott, James, 43, 44
Employers' Liability, 191
Empress, England, 195
Emu, 276
English History, 308
English Ins. Co., 200
Enjine! Enjine!, 15, 307
Eno, Amos R., 74
"Enoch Story's Inn," 52
Enterprise, Cincinnati, 99
Equitable, Australia, 289
Equitable, England, 191
Equitable, Indianapolis, 65, 71
Equita, Italy, 268
Equitativa, Spain, 292
Escaut, Belgium, 211
Espanola, 292
Esperance Belge, 213
Essentials of The Fire Insurance Business,
    308
Essex & Suffolk, 159, 161
Essex Economic, 173
Estonia, 294
Estrella, 207
Ethniki, Greece, 256
Ethniki Zoe, 257
Etna, Ireland, 189
Europea, Portugal, 284
Europe, Bulgaria, 219
Evans Mills, N. Y., 74
Evans, Oliver, 31, 38
Evil Spirits, 231
Ewbank, Thomas, 245
Excess, England, 193, 231
Exchange House Fire Office, 127, 128
Exeter, England, 165

Factory Act, 168
Fagots, 166
Fakes, 120, 201, 202
Fame, Philadelphia, 120, 121
Famous Fire Insurance Companies
    Insurance Register, 308
Far Eastern, 225
Farmers and General, 183
Farmers & Merchants, Dayton, 95
Farmers & Merchants, Indianapolis, 97
Farmers & Merchants, Quincy, 93
Farmers Clubs, 55
Farmers Fire, York, 79
Farmers, Freeport, 85
Farmers, Merch. & Mfrs., Miami Valley, 103
Farmers Migrate, 62

Farmers Mutual, Barry County, 117, 119
Farmers Mutual, Dayton, 106, 109
Farmers Mutual, Detroit, 95
Farmers Mutual, Kewanee, 106, 109
Farmers Mutual, Nazareth, 67
Faroes, 278
Faulkner, Cecil E., IX, 14, 15
Federal, England, 193
Fenwick, John, 21
Fidelidade, 283
Fidelity Phenix, 117, 119
Field, Cyrus, 91
Fife, England, 201, 202
Fifth Ave. Hotel, 74
Filipinas, 280
Fillmore, Millard, 63, 270
Finland, 235, 294
Finland's Code, 235
Fire & Tornado, Freeport, 95
Fire Association, 44, 47, 73
Fire Boats, 217
Fire Department Ins. Co., 57, 61
Fire Hose, 44, 257, 258
Fire Insurance Classes, 39
Fire Insurance History, XIII
Fire Insurance House Marks of the
    United States, 307
Fire Insurance Offices and Fire Marks in
    Australasia, 307
Fireman's Fund, 91, 95
Fire Mark Circle, VIII, IX, 12
Fire Marks and Insurance Office Fire
    Brigades, 308
Fire Marks of American Fire Insurance
    Companies, 307
Fire Mark, Origin, 2, 3, 4, 6, 8; use of, 1,
    57, 64, 73, 91, 111, 114, 117, 118, 125,
    126, 127, 128, 129, 181, 201, 214, 217,
    218, 231, 233, 235, 245, 255, 258, 261,
    263, 264, 270, 271, 272, 273, 274, 275,
    276, 278, 279, 280, 282, 284, 287, 288,
    289, 294, 295, 299, 300, 301, 303. See
    also House Signs, Plaques, Plates, Signe-
    viery, Signevierist.
Fire Marks, American Reserve, 307
Fire Marks—Their Origin and Use, 308
Firemen's, Dayton, 87
Firemen's Ins. Co., Balti., 51, 54
Firemen's Ins. Co., Georgetown, 55, 61
Firemen's Ins. Co., Pittsburgh, 56, 59, 122
Firemen's, New Jersey, 74, 83
Firemen's, New Orleans, 106, 109
Firemen's Ticket, 44
Fire Office, The, 3, 126, 147
First American Fire Ins. Co., 19
First Fire Marks, VII
First Hundred, The, 307
First Known American Mark, 24
    See also Fire Mark
First Russian, 287
First Steam Fire Engine, 73
FitzPernell, Robert, 179
Fiume Societa, 269
Flack, James, 143
Flambeau, 64
Flaming Brazier, 195
Flandre, France, 243
Flax Bushes, 277
Fleming, George Thornton, 307
Fleur-de-lys, 173
Flying Shuttle, 147

Folsom, Joseph F., 307
Fonciere, Hungary, 261
Fonciere Incendie, France, 243
Fondiaria, Italy, 267
Fook On, China, 225
Forbush, Gayle T., IX, 14
Ford, Henry, 113
Ford, Henry A. and Kate B., 307
Forest City, Rockford, 106, 109
Forest Mark, 235
Formosa, 280
Fort Sumter, 90
Fothergill, George A., 10, 307
Foyer, Luxembourg, 273
France Incendie, 239
Franco Americaine, 263
Franco, Argentina, 207
Franco Romana, 286
Frankish Crusaders, 279
Franklin, Benjamin, 23, 24, 307
Franklin, Columbus, 95
Franklin, Pa., 14, 15, 52, 53, 54, 72
Franklin, Saint Louis, 83
Fraternelle Parisienne, 239
Freeman, Edmund, 64
Frelinghuysen, Senator, 14
French Fire Engines, 235
French Huguenots, 31, 127
French Influence, 159
Friendly Society, Charleston, 20, 21, 24
Friendly Society, Edinburgh, 135, 139, 141
Friendly Society, London, 127, 129
Fuller, George N., 307
Furlong, James, 28

Gaeo, 165
Garantia Funchalense, 274
Garantia, Portugal, 283
Garantie Nationale, 213
Garfield, James A., 107
Garter, 179, 193
Gattegno, Michel H., IX, 255
Gaudiano, 157
Gauls, Ancient, 235
Gazdak, Hungary, 261, 262
Gazette, 56
General Accident, Fire and Life Assurance,
    197
General Accident, Scotland, 193
Generala, Rumania, 286
General, Dublin, 151
Generale D'Assurances (1906), France,
    243
General Electric Co., 113
General, England, 179
General Espanola, 292
Generales Incendie (1819), France, 235,
    237
Generali & Globo, Italy, 269
George, King of England, 14
George II, King, 136, 139, 146
George III, 146, 159
George IV, 167, 168
George V, 196
George, W. S. & Co., 307
German American, N. Y., 109
Germano, Argentina, 207
German, Dayton, 101
German, Freeport, 97
German, Wheeling, 103
Germania, Cincinnati, 97

Germania, New York, 87
German Provinces of Russia, 234
Gheniki Asphalie, Greece, 256
Gibraltar, 289
Giguilliat, 20
Gilde Deutsche Versich., 253
Gillespie, George C., 14
Gillespie and Walsh, 29, 73, 307
Gillingham, Harrold, 14, 307
Girard College, 73
Girard Fire, 73, 79
Girard, Stephen, 53
Glasgow Ins. Co., 159, 163
Glasgow, Scotland, 143
Glatzer, Germany, 251
Glendining, D., IX
Glendining & Co., 307
Glens Falls Ins. Co., 63, 69, 307
Globe, Belgium, 213
Globe, Cincinnati, 99
Globe, London, 161
Globe and Rutgers, 114, 116
Globus, Austria, 210
Globus, Germany, 253
Glover, Abbie G., IX
Goforth, Nathaniel, 4
Gold, Pleasant Daniel, 307
"Golden Lion," 52
Good Intent, 44
Good Luck Device, 221, 231
Gookin, Governor, 22
Gorgons, 175
Gosstrakh, Russia, 287, 288
Gothaer, Germany, 247
Grading of Marks, 8
Graff, Jacob, Jr., 29
Grain Elevator, 31
Grand Duchy of Luxembourg, 273
Granite State, 110, 111, 112
Grant, David, 55
Grant, Ulysses S., 55, 90, 91
Grapes, 179
Gray, Jerome B., 307
Great American, N. Y., 105, 109
Great Boston Fire, The, 1872, 308
Great Britain, 191
Great Fire, New York, 57
Great Trek, 288
Greater Indianapolis, 307
Greece, Influence on Design of Fire Marks,
    153, 171, 175, 185, 187, 189, 191, 193,
    195, 199, 200, 209, 213, 237, 239, 241,
    243, 244, 247, 251, 253, 254, 256, 257,
    265, 267, 269, 289, 291, 295, 297, 303
Greek Gods, 6
Green, J. R., 307
Green Tree, 29, 52
Greenwich Village, 50
Greenwood, Miles, 65, 73
Greenwood Mutual, 55, 59
Gregorian Calendar, 24
Gregory, R. C., 90
Griffith, A. E., 307
Griffiths & Browett, Ltd., 193
Griswold, J., 307
Guaranty Trust Co., 74
Growth of English Industry and Commerce,
    The, 307
Guardian Eastern, 200
Guardian, England, 169
Guardian, Phila., 103

Guardian, Pittsburgh, 117, 119
Guntzel & Schumacher, 233
Gustavus Adolphus, 294

Haagsche Assurantie, 259
Hadrian, Emperor, 10, 141
Haines, Frederick H., 307
Hale, William, 127
Half Century of History, 308
Hamburg Bremer, 251
Hamburg Magdeburger, 251
Hamburg Munchener Lloyd, 254
Hamburger Feuerkasse, 245
Hamilton, Ohio, 77
Handbook of United States Coins, 308
Hand-in-Hand, British Guiana, 217
"Hand-in-Hand," 44
Hand-in-Hand, London, 3, 127, 129, 130,
    134
Handy, D. N., IX
Hannover, Germany, 247
Hanover Fire Insurance Company, The,
    New York, 74, 307
Hansa, Estonia, 234
Hants Sussex & Dorset, 159, 161
Happisburgh, England, 145
Hardy, Edward R., IX
Harmony of Interests, 72
Harp, 149, 163, 171
Harris, Linden T., IX, 14
Harrison, Benjamin, 74
Hartford Agent, The, 307
Hartford County Mutual, 55, 59, 307
Hartford Fire, 40, 41, 42
Hasicska, Czechoslovakia, 229
Hassneh, Palestine, 279
Hatch, Charles B., 74
Hawaiian Republic, 113
Haydock, Robert, 30
Hazai, Hungary, 261
Hazard, Erskine, 52
Heaton, Birmm., 179
Heisz, Frederick, 33
Hekla, Madison, 91, 101
Hellas., 255
Helvetians, 294
Helvetia, St. Gallen, 295, 297
Hengst, 161
Henry II, 153
Henry the Navigator, Prince, 273
Heraldry, 6
Hercules, Scotland, 166
Herkon, M., 1
Hermes the God, 166
Hertford, Borough of, 173
Hertfordshire, Cambridgeshire & Country,
    173
Hertogenbosch Van 1838, 259
Hertogenbosch Van 1841, 259
Herts & Cambridge, 173
Hessische, Germany, 247
Hewson's at Kensington, 38
Heyser, William, 56
Hibernia, Cleveland, 107
Hibernian, Dublin, 146, 149
Hicksville Fire Dept., 103
High Veld, 288
Hill Caves of Gibraltar, 255
Hilterfingen, Switzerland, 237
Hind, Arthur, 14
Hine, C. C., 307

Historic Michigan, 307
Historical Collections of Ohio, 308
History of Baltimore City, 308
History of Baltimore, Its Men and
    Institutions, A, 307
History of Cincinnati, Ohio, 307
History of Duval County, Florida, 307
History of Fire Fighting, 307
History of Kentucky, A, 307
History of Lexington, 308
History of Lycoming County, Pa., 308
History of Maryland, 307
History of Pittsburgh, The, 308
History of Pittsburgh and Environs, 307
History of Saint Louis City and County,
    308
History Stories and Legends of South
    Carolina, 308
History of the American Steam Fire
    Engine, 308
History of The Home Insurance Company,
    308
History of The North River Insurance Co.,
    308
History of The Southern Mutual Insurance
    Company, 307
History of Washington County, Maryland,
    308
History of West Virginia, 307
History of Western Maryland, 308
Hodge, William, 4
Holando Sudamericana, 207
Holland Purchase, 103
Holland Van 1859, 260
Hollandsche-Nederlandsche, 259
Hollowell Paper Mill, 56
Holmes, Isaac, 21
Home, Cincinnati, 85
Home, Columbus, 95
Home Insurance Co., N. Y., The, IX, XIII,
    53, 74, 75, 79, 81, 307
Home Insurance Company—1853-1903,
    The, 307
Home, Lafayette, 90, 97
Home, New Haven, 73, 87
Home, Omaha, 112
Home Mutual, St. Louis, 65, 67
Homestead Act, 90
Hongkong, China, 223
Hope, England, 165
Hope Mutual, Pa., 14, 73, 81
Hope Mutual, St. Louis, 87
Horses, 105, 106
House Signs, 1
How to Build a Stamp Collection, 308
Howe, Elias, 64
Howe, Henry, 308
Hudson, J. L. Co., 308
Hudson, N. Y., 117, 119
Hudson River R. R. Co., 63
Huguenot Society of South Carolina No.
    56, Transactions of The, 308
Humpleby, Joseph, 141
Hunt, W., and Poole, R. L., 308
Huskisson, William, 167
Hydraulics, 245

Iberica, Spain, 291
Iceland, 278
Iconography of Manhattan Island, The, 308
Il Duomo, Italy, 269

Illinois Mutual, 61
Imperial, England, 161, 163
Indemnisa Dora, 283
Independence Hall, 52
Indiana Central, 90, 95
Indiana Fire, Indianapolis, **77**
Indian Ocean, **285**
Indianapolis Fire, 114, 116
Indigo, 22
Indische Lloyd, 233
Indonesia, 231
Industrial Advance, British, 159
Industrial Revolution, 62
Industrielle du Nord, 241
Insurance Blue Book—1876-1877, 24, 307
Insurance Company Coins, 7
Ins. Co. of Fla., 64, 67
Insurance Co. of No. Am., 12, 14, 30, 31, 35, 122, 308
Ins. Co. of Scotland, 171
Insurance Cyclopaedia—Vol. 3, 308
Insurance in Connecticut, 308
Insurance Law Journal, 106
Insurance Laws, N. Y., 43
Insurance Monitor, 72
Insurance Office Signs, 308
Intag Phobus, 253
Interesse Publico, Brazil, 215
Internacional, Brazil, 216
Internacional, Panama, 280
International, China, 225
International Postal Union, 2
Into Another Century, 308
Invicta, 161
Iowa State, Keokuk, 83
Irish Alliance, 173
Irish Parliament House, **175**
Iron Curtain, 228
Irving, N. Y., 77
Istanbul, 141, 177, 193, 195, 199, 201, 202, 209, 219, 237, 239, 241, 243, 260, 291
  See also Constantinople
Italia, Italy, 267
Italiana Incendio, Milan, 267
Italian Excess, 269
Italian Screw Press, 5
Italica, Milano, 268
Ivan III, 287
Ivan IV, the Terrible, 287

Jackson, Andrew, 53, 55
Jackson, William, 143
James II, 126, 127
James, Marquis, 308
James River & Kanawha Co., 56
Janney, Benjamin S., 47
Java, 231
Javasche Zee en Brandassurantie, 232
Jefferson, St. Louis, 99
Jefferson, Steubenville, 99
Jefferson, Thomas, 29, 33
Jerusalem, 175
John, King of Bohemia, 139
Jones, Capt. William, 39, 40
Jones, Joel, 73
Judah & Israel, 279
Jugoslavija, 305
Jura, France, 241
Justice, 157, 191

Kangaroo, 276, 301

Khan, Kublai, 270
Kali Pistis, 257
Kane, John K., 52
Kansas City Fire, 101
Kansas Farmers, Abilene, 111
Karelia, 294
Karntnerische, Austria, 209
Karpatia Rolnicka, 230
Katholikus, Hungary, 262
Keely, John Ernest, 106
Kelly, J., IX
Kent Fire, 159, 161
Kenton, Ky., 103
Ketcham, Edward A., 308
Kiesler, Edward P., IX
Killikelly, Sarah H., 308
Kinetographic Camera, 113
Kingdom of Yugoslavia, 303
King Ins. Co., England, **195**
King, John, 56
King, Moses R., 74
King, William T., 308
Kisbirtokosok, 262
Kiwi Birds, 277
Knickerbocker Fire Insurance Company, 30, 308
Knost Bros. & Co., 56
Knox Co. Mutual, 56, 61
Kobe Kaijo Kasai, 271
Koruna, Prague, 229
Kozepeuropai es Minerva, 262
Krakowskie, Florjanka, 281
Kurzeme, 271
Ky. & Louisville, 57, 61
Kykladiki, 257

Labor Saving Devices, 159
Laclede, St. Louis, 89
Lafayette, General, 52
Lambeth, Coade, 153
Lancashire, 177
Lancaster Castle, 193
Lancaster, Duke of, 149
Land of Canaan, 279
Landowners—British, 168
Lansing, The Capital of Michigan, 307
Latrobe, John H. B., 308
Latta, Moses, 73
Latvia, 294
Latvijas Lloids, 272
Laurens, John, 21
Laver, 151
Law, Insurance, 43, 72
Lawrence, William L., 308
Lawson, Douglas, IX, 12
Law Union and Crown, 193
Law Union & Rock, 199
Lealdade, Brazil, 216
Leech, Thomas, 23
Leeds & Yorkshire, 173
Leeds Fire Office, 151
Legal & General, 179
Legal, England, 199
Legal Intelligencer, 64
Legg, L. G. Wickham, 308
Legie, Prague, 230
Leicestershire, 179
Leipziger, Germany, 247
Lenin, 287
Le Nord, France, 239
Leon, Spain, 292

Leopards, 151
Levy, Benjamin, 47
Lewis, Faulkner, X
Lewis, John, 143
Lexington Fire, 57, 59, 122
Liberty Bell, 23, 24, 25
Licensed Victuallers, 179
Licenses and General, 193
Lichtenstein, Alfred, 14
Lidova, 229
Lietuva, 273
Lietuvos Lloydas, 273
Ligure, Lavor, Latta & Fre., 197
Linaker, E. Nugent, IX
Lincoln, Abraham, 57, 72, 91
Lind, Jenny, 63
Lion, 149, 155, 157, 158, 163, 177, 179, 189, 191, 197, 199, 200, 216, 265, 293
Lion, England, 181, 191
Litchfield Mutual, 64, 67
Little Miami R. R., 65
Littlemore, England, 143
Liver Bird, 151, 183, 185, 189
Liverpool and London, 185
Liverpool and London and Globe, 189
Liverpool Fire, 151
Livonian, 234
Lloyd Amazonese—1910, 216
Lloyd Belge, 213
Lloyd Paraense, 216
Lloyd, Prague, 230
Locksley Hall, 181
Locre, Belgium, 214
London Assurance, 135, 136, 141
London Assurance, 1720-1920, 308
London Assurance Fire Marks, The, 307
London & Lancashire, 187
London and Provincial, 185
London Brigade, 126
London, City Arms, 147, 149
London, City of, 141
London Conflagration, 105, 126
London Guarantee and Accident, 191
London Slums, 126
Longacre, John, 14
Long Distance Telephone, 110
Loomis, S. L., 74, 75
Lorillard Fire, 74, 77
Louis XIV, King, 235
Louisiana, 6
Lovejoy, Elijah, 57
Low, J. Herbert, 308
Luanda, Angola, 284
Lubecker Brandkasse, **247**
Lucas, Col. George, 21
Lucas, Elizabeth, 21, 22
Luce, Edgar P., 14
Lumbermen's, Philadelphia, 106, 109
Lun Tai Mutual, 223
Luxembourg, House of, 273
Lycoming Co. Mutual, 56, 61

McAdam, John, 167
McCants, E. C., 308
McConnell and Liggett, 308
McCormick, Cyrus, 62
McCulloh, T. G., 56
McKeen, Levi, 43
McNamee, Theodore, 74

Macadamizing, 167

Macedonians, 279
Macmillan Co., X
MacPhail, John, 143
Madagascar, 274, 285
Madeira, Louis C., 14
Madeira Wine, 273
Madison, Pres. James, 39, 40, 43
Madura, 231
Magdeburger, Germany, 249
Magellan, Ferdinand, 280
Magnetic Telegraph Co., 64
Magyar Francia, 261
Magyar Hollandi, 262
Making of South Carolina, 308
Malacca, 293
Malayan Confederation, 293
Maltese Cross, 223
Mamaku Tree, 277
Mammoth Cave, 255
Mammoth Paper Mill, 56
Manchester City Arms, 173
Manchester Fire Ins. Co., England, 173, 175
Manchester Fire Office, 146, 149
Manchester Massacre, 159
Manchurian Company, 271
Manganese, 284
Manhattan, 50, 74
Manhattan, Bank of, 307
Manhattan Fire, N. Y., 105, 109
Manhattan Library, The, 307
Manigault, Gabriel, 21
Mannheimer, 253
Manufacturers' & Merchants, Pittsburgh, 99
Marble Palace, 74
Marconi, Guglielmo, 114
Mare Nostrum, Spain, 292
Maria Theresa, Empress, 13
Maritime Refrigeration, 206
Marks, Chief Isaac N., 14
Martin, Charles J., 53, 75
Martin, Charles J., 308
Martinique, 145, 163, 169, 187, 239, 243, 244, 260
Maryland, 6
Mauritius, 2
Mauritius Fire, 274
Marx, Karl, 62
Mecklenburgische, 247
Medusa, 175
Meginness, John F., 308
Meiji Fire, 270
Melbourne Fire, 301
Melksham, England, 146
Mellen, William H., 74
Memorial History of Boston, 3 Vols., 308
Memphis City, 105, 109
Menes, King, 233
Mercantile, Australia, 276
Merchants', Chicago, 93
Merchants, Galveston, 106, 109
Merchants, Hartford, 87
Merchants, New York, 117, 119
Mercurio, Argentina, 207
Meridith, Hugh, 23
Merkur, Prague, 231
Metropole, France, 243
Metropolitan Fire Brigade, 3
Mexico City Agency, 189
Meyers, Joan, IX
Miami Valley, Ohio, 93

Michigan Central, 97
Michigan State, Adrian, 97
Middle Ages, 278
Middlesex, England, 191
Middlesex Mutual, 55, 59
Middlewest Fire, 117, 119
Midlands Movement, 159
Migdal, 279
Milano, Italy, 265
Miles, Richard, 143
Milestones, 24, 25
Milestones, Home, 307
Miller, George H., IX
Miller, Thelma Gorman, IX
Mills, Johnson & Co., 105
Milwaukee Mechanics', 77
Minerva, Belgium, 214
Minerva (Pallas Athene), 169, 175
Mines Royal Co., 135
Misr, Egypt, 233
Missouri State Mutual, 65, 71
Mitchell, Walter, 40
Mobile Fire, 101
Mogul Empire, 263
Mohammedan, 263
Moldavia, 285
Moldavia Generali, 230
Moluccas, 231
Monarch, England, 199
Monde Incendie, France, 241
Mongols at Kiev, 287
Monmouth, England, 143
Monroe, James, 44, 45
Montgomery Co. Mutual, 64, 67
Moravskoslezska, 229
Mordecai, Samuel, 308
Morgan, Joseph, 45
Morgan, J. Pierpont, 45
Morgan, Junius Spencer, 45, 74
Morgan's Coffee House, 45
Morrison, William, 113
Morse, Samuel, 62
Morton, William, 308
Morton, Gov. O. P., 90
Morton, Levi P., 74
Motorcycle, First, 110
Motor Union, England, 199
Motte, Jacob, 20, 21
Mound City Mutual, 85
Moving Pictures, 113
Muhlen Zu Osnabruck, 253
Mullets, 151
Mundial, Spain, 291
Municipalities of Essex County, N. J., 1666-1924, The, 307
Murdock, Harold, 308
Museum Catalog, Chartered Ins. Inst., 307
Mutua Catalana, Spain, 291
Mutua General, Spain, 291
Mutual Assur., N. Y., 30, 35, 55
Mutual Assur., Phila., 29, 33, 34, 55
Mutual Fire, Coatesville, 61
Mutual Fire, Frederick, 64, 67
Mutual Fire, Germantown, 67, 122
Mutual Ins. Co., Charleston, 31, 37
Mutual Ins. Co., Hagerstown, 64, 67
Mutuelle de Limoges, 243
Mutuelle de Poitiers, France, 239
Mutuelle de Valence, 237
Mutuelle d'Orleans, 243
Mutuelle du Mans, 237

Nacional, Venezuela, 300, 301
Nagasaki, 270
Napoleon, 159, 236, 289
Napoleonic Wars, 278, 288
Nassauische, 247
Natal, 288
Natal Fire Office, 288
National Benefit, England, 193
National Board of Fire Undr., 62, 91
National British & Irish Millers', 195
Nationale Balkan, Bulgaria, 219
Nationale, France, 237
National, Egypt, 233
National, England, 191
National General, England, 199
National, Germany, 249
National, Hartford, 105, 107
National, Ireland, 171
National Land Survey, 45
National, New Zealand, 277, 278
National of Great Britain, 195
National Protector, 199
National Turnpike, 65
National Union, England, 195
Nazi War Machine, 255
Nebraska & Iowa, 112
Nederlanden Van 1845, 260
Nederlandsche Lloyd, 260
Nederlandsche, Tiel, 259
Nelson, John G., 74
Nelson of Trafalgar, 159
Neolithic People, 272
Nero, 264
Neuchatelois, 297
Neue Frankfurter, 254
Newark Firemen's Insurance Co., 74
Newark Gas Light Co., 64
Newbold, 127
Newcastle-Upon-Tyne, 147, 153
Newcomer, Stephen, 143
New England, Hartford, 87
New Granada, 226
Newhall, Daniel, 14
New Hampshire Fire, 103
New India, 263
New Orleans Fire Dept., 14
New Orleans Mutual, 103
Newport Association, 159, 166
Newport, R. I., 31
New York Central, 93
New York City, 50; Great Fire of 1835, 57, 105
N. Y. Gas Light Co., 50
New York Post, 50
New York State, 5
N. Y. State Laws, 63
New York, The World's Metropolis, 1623-1923, 307
New Zealand, 277
Niagara District, 56, 59
Niagara, N. Y., 64, 71
Nile, 233
Ninth Ave. El., 110
Niveze Prevoyance, 214
Nolan, James B., 308
Noordhollandsche, 259
Nord-Deutsche, 251
Norske Kjobmaend, 279
Norske Merkantile, 279
Nordstern, 251
Norris, Isaac, 23

North British, 159, 166
North British & Mercantile, 187, 189
North China, 223
North-Eastern, England, 199
Northern Bank of Ky., 57
Northern, England, 179
North River Bank, 50
North River Insurance Company, The,
    50, 53, 57, 307, 308
Northwestern National, 103
Northwest Ordinance, 45
Norway, 294
Norwich General, 147, 155
Norwich Union, 155, 157
No. St. Louis Mut., 95
Nottingham and Derbyshire, 179
Novgorod, 287
Numismatics, 1
Numismatist, 1
Nuremburg Engines, 245

Oakland Co. Farmers', 93
Oberschlesische Provinzial, 247
O'Connor, Harvey, 308
Odd Fellows, 45, 49
Odin, Steed of, 161
O'Gaunt, John, 149, 177, 183, 193
Ohio, 5
Ohio, Chillicothe, 101
Ohio, Dayton, 99
Ohio Farmers, 64, 69
Ohio Land Co., 45
Ohio Mutual, Salem, 109
Old Fire Marks, 308
"Old Man on Fence," 64
Old Merchants of New York City (3 Vols.),
    The, 307
Olds, R. E., 110
Olive Branch, 179
Oma Eesti, 234
Omikami, Amaterasu, 270
Omnia, Spain, 292
Onderlingen Brand., 259
One Hundred Years, Phila., 307
One Hundred Fifty Years of Providence
    Washington Insurance Company, 308
Onslow, Thomas Lord, 135, 136
Orange Free State, 288
Orange River, 288
Order of the Garter, 185
Orel, Bulgaria, 219
Orient, Marks in, 175, 195
Orient, Turkey, 300
Orkney Islands, 278
Ottoman, 285
Ottoman Empire, 299
Ottomane, Turkey, 299
Ouzel Galley, 158
Overseas, Singapore, 293

Pace, Italy, 269
Pacific, Australia, 276
Pacific, San Francisco, 95
Paid Fire Departments, 4, 91, 105
Palatine, England, 193
Palestine, 145, 193, 197, 265, 297
Palestine General, 279
Palestine Lloyd, 279
Palladium, 175
Pallas, 175
Palmer, Clarence, 14

Panama Canal, 280
Panellinios, Greece, 257
Paraense, Brazil, 215
Paraguay, 300
Parana, Brazil, 251
Paris, 235
Parker, Samuel, 29
Parsons, John, 126
Paternelle, France, 241
Patria Hispana, 291
Patrie, Belgium, 213
Patriotic, Ireland, 175
Patriotique, Belgium, 213
Patrons Mutual, Glastonbury, 111, 112
Payridon, 206
Peabody, Wheeling, 104
Peace of Amiens, 159
Pearl, England, 199
Pearsall Bros., 91
Peel, Sir Robert, 180
Penal Colony, 275, 298
Penang, 293
Penn Fire, Pittsburgh, 64, 67
Peninsular War, 159
Pennsylvania, 5
Pennsylvania Fire, 51, 54
Pennsylvania Gazette, 23, 24
Pennsylvania Ins. Co., Pittsburgh, 77
Pennsylvania Railroad, 52
Penn, William, 22
Penny Black Stamp, 1, 2
Penzintezetek, 262
People's, New Orleans, 104
People's, St. Louis, 87
Pepys, Samuel, 141
Pere Marquette R. R., 90
Perier Bros., 235
Perier, Sieur du, 235
Peronneau, Henry, Jr., 21
Perpetual Motion, 106
Perry, Commodore, 270
Perseverance, 44
Persians, 279
Peter the Great, 234, 271, 287, 294
Petriken, William Alexander, 56
"Pewter Platter, The," 52
Phenix Belge, 214
Phenix, Brooklyn, 81
Phenix Bulgare, 219
Phenix Fire Ins. Co., 74, 308
Phenix, France, 237
Phila. Contributionship, 4, 5, 24, 25, 27,
    28, 29, 55, 308
Philadelphia, 23, 39, 52
Philadelphia Inquirer, 52
Philadelphia Ins. Co., 39, 41
Phila. Gas Light Co., 51
Phila. Saving Fund Society, 52
Philanthropist, 56
Philatelist, 1
Philately, 1, 2, 9
Philippa of Hainault, 139
Philippines, 289
Phoenicians, 205
Phoenix Bank, Hartford, 45
Phoenix, Hartford, 83
Phoenix, Legend, 153
Phoenix, London, 39, 147, 153, 201, 202
Phoenix Office, 1705, 126
Phoenix Mutual, Cincinnati, 106, 109
Phonix, Austria, 209

Phonograph, 106
Picture of Baltimore, 308
Pig & Lilies, 151
Pimpernel, 179
Pinckney, Captain William, 21
Pinckney, Charles C., 20, 21
Pinckney, Charles Cotesworth, 22
Pinckney, Thomas, 22
Pincon, Vincent Yanez, 214
Pioneer, St. Louis, 101
Pirates, 158
Pirma Rigas, 271
Pitman Fire Patrol, 114, 116
Pittsburgh Conflagration, 64
Pittsburgh Navigation, 56, 59
Pittsburgh & Ohio R. R., 73
Pitt, William, 159
Plaques, 1
Plaques in France, 236
Planters, Pine Bluff, 114, 115
Plates, 3, 72, 105
Platform Elevator, 63
Platt, Edmond, 308
Plenty, Figure of, 169, 171
Plumber in Britain, 5
Plus Ultra, Spain, 291
Polaris Eesti, 234
Polar, Spain, 291
Political History of England, The, 308
Pommersche Feuersozietat, 247
Ponta Delgada, 210
Poor Richard's Almanac, 23
Pope, Daniel, 51
Pordage, A., 14
Port Hill, 177
Port, Poland, 282
Portugal, Cia. de Seguros, 283
Postage Stamps, 1, 2, 5
    See also "Penny Black"
Poughkeepsie Eagle, The, 308
Poughkeepsie, N. Y., 43
Poulson's Advertiser, 38
Povey, Charles, 127
Power Loom, 147
Powszechny Zaklad, Poland, 281
Prager Phonix, 230
Pratten, A. S., IX, 14, 15
Prazska Mestska, 229
Preservatrice, France, 241
Preussische, Germany, 251
Previdente, Brazil, 215
Previdente, Italy, 269
Previdenza, Italy, 269
Prevision Espanola, 291
Previsora, Venezuela, 300, 301
Prevoyance Agricole, 213
Prevoyance, France, 244
Prevoyance Sociale, 213
Prima Ardeleana, 286
Prince of Wales, 134, 139, 159, 179, 181,
    201, 202
Proctor, John Clagett, 308
Prohibiting Foreign Concerns, 40
Pronia, Greece, 256
Property Fire Office, 193
Property Ins. Co., England, 195
Property Insurance Review, 308
Propontis, Greece, 257
Proprietaries Reunis, 213
Prosperidade, 283
Protection, Boston, 71

316

Protection, Charleston, 115
Protection, Goshen, 95
Protection, Thomaston, 64, 69
Protector, England, 177
Protectrice, France, 243
Providence Bank, 31
Providence, France, 239
Providence Insurance Company, 31
Providence Washington, 37
Providentia, Germany, 251
Providentia, Hungary, 262
Provident Institute, 302
Providenza, Italy, 267
Provinces Reunies, 213
Provincial, England, 197
Provinz Brandenburg, 245
Provinz Ostpreuszen, 247
Provinz Sachsen-Land, 247
Provinz Sachsen, 249
Provinzial, Rheinprovinz, 249
Prudential, England, 185
Prvni Ceska, 229
Puerto Rico, 32, 289
Pullman Co., 113
Puritans, 125, 128
Putnam, Hartford, 97
Putnam, Rufus, 45
Pye, David, 14
Pyramids, 233

Quebec Engine, 220
Quebec Fire, 220, 221
Queen City, Ohio, 73, 77
Queen, England, 181, 185
Queen, New York, 113, 115
Queensland, 276
Queen Victoria, 2
Quincy Mutual, Mass., 77
Quinine, 231

Rakestraw, William, 4
Ram, 151
Ranck, Geo. W., 308
Ransom's Inn, 40, 45
Rawle, William, 52
Rayner Heusser, 225
Reading, England, 171
Reale Mutua, Italy, 265
Reanie & Neafie, 73
Record of The International Fire
    Exhibition, A, 308
Red Cross of St. George, 179
Reeker, Gustav, IX
Reelfoot Lake, 120
Reform Act—1832, 180
Reigart, Adam, 28
Reinsurance & Guarantee, 199
Reliance, England, 191
Reliance, Phila., 93
Relief, 44
Relton, Francis Boyer, 147, 308
Remington, E. & Sons, 106
Remoises, France, 243
Report on One Hundred Years, A, Glens
    Falls, 307
Republic, Chicago, 99
Residence, Cleveland, 106, 109
Rheinland, 253
Rhinelander, William C., 50
Rhin et Moselle, 243

Richards, Benjamin W., 52
Rich, King, X
Richland, Mansfield, 64, 71
Richmond, Duchess of, 141
Richmond, Her Past and Present, 307
Riddle & Co., 56
Rieg, Otto F., IX
Rigas Unions, 272
Riunione Adriatica, 267
Riveted Hose, 40
Roach, Mayor George, 22
Roberts, Hugh, 24
Rockford Ins. Co., 101
Rock, Gibraltar, 255
Rock River Mutual, 79
Rodina, Bulgaria, 219
Roe, George Mortimer, 308
Roelker & Collins, 308
Roettiers, John, 141
Rolnicka, 229
Roman Conflagration, 264
Roman Empire, 264
Romance of Insurance, A, 308
Romance of the Insurance Business as Dis-
    closed Through Ancient Fire Marks, 307
Romans, 279
Roosevelt, Franklin D., 14
Rose of England, 195
Rosija Fonsier, 305
Rossia Ins. Co., 287
Ross, Robert, 141
Ross, Thomas, X
Rothschild, Baron, 13
Round Lake, Illinois, 117, 119
Royal, England, 183, 185
Royal Exchange, 135, 136, 143, 145
Royal Exchange Assurance Magazine, 308
Royal Exchange, Dublin, 155
Royal Farmers' and General, 183
Royal, France, 237
Royal Irish, 171
Rubber, 231
Rubicam, Daniel, 52, 53
Rubicam's Tavern, 52
Rural Free Delivery, 114
Rurik the Viking, 287
Russian Revolution, 271
Rutherford, Dwight, IX

St. Andrew, 166
St. Catherine's, 177
St. Denis, 285
St. Ferdinand Fire, 121
St. George, 187
St. Helena, 159
St. Joseph Fire, 103
St. Louis Mutual, 77
St. Lucia, 199
St. Mary's Canal, 92
St. Michael, 210
St. Michael's Cave, 255
St. Mungo, 163
St. Patrick, Ireland, 175
St. Paul F. & M., 91, 99
St. Petersburg, 287
Sabiedriba Latvija, 272
Sachs, Edwin O., 308
Sagres, Brazil, 216
Sagres, Portugal, 284
Salamander, 171, 185, 187, 287
Salamander, England, 171

Salamander, Russia, 287
Salamander V. 1888, Holland, 260
Sale Catalogs of Fire Marks, 307
Salmon River, 163
Salop Fire, 151
Salvage Bag, 23
Salvage Corps, 128
Salzmann, Alfred Co. Ltd., 175
Samarangsche Zee en Tweede
    Samarangsche Zee, 232, 233
San Francisco Earthquake, 117
San Francisco's Great Disaster, 308
Sarum, England, 146
Sault-au-Matelot, 220
Sauvegarde, 213
Sava Opce, Zagreb, 305
Savoia, Italy, 267
Savoy, House of, 264
Scales, 157
Scharf, Col. J. Thomas, 308
Scheldt River, 211
Schlesische, Germany, 249
Schleswig Holsteinische, 247
Schulman and Holzer, 308
Schweizerische National, 297
Scimitars, 191
Scottish Commercial, 189
Scottish, Edinburgh, 191
Scottish Imperial, 189
Scottish Union, 177
Scottish Union and National, 191
Sct. Florian, 229
Sea, England, 191
Sea Horses, 173
Second Balkan War, 285
Securitas, Belgium, 211
Securite Francaise, 243
Security, Cincinnati, 110, 111
Security, N. Y., 85
Self Government, 146
Seminole Indians, 64
Seneca Falls, N. Y., 73
Serbs, 303
Serpents, 175
Seventy-five Years, Agricultural, 307
Seventy-five Years of Progress, Hanover, 307
Severus, Emperor Alexander, 264
Sewing Machine, 64
Seymour, Queen Jane, 153
Shamrock, 171, 195
Shamrock Fire, 171
Shanghai, China, 225
Shang-Yin, 221
Shawk, A., 73
Shawnee, Topeka, 115
Sheffield, England, 165
Shepard, Charles, 55
Sherman Anti-Trust, 110
Sherman, C., 308
Sherwood, Royal Forest, 179
Shetlands, 278
Shippen, Edward, 4
Sholes, Christopher Latham, 106
Short History of The English People
    (IV volumes), A, 307
Short History of The Oldest American Fire
    Insurance Company, 308
Shorter History of England and Greater
    Britain, A, 307
Shrewsbury, Arms of, 151
Shropshire and North Wales, 179, 181

Shulze, Gov. J. Andrew, 52
Signeviery, 1, 2, 19, 72, 117, 120, 281
    See also Fire Marks
Signevierist, 1, 90, 120, 126, 201
Sila, Bulgaria, 219
Silesia, Poland, 282
Silk Manufacturing, 127
Sill, Joseph, 14
Silsby Mfg. Co., 73
Silver Ingot, 2
Sincere, Singapore, 293
Singapore, 293
Singapore Ins. Co., 293
Singer Company, 308
Sinking Fund—British, 167
Siphones, 264
Sixty Years, Detroit, 308
Skandinavien, 294
Skelton, Richard, 143
Slavery, 56, 65, 168
Slavia, Prague, 229
Slavija, Ljubljana, 306
Slavonic People, 303
Slovanska, Prague, 229
Slovenes, 303
Slovenska, Bratislava, 230, 231
Smallpox, 153
Smith, Daniel B., 28
Smith, Elizabeth, 143
Smith, Harold V., IX, 14, 53
Smith, H. V. Museum, XIII, 12, 13, 14, 15, 75
Smyrna, 158
Societa Cattolica, Italy, 267
Societe Cooperative, Bulgaria, 219
Soleil, France, 239
So. African National, 288
Southampton Arms, 183
South Australia Co., 289
South British, 277
South Carolina, 6, 22, 90
South Carolina Gazette, 20, 21
Southeastern Pennsylvania, 308
Southern Cross, 302
Southern Mutual, Athens, 64, 69
South of England, 183
South St. Louis Mutual, 89
South Sea Bubble, 135, 136, 146, 201
South Sea Co., 134
South Shields, England, 143
Southwark Cross, 177
Southwark Hose, 44
Southwestern Pennsylvania, 308
Sovereign, England, 201, 202
Soviet Union, 281
Spalding, W. R., 55
Spanish-American War, 227, 289
Specimens of British Fire Marks, 308
Spectator, The, 308
Sphinx, 233
Spink, William, 143
Spinning Jenny, 147
Springfield, Ohio, 97
Springfield Fire, Mass., 64, 71
Srbija, Belgrade, 305
Stadernas, Sweden, 294
Stadtische Berlin, 245
Stamp Collector, see Philatelist
Stagecoach, 167
Standard, New Zealand, 278
Star, England, 185

Star Fire, Ogdensburg, 74, 83
State Assurance, England, 193
State, Des Moines, 114, 115
State Fencibles, 52
State House, Phila., VII, 47
State, Lansing, 103
State Mutual, Hannibal, 99
Statue of Liberty, 74
Steam Propelled Boats, 38
Steaua Romaniei, 286
Steelyard, 157
Steirer, Austria, 209
Stephen, King, 155
Stephenson, Freeport, 81
Stettiner, Germany, 245
Stevenson, H. J., 14
Stockdale & Darlington R. R., 167
Stockholms Stads, 294
Stokes, I. N. Phelps, 308
Storebrand, 279
Stork, 259
Story of The Derwent & Tamar Assurance
    Company, Limited, 308
Stow, John, 4, 25
Straits Fire, Singapore, 293
Street, G. S., 308
Stroud, E., 14
Stroud, James P., 14, 15
Suction Pumps, 258
Suffolk and General, 158, 201, 202
Suisse Mobilier, Berne, 295
Sumadija, Belgrade, 305
Sumatra, 231
Sun, Cleveland, 97
Sun, Dublin, 161
Sun, London, 14, 128, 131, 133, 134, 201, 202
Suomen, Finland, 235
Surrey, Sussex and Southwark, 177
Sutters Mill, 64
Swan River, 303
Swedish-Norwegian Union, 294
Swerig, Mabel, IX
Swigart, W. Emmert, IX, 14, 308
Sydney Fire, 276

Tagus, Portugal, 283
Taisho Marine, 271
Talmadge, James, Jr., 44
Tamar Fire, 298
Targe or Scottish Shield, 189
Tasman, Abel, 298
Tasmanian, 298
Taverns, 52
Tax, Argentina, 206
Taxes, 50
Taylor, Pres. Zachary, 63
Telephone, Electric, 106
Temple Bar, 179
Tenno, Jimmu, 270
Tennyson, 181
Terra Haute & Alton R. R., 64
Terry, Nathaniel, 40
Tetbury, England, 146
Teutonia, Cleveland, 97
Teutonia, Dayton, 99
Teutonic, 294
Textile Machines, 38, 180
Thirty Years War, 294
Thistle, 163, 195
Thornbill Collection, 13

Thorp, Prescott Holden, 308
Thouron, Peter, 27
Thuringia, Germany, 251
Tin Fire Marks, 55
Tiptonville Mutual, 120, 121
Tiroler Landes, 209
Titan, Greece, 257
Tobin, C. R., IX
Todd, Frank Morton, 308
Tokio Marine, 270
Tokyo Bay, 270
Toland, Robert, 52
Tom's Coffee House, 127
Tools, Hand, XIII
Torino, Italy, 267
Tories, England, 146, 159
Townsend, Joseph, 31
Toyo Fire, 271
Toys, 56
Traders, Chicago, 99
Trade Signs, XIII
Tranquilidade, 283
Transatlantische, Germany, 251
Transportation—Britain, 167, 180
Transsylvania, Rumania, 285
Transvaal, 288
Treaty of Cordoba, 275
Treaty of Kiel, 278
Treaty of Paris, 146, 274
Treaty of Utrecht, 289
Treaty of Westphalia, 294
Trinity College, 141
Trotsky, 287
Trow's New York City Directory, 308
Troy, 175
Tuckett's Monthly Insurance Journal, 72
Tudor, House of, 139
Tung Yih Trust, 225
Tuscarora, Cincinnati, 120, 121
Tyler, Sydney, 308
Typewriter, First, 106
Typhoon in Japan, 270

Ulpian, 264
Ultramarina, 283
Ulysses, 175
Uniao, Brazil, 215
Union & Fenix, Spain, 289, 291
Union & Rhein, Germany, 251
Union, Bangor, 93
Union Belge, 213
Union, China, 223
Union, Dayton, 97
Union Des Assureurs, 214
Union Des Proprietaires, 213
Union Fire Company, 23
Union Fire, Nashville, 43, 104
Union, France, 237, 239
Union Generale du Nord, 241
Union Geneve, 297
Union, Germany, 251
Union Hispano Americana, Cuba, 227
Union Ins. Co., Charleston, 39, 41
Union Jack, 179, 185, 197
Union Levantina, 291
Union, London, 134, 137, 139
Union, Mexico, 275
Union Nationale, Turkey, 300
Union New Zealand, 278
Union of South Africa, 288
Union of Soviet Soc. Rep., 287

Union, Prague, 231
United, Australia, 276
United Counties, 199
United, Covington, 101
United Firemen's, 73, 89
United States Branch Bank, 45
U. S. Fire Companies, 44
United States Fire, N. Y., 51, 53, 57
United States Ins. Co., Balti., 55, 59
United States of Colombia, The, 226
Universal Tontine, 30
Unknown, American, 121
Unknown, British, 202
Urals, 218
Uranus, 165
Urbaine, France, 239
Uruguay, Republic of, 300
Utrechtsche, Holland, 260

Valstybes, 273
Van der Heide (or Van der Heyden),
    John & Nicholas, 257
Van Diemen's Land, 298
Van Diemen's Land Ins. Co., 301
Van Duzen & Tift, 56
Van Valsen, Capt. Gerrit, 21
Vardar, Herceg-Bosna, Triglav, 306
Vascongada, Spain, 292
Vaterlandische, 247
Venus, China, 225
Vesta, Goddess, 161
Victor Emanuel, King, 13
Victoria, Alexandrina, 180, 181, 185, 195
Victoria, Australia, 301, 302
Victoria, Germany, 251
Victorian Historical Magazine, The, 308
Victor Talking Machine Co., 14
Viking Fleets, 278
Vincent, Samuel, 126
Virginia F. & M., 56, 59, 120
Virgin Mary, 151
Virginia, Especially Richmond in By-Gone
    Days, 308
Vittoria, Italy, 268
Vogel, F. B., 308
Volga, 218
Volksfursorge, 253
Volunteer Fire Departments, 51, 73, 74, 91
Von Ferrari, Count, 13
Voss, Carolyn, IX

Wah An, China, 223
Walachia, 285
Walch, Charles E., 308
Walford, 308
Wallace, A. C., IX

Waller, Richard, 141
Walpole, Sir Robert, 136
Walsh, Stevenson H., 14
Walton, Coates, 14
Wappoo Creek, 21, 22
Ward, A. W., Prothero, G. W.,
    Leathes, Stanley, 308
Warder, John, 28
War Hawks, 39
Warner, Edward, 23
Warner, Peter R., 308
War of 1812, XIII
Warszawskie, 281
Washington Guards, 52
Washington Insurance Co., 32
Washington Mutual, Boston, 64, 67
Washington Mutual, Ky., 87
Water Frame, 147
Waterloo, 159
Waterlow & Sons, 193
Waterman, Henry, 63
Watermen, 127, 177
Watertown, N. Y., 103
Water Works of Paris, 235
Watson, Thomas A., 106
Webb, Elisha, 145
Wechselseitige Brand. und Janus, 209
Wechselseitige in Graz, 209
Weekly Underwriter, N. Y., 308
Westchester Fire, 81
Western Australian, 303
Western, Canada, 221
Western, England, 189
Western Isles, 278
Western Mutual, St. Louis, 87
Western Pioneers, XIII
Westfalische Provinzial, 245
West Indies, 21, 22
Westinghouse, George, 106, 113
Westminster, 134, 139, 201, 202
Westminster Abbey, 139
West of England, 159, 165
West of Scotland, 193
West Virginia, 5, 113
Weydemeyer, General, 62
Wharton, Thomas I., 52, 53
Wheat Sheaf, 183
Wheeling's First 250 Years, 308
Whelen, Israel, 40
Whig Control, 146, 147
Whiley, Capt. Richard, 50
Whitby, England, 143
White, Henry A., 308
Who Is Who in Insurance, 308
Wilderness Conquered, XIII
Willemson, Verner R., IX

William IV, 168
William & Mary, 127
William the Conqueror, 153, 155
Williams, Bertram, IX, 5, 12, 308
Williams, John, 14
Williams, Thomas J. C., 308
Williamsburgh City, 74, 79
Willing, Richard, 52, 53
Wilmott, John, 143
Wilson, H., 308
Wilson, Woodrow, 228
Windham Co. Mutual, 55, 61
Windmill, 195, 257
Wing On Fire, 223
Winnesheik, Freeport, 93
Winsor, Justin, 308
Winton, Alexander, 114
Wister, Alexander W., 14
Woodin, William H., 13
Wood, Oliver E., 74
Woodward, P. Henry, 308
Wool Combing, 147
Worcester Fire, 147, 155
World Auxiliary, 200
World Marine and General, 195
World War I, 196, 207, 228, 234, 261, 272,
    281, 285, 287, 303
World War II, 228, 245, 264, 303
Wragg, Joseph, 21
Wurttembergische, 249
Wyoming, Wilkes-Barre, 85

Yangtsze, China, 223
Yao and Shun, 221
"Yellow Cat," 52
Yeung Shing, China, 223
Yeoman, Hewitt and Green, 308
Yonkers & New York, 95
York and London, 179
York & No. of England, 179
York Co. Mutual, W. Buxton, 64, 71
York Minster, 177
Yorkshire, 177
Young America, 73
Young, Archibald, 21

Zaklad, Posnan, 281
Zavarovalnica, 305
Zeus, 165, 169
Zinc Marks, 65
Zinc Mines, 6
Zinsman, Samuel, 14
Zionists, 279
Zion, Palestine, 279
Zoides, Alexander J., IX, 255
Zuider Zee, 257